THE THRONE OF THE GODS

The German original, entitled *Thron der Götter*, was published
in 1938 by the Morgarten-Verlag A.G., of Zurich, Switzerland

THE
THRONE OF THE GODS

AN ACCOUNT OF THE FIRST SWISS EXPEDITION
TO THE HIMALAYAS

by

ARNOLD HEIM AND AUGUST GANSSER

WITH 220 PLATES IN PHOTOGRAVURE
18 SKETCHES IN THE TEXT
11 MUSICAL ITEMS, 2 PANORAMAS
AND 1 RELIEF MAP

translated by

EDEN AND CEDAR PAUL

NEW YORK
THE MACMILLAN COMPANY
1939

MGE

Photogravure Plates printed by
Messrs. Conzett and Huber, Zurich

PRINTED IN GREAT BRITAIN
BY R. & R. CLARK, LIMITED, EDINBURGH

ACKNOWLEDGMENTS

AFTER the Swiss Scientific Society provided the sinews of war for our expedition, various other societies and private persons furnished valuable aid, both financial and in the way of supplies.

Financial Aid came from :

Iwan Bally, of Schönenwerd, who from the first showed great interest in our scientific aims.

Alfred Dürler-Tobler and Hans Tobler, of Zurich.

Dr. A. Wander of Berne, per Dr. Gossweiler and Director Schaffner.

Firm of Jelmoli, per Director Leuthold, of Zurich.

Swiss Reinsurance Society, of Zurich, per Dr. Charles Simon and Director Bebler.

Swiss Alpine Club, per Herr von Kalbermatten, of Sion.

Barth Foundation of the Federal Technical Academy, per Dr. Rohn.

Joachim de Giacomi Foundation, per Dr. R. La Nicca, of Berne.

Dr. Charles Simon, of Au.

Paul Montandon, of Thun.

For *Donations in Kind* we have to thank the following firms :

A. SPORTING REQUISITES, INSTRUMENTS, AND DRUGS

Jelmoli, of Zurich (Tents, etc.).

Skifabrik Attenhofer, of Zurich (Hinged Skis).

Gustav Metzger, of Basle (Raincoats).

Bally, of Schönenwerd (Mountain Boots).

Urania-Apotheke, of Zurich, per Dr. L. Bächler (Drugs).

F. Hoffmann-La Roche & Co., of Basle (Drugs).

I. G. Farbenindustrie-Ges., Zurich Branch (Chinoplasmin).

Wilhelm Koch, of Optisches Institut, Zurich.

Perutz of Munich (Perpantic-Film).

Kern & Co., of Aarau (Prismatic Binoculars).

Elsener, of Schwyz (Cutlery).

A. Türler & Co., of Zurich (Alarums).

v

Johann Faber (Sketching Materials).
Burger-Kehl (PKZ), of Zurich.
Gaba Company, of Basle.

B. PROVISIONS

Tobler, of Bischofszell (Pomol).
Dr. A. Wander, of Berne (Ovomaltine).
Nestlé & Anglo-Swiss, of Vevey (Milk Powder).
Nobs & Co., of Münchenbuchsee (Vierkorn-Biscuits).
Maggi, of Kemptthal (Packet Soups).
Reformhaus Egli & Co., of Zurich (Dried Fruits, etc.).
Migros Company, of Zurich, per Councillor Duttweiler (Varia).

For Valuable *Recommendations, Advice, and Other Help,* we have
to thank :

The Head of the Political Department, Councillor Motta, of Berne.
Swiss Embassy, London.
Geological Survey of India, Calcutta.
Consul Max Staub, of Calcutta.
Dr. P. G. H. Boswell, of London.
Professor Kenneth Mason, of Oxford.
Hugh Ruttledge, Chief of recent Everest Expeditions
Dr. Sven Hedin, of Stockholm.
Dr. G. Dyhrenfurth, of Zurich.
Drs. O. Hug and H. Winzeler, of Zurich.
Drs. C. Schröter and Albert Heim, of Zurich.
Dr. Erich Tilgenkamp, of Kilchberg.
Dr. W. Knopfli, Zoologist, of Zurich.
Drs. Rudolf Staub and A. Jeannet, of Zurich.
Dr. Emil Abegg, of Zurich.
Dr. Eugen Wegmann, Geologist, of Schaffhausen.
His Excellency Professor Giuseppe Tucci, of Rome.

With apologies and cordial thanks to any whose names may have
been overlooked.

PREFACE

For more than twenty years I was mainly occupied with geological researches in the Alps. During the years 1929–1931 I made acquaintance with the Sino-Tibetan ranges, and then, in 1935, with the Farther-Indian chains bordering on Siam. Steadily the desire grew to make comparative studies in the Himalayas, for it seemed to me that there, among the highest and most recent mountains of our planet, a geologist already versed in Alpine technology had a good chance of solving some of the basic problems of mountain structure.

I made a short stay at Darjeeling, where, as also at Simla in the summer of 1935, and during two visits to London, my plans ripened. But what chiefly promoted the advance towards practical realisation in the shape of the first Swiss expedition to the Himalayas was the vigorous encouragement of the Central Committee of our national academy, the Swiss Scientific Society.

From the start I was mainly concerned with the Central Himalayas, which offered the greatest interest and were the least known. Seeing, however, that the kingdom of Nepal contains the highest peaks in the world and (though access is more and more rigorously restricted) has lateral valleys offering unrivalled paths to the central Himalayan massif, it seemed desirable to approach the goal by way of the bordering British-Indian province of Kumaon. Our journey was to show that the formidable gorge of the frontier stream of Kali does indeed furnish the best of all insight into the structure of these mighty mountains.

As a glance at the relief map of the Central Himalayas will show, we had to leave British territory and enter the forbidden lands of Nepal and Tibet in order to extend our observations into those peculiarly interesting and little known regions. The remarkable results we were able to achieve have more than compensated for the difficulties we faced and the hardships we endured.

The name of this book, *The Throne of the Gods*, was chosen after our visit to the Himalayan and Transhimalayan mountains which the Indians and the Tibetans, the Hindus and the Buddhists, regard with such veneration because there the gods live and reign. Towards Kailas are directed the yearnings of several hundred million Asiatics, as also towards Badrinath and the neighbouring peaks where the Ganges takes its rise. As pilgrims of science we approached these stupendous masses with no less reverence.

In the present work, which we hope to make thoroughly comprehensible to the general reader, little is said about our geological researches, a detailed account of which is reserved for a study now in course of preparation, to be first published in English. Here we recount our experiences and discoveries, the lives of men, animals, and plants, not only among the crags and glaciers of the high mountains, but also on the way thither. In these respects the work differs from the publications of Himalayan expeditions whose main purpose was the ascent of previously unscaled peaks.

As in my books *Minya Gongkar, Forschungsreise ins Hochgebirge von Chinesisch-Tibet,* and *Negro Sahara, von der Guinea-Küste zum Mittelmeer* (both published by the Verlag Hans Huber of Berne), to avoid exaggerations and the play of uncontrolled fancy the writers have kept strictly to the data furnished by their careful diaries.

The text is, perhaps, somewhat overburdened by the figures relating to altitude (which were largely determined by our own barometric observations), and by the numerous names of places and plants. But the omission of these would have been a matter of regret for naturalists, who seek accurate information as well as entertainment.

Acknowledgments to the many persons who have helped us in our enterprise will be found. I should like here, however, to say a special word or two about my companions. Werner Weckert, the noted mountaineer, made all the arrangements for equipment, which he brought to India on board the s.s. " Strathmore ". Then, on the third day of our tramp into the mountains, he went down with appendicitis, and was thus lost to the expedition. Our trio had become a duet. If nevertheless, during what was described as " the worst summer on record ", we were able to achieve more noteworthy scientific results than I had ventured to expect, this was mainly due to my young colleague Dr. August Gansser. Throughout our eight months' journey he was a good comrade, a shrewd and indefatigable collaborator, and a leader in the difficult glacier country. He contributes his own report of various independent expeditions.

All the sketches and photographs are our own, being respectively marked (H) and (G).

Dr. E. Schmid was good enough to examine the botanical specimens we brought back to the University of Zurich. Most of the Latin names in the text were supplied by him, and he contributes the section on Botanical Results.

To the Cartographical Institute of Kümmerly and Frey, and above all to Dr. Heinrich Frey of Berne, we are deeply indebted for the preparation of the Relief Map and for the help given in other cartographical matters. I believe ours to be the first Relief Map of the Himalayas in natural illumination (from S.W. instead of from N.W.).

Lastly I wish to express my gratitude to the Morgarten-Verlag of Zurich and to Dr. E. Huber for the cordial way in which our wishes have been fulfilled.

ARNOLD HEIM

ZURICH, *October* 1937

CONTENTS

CHAPTER ONE

CHAPTER TWO

CHAPTER THREE

CHAPTER FOUR

CHAPTER FIVE

CHAPTER SIX

CHAPTER SEVEN

xi

CHAPTER EIGHT

CHAPTER NINE

CHAPTER TEN

CHAPTER ELEVEN

CHAPTER SEVENTEEN

CHAPTER EIGHTEEN

APPENDIX

LIST OF ILLUSTRATIONS
IN THE TEXT
(H = by Heim ;   G = by Gansser)

Musical Items are given on pp. 14, 15, 25, 26, 32, 54, 77, 178, 181

PLATES MADE FROM PHOTOGRAPHS
(Taken by Heim, marked H ;   by Gansser, marked G)

xvi

B

xvii

xix

xxii

PANORAMAS AND MAP
(*At end of Volume*)

I. PANORAMIC SKETCHES
(Drawn from Nature by A. Gansser)

a. Central Himalayas (Kumaon-Nepal) from Jandi (7870 feet), above Binsar. (The whole stretch measures 250 miles.)

b. View of the Trisul-Nandakna Group (from Gwaldam, 6560 feet, on the Almora-Garhwal border).

c. View of the Dunagiri Group from the Kuari Pass (11,808 feet).

II. PANORAMIC PHOTOS

a. Mountain Chain of North-West Nepal, photographed from the head of Nampa Valley, at an Altitude of 17,384 feet. (Cf. Fig. 10 in text.) June 1936. (G)

b. Badrinath Group from the Northern Side of the Bhagat-Kharak Glacier, extending from South-East by Way of South to W.N.W. October 3, 1936. (H)

MAP
(*In Pocket*)

Relief Map (1 : 650,000) of the Central Himalayas as far as Transhimalaya, in natural South-Western illumination, prepared by Kümmerley and Frey of Berne upon the foundation of the Survey of India official Maps, with emendations based upon sketches by the present authors. (On this map heights are printed in metres. Throughout the text they are given in feet.)

CHAPTER ONE

BY AIRPLANE TO INDIA

WE were ready to start by the beginning of March 1936. Although bedridden from age, my father bade farewell to me without anxiety. My young colleague August Gansser joined me at Lugano, having come by the St. Gotthard route. In Rome we had just time to call on the famous orientalist Professor Giuseppe Pucci, who the summer before had visited Kailas with special permission from the Tibetan Government, making the same sort of journey which we were proposing as geologists. Our reception was most cordial. Pucci made no secret of his belief that we should encounter political difficulties, which indeed our correspondence had already led us to expect. The good old days of a von Richthofen or a Sven Hedin are over and done with. As time passes, these countries in a critical position are more and more inclined to close their frontiers. That is readily comprehensible in view of the way in which the white " Christians " have ruthlessly pursued materialistic aims in Asia. Still it was hard to understand why obstacles should be placed in the way of accredited scientists like ourselves who were politically neutral. However, we knew that Nepal is a fenced precinct, and that we were likely to be hindered from entering Tibet. We could hardly hope to do more than visit the British province of Kumaon in Central Himalaya, a region whose geology was still practically unknown, so that there were numerous and important problems to solve.

ROME TO HELIOPOLIS

The stars were still shining in the early morning of March 19th when we drove by autobus to the aerodrome. Italian officers explored our baggage and carefully examined the photographic apparatus. Fortunately, through the instrumentality of the Political Department in Berne, I had been able to secure from the governments concerned permits to take photographs in the parts of Asia we intended to explore.

I

With remarkable punctuality, precisely at sunrise, after fifteen seconds' run on the level, the twin-motor "Douglas" airplane of the Dutch Air Transport line (K.L.M.) quitted the ground on its south-eastward course (Plate 1).

In three-quarters of an hour we sighted Vesuvius, to the north of which we passed. The volcano was emitting a yellowish pillar of smoke, deflected by the N.E. wind. The peaks of the Apennines were capped with clouds, above which we soared. These clouds, as we looked on them from a height of 13,000 feet, reminded us of the inland ice-sheet we had seen in Greenland.

Eastward of the Apennines there were no clouds. To our left lay the harbour of Taranto, in brilliant sunshine.

A few minutes later we were crossing the blue waters of the Adriatic. We headed for the island of Corfu, which has so often changed hands, and is now a Greek possession. The soil of Greece, with its numerous dentated islets, peninsulas, bays, and sounds, was only visible through gaps in the clouds. Above the cloud-sheet projected peaks bestrewn with recently fallen snow. At Athens, after our journey had lasted four hours, we had for the first time to put on our watches by one hour. At a speed of 150 to 200 miles per hour one has, moving eastwards, to put on one's watch about ten minutes every hour if one wishes to keep local time. To be precise, the difference in time is four minutes for each degree of longitude.

Only a year ago, the traveller who made a journey to the East by air had to pass the night at Athens. Now, however, after an hour's rest, our air-liner took off once more and we flew over the splendid city with the conspicuous Acropolis to reach the Aegean. The bare cliffs of the Cyclades rose steeply out of the sea. Then came a wonderful view of Santorin with the ring of its broken crater. The villages on the slopes were dazzlingly white in contrast with the blue waters. Mount Caldera is more than five miles wide. In the dawn of history it was a gigantic volcano. During a long period of quiesence, the floor of the crater sank over a thousand feet beneath the water. Then, in the year 1925, came a period of fresh activity, when the lava and scoria of the Island of Neokaimeni were extruded. The surrounding craterine lake is turbid from the washings of the cinders.[1]

We said goodbye to Europe as we passed Crete, half-hidden in the clouds which veiled its mountains on our right. Then for two hours we flew S.E. over the Mediterranean, not in a seaplane but in an ordinary airplane not provided with any cork-jackets for the passengers

[1] Cf. Mittelholzer, Gouzy, and Heim, *Afrikaflug*, 1927, Plates 15-17 and text p. 221.

in case of mishap. From a height of eight to ten thousand feet, the foaming waves were no more than tiny spots upon the sea. Then, through a yellowish dust-haze, appeared the flat shore of Africa. Quickly the scene changed. In place of the yellow desert, we saw the irrigated expanse of the Nile Delta, with its quadrangular green and brown fields and its rounded peasant villages.

At length, in the gentle evening light, we reached the aerodrome of Heliopolis. Thence it was only a short drive to the Palace Hotel, a pre-war building in the Arabian style, which charms every visitor. Unique is the domed hall with its huge Persian carpet, and splendid are the gardens with palm-trees and luxuriantly flowering Bougainvillias with their bright, violet-coloured bracts. Only two days before we had left the Alps under snow and in a biting north wind. Here it was mild and warm, with insects chirping merrily far on into the night.

HELIOPOLIS TO BAGDAD

Next morning we crossed the Suez Canal, busy with warships and transports. Beyond lay Eastern Egypt with its remarkable landscape, that of inhabited sand-dunes. For beyond each huge wall of migratory sand-dunes was a yellow stretch of sand showing detached curved areas, in whose declivities grow date-palms, partially sheltered from the wind. Many of them, however, had half disappeared beneath the shifting sands. These are the extremely isolated settlements of the nomads of the desert. From shallow wells dug in the sand sufficient water can be secured to irrigate a small orchard and provide an exiguous livelihood for a family. (See Plate 4.)

As we reached Palestine there was a change both in climate and in scenery.

At first came big abandoned settlements surrounded by quadrangular walls, but overwhelmed by the desert. By degrees, however, as we coasted the Mediterranean, we could see freshly ploughed fields amid which stood wattle-and-dab houses. But sooner than we expected we reached Gaza. Here, in the fine aerodrome, we were served with tea and coffee and a " second breakfast " of ham and eggs. The " Douglas ", too, received its rations. The flying-ground is encircled by orange and grape-fruit plantations. These must be irrigated, but the scanty rainfall suffices for the growth of cereals. From the plain, however, as we continued on our way, we could see ever and again the dendriform figures made by recent erosions, which are threatening the wheatfields. (See Plate 2.) Now to the S.E. appeared the terraced limestone hills, harsh ribs in a desolate country which give Eastern Palestine its typical aspect (Plate 7). The friendly pilot circled over Bethlehem (Plate 5), and then deviated slightly to the north to show us sunlit Jerusalem with its cupolas and spires (Plate 6). We were fully occupied looking and photographing, so far as these were possible through the rear windows.

We had crossed the serrated spine of the Judean Mountains which reach an altitude of a few thousand feet, to soar above the deep depression of the Dead Sea whose waters are nearly 1300 feet below sea-level. Since there is no outlet from this lake, and its tributaries have for ages been bringing down saline matter from the hills, the Dead Sea consists of extremely concentrated brine.

Having crossed the Jordan (Plate 8) we could see more settlements upon limestone terraces, like those of Judea. Then came the wide expanse of the Syrian Desert, in whose desolation no more than a few isolated dark rings could be distinguished. These must be walled enclosures built by nomads to herd their sheep. Now limestone terraces and red clays gave place to regions spotted with black. These are areas of basaltic lava. A few small craters could be made out, until the sand predominated once more. As we crossed Transjordania at a height of about 10,000 feet, we noted in our diaries that the country here was "zebroid". The zebroid markings appeared to be the beds of dried-up rivers and pools, while upon the transversely disposed dunes scanty brushwood grew (Plate 9).

Now to the left we could make out a fine line traced across the desert. This was the great pipe-line with its road and its power-stations, by which the crude petroleum from the newly-bored fields in Persia and Irak is conveyed to the Mediterranean.

Towards noon there began to open beneath us the vast sandy plain of Mesopotamia—a desert which needs only water to become a garden. To this Bagdad bears witness, the huge town with a loamy soil on the banks of the Tigris with its extensive groves of date-palms and its green wheatfields (Plate 10).

Since we reached Bagdad early in the afternoon, we had plenty of time to study the capital of the kingdom of Irak from the ground-level as well as from the air. One who, a good while ago, became acquainted with the indescribably foul streets and alleys of this giant town, and who spent sleepless nights there, plagued by heat and dust, tortured by vermin, could not but be astonished to find a new hotel with an attentive staff. The fine veranda commands a view of the busy, turbid river, the flat roofs, and towering amid them the golden domes of the mosques.

4

BAGDAD TO JODHPUR

Our longest day's flight, nearly 2000 miles, was before us. We were called at half-past two, and were driven to the aerodrome beneath a cloudless starry sky. The huge metallic bird which was to carry us shone in the searchlight like a ghost. The cylinders worked under a full charge of fuel, and sparks emerged from the exhaust. We took another hour's snooze in long chairs, to be awakened by flashes of lightning from a wall of storm-clouds we were approaching. The crew of the plane were uneasy as well as its passengers. The pilots were issuing light-signals and the wireless was continuously at work. To the right we could see a red glow from the petroleum wells of Muhamera. We were rapidly sinking towards the ground. Why? Soon the aneroid registered an altitude of less than 1600 feet. Day was dawning, and we could discern a labyrinth of winding channels amid the mud of the Shat-el-Arab Delta—the lower course of the Euphrates after its junction with the Tigris. There were repeated flashes of lightning. A forced descent here might be the end of us all. But it was growing much lighter, and we planed smoothly above the smooth, shallow waters of the Persian Gulf. Our pilots had managed to pass safely beneath the threatening clouds. The danger was over.

We glided down to the petrol tanks on the desolate, flat island of Bushire. The next stretch of our journey, along the Persian Gulf over the lower slopes of the Iranian chains, was so lovely that it could not fail to delight the eyes of a geologist privileged to have a bird's-eye view. While the other passengers slumbered peacefully on their long chairs, Gansser and I were busily engaged in making observations and taking photographs. So clearly were the strata exposed, so nakedly displayed, that one might have made a geological map from the airplane and could have pointed out anticlinal sites likely to repay boring for petroleum. The convolution was so recent and the surface corresponded so closely with the internal structure, that every anticline formed a mountain ridge and every furrow a longitudinal valley (Plate 11). The roots of the ridges are connected by wonderful convex folds in which the upheaved strata slope down from the axes in opposite directions.

Now came a most remarkable coastal region, near Lingeh at the entrance to Ormuz Strait. Here the folds are suddenly interrupted by gigantic brown or violet cakes, which from an altitude of 10,000 feet look like huge cow-pats (Plate 12). At first sight one thinks of an out-flow of lava. Really we had to do with a phenomenon met with in other parts of the world (Rumania, Adour, Southern Spain, Northern Africa, the Southern States of the American Union, Mexico, etc.), but nowhere so clearly displayed as here. They are called " diapers ". In consequence of excess of pressure, the more plastic underlying rocks—in this case motley clays with rock-salt and gypsum—have been forced through the superimposed and more recent strata to spread on the surface (Plate 12). Along the coast here about a dozen such diapers with a diameter ranging from three to eight miles can be seen from the plane.

As regards landscape, the most striking is that seen when flying over the savage, barren crags of the Ras-el-Djebel and the adjacent islands. This is the place where the Iranian chains turn sharply southward towards Oman in Arabia to make the narrows of the Persian Gulf. Whereas just now, except for the diapers, the only rocks in sight were tertiary, here the brown crags are formed from much older strata. They have been not only much denuded by erosion, but have actually for the most part been submerged, so that only the spines and crests show above the blue waters (Plate 13). We had a second pause for rest and fuel on the promontory of Jask close to an impoverished Iranian fishing village built upon a dazzlingly white terrace of coral and desert sand. In a few vigorous words the local representative of the air-transport service told us what life was like in this God-forsaken spot. Not merely was the heat almost intolerable as judged by the thermometer, but in summer the air was almost saturated with moisture, to the extent of 95 per cent.

Eastward of Jask, the mountains recede from the coast. The desert sands are of a monotonous yellow tint. Not until we attained a height of 13,000 feet did we escape from the heat. Here and there spurs of the hills came down to the coast, forming wide and wonderfully convoluted inlets. First Chahar, then Gwadar, where we were already in British Baluchistan. An hour and a half later we could see the rectangular figures of salt-pans along the coast, and very soon we sighted the big commercial city of Karachi. So rapid was our descent to the landing-stage that the sudden change of air pressure made us deaf and giddy for several minutes. Our first surprise on reaching Hindustan was to be welcomed by the Vögelis, Swiss like ourselves, who brought us some pinks from their garden.

We made only a brief stay for customs examination, but had a chance to stretch our legs. The doctor, whose business it was to make a physical examination, laughed when he heard why we had come to India. Then we made our fourth start.

6

On either side of the reddish-brown winding Indus, stretched yellow cornfields and plantations of young trees (Plate 14). Irrigation extends far eastward into the desert of Thar, so that wheat and cotton can be grown. These irrigation works have been one of the great achievements of the British in India.

The dust of the desert rose to an altitude of over 6000 feet. The setting sun striped the heavens with yellow and red rays. The wireless operator was kept hard at work during the next two hours until, through the starlit night, there loomed the revolving red projectors of Jodhpur Lighthouse. Red light-signals and big illuminated letters gave the direction of the wind and the course in which a landing should be made. We had to put on our watches two and a half hours. By local time it was ten minutes past eight, so we were ten minutes late on arrival.

Again we were surprised by a warm welcome. This was given us by our Australian friend F. F. Fergusson who, as civil engineer to the State of Jodhpur, has planned and executed an important irrigation scheme. He and his charming wife, a Parisian, promptly carried us off as guests to his pleasant tropical mansion surrounded by a sweet-scented flower garden.

CHAPTER TWO

IN THE PLAINS OF INDIA

JODHPUR

As if fallen from the skies, we found ourselves in an ancient world, which to us was a new one. The town of Jodhpur is not on the frequented routes of travel, is not an over-Europeanised and much-visited city, but a fragment of primitive India. Since the Hindu abstains from killing and regards many animals as sacred, primitive animal life abounds. On the aerodrome we already encountered gazelles, wild pig, and foxes. But our great surprises in this respect were reserved for our first excursion in an automobile.

The landscape reminded us of Africa. High above the white buildings of the city towered a mighty fortress built four and a half centuries ago, firmly planted, together with the Maharajah's palace, upon a huge block of old red sandstone, itself emerging from vastly older rhyolithic lava, which must have been erupted about five hundred million years ago (Plate 17). The general aspect of the country—a steppe adorned with candelabra-euphorbias, strongly reminding us of cactuses, with tamarinds and acacias, and with outcrops of granite and gneiss—cannot fail to recall the African landscape. A superficial glance is enough to make the expert understand why the famous geologist Eduard Suess came to the conclusion that the plains of India had originally formed part of the same continent as Africa. To this primitive hypothetical continent, before it was broken in sunder, he gave the name of Gondwanaland (the name was taken from the extant Gondwana, an ill-defined region in the Central Provinces of India, peopled largely by Gonds).

Scared by our auto, thousands of antelopes with long straight horns (oryx or kindred beasts), white, yellowish brown, spotted, or black, scattered across the plain, kicking up clouds of dust. The shores of the pools and ponds swarmed with giant crocodiles, sluggish beasts which are not inclined to get out of one's way (Plate 16). Close by were storks, herons, pelicans, and flamingoes. On the red rocks behind the fortress were families of sacred monkeys, so tame that they would snatch bananas out of our hands. The antics of these beasts were most amusing to watch. Loud were the anxious cries of the little quadrumana when a boar came in sight. They fled for the trees, and climbed swiftly into the tree-tops. Some of them were handsome creatures, with black faces amid a bush of white hair, and with tails a yard long. Bird-life, too, was abundant and varied. India would smell much of carrion if dead beasts were left to rot untouched where they fall, instead of being promptly cleaned up by the sanitary authorities — the vultures, to wit. Very numerous, too, were small crows, which began to make a noise early in the morning, rivalling the kites ; also the air was alive with turtle-doves, partridges, wild peacocks, green parrots, and sparrows (man's universal companions). Down from the quarries came one-humped camels, laden with blocks of sandstone weighing as much as 5 cwt.

But the natives and their buildings are very different from those of Africa (Plates 18 and 19). Though most of the former are dark-skinned, they are not negroid in type or colour, but Indians of Aryan descent, mainly Hindus by religion, divided into castes, the caste-mark being painted on the forehead. They are vegetarians. The population of Jodhpur native city is about 100,000, and the town is separated by walls and gates from the wide-spreading European settlement. The white invaders have learned how to build fine edifices of red sandstone ; government buildings, hospitals, banks, and bungalows. Here in Jodhpur there was no sign of the ill-feeling which exists in many parts of India between the natives and the British authorities, although wages are still very low, being about 3 annas (equals approximately 3d.) a day. In Rajputana the natives make a friendly return to a European's greeting. After all, the beneficial results of the skill of white engineers are plain to all men's sight.

TO MOHENJO-DARO, THE OLDEST TOWN
IN INDIA

Since we shall not subsequently have occasion to speak of the plains of India, I shall give here a few observations, some of which were made at a later date.

After so much information had been gleaned from excavations made in the early foci of Egyptian and Mesopotamian culture, in India the same method was used and bore good fruit.

Just as on the Nile and along the Tigris and the Euphrates, so in

9

Hindustan civilisation mainly began in the alluvial plain of a mighty river — a plain which had become a desert. Mohenjo-Daro is on the west bank of the Indus. The oldest civilisation in India grew up here, and is known as the Indus Civilisation. From an examination of sculptures and seals, which closely resemble those of the ancient city Ur of the Chaldees, it would appear that this civilisation dates back 4500 to 5000 years.

From Jodhpur we took the night-train northward across the desert of Thar to Hyderabad, Sind. Thence, again by night, we travelled by train in seven hours to the station of Dokri. Then came a ten-mile drive in a tonga, or two-wheeled cart, at first through a shady avenue, then through the village of Dokri, well planted with date-palms, and over huge irrigated fields, until the ruins which had been excavated from amid the jungle were suddenly exposed. There have been several different settlements, and the uppermost of them is crowned by a ruined Buddhist temple.

The buildings are of brick, and the narrow alleys intersect at right angles. The aqueducts and baths recall those of the ancient Romans. The excavations have shown that the town was rebuilt no less than seven times after being swept away by inundations, until at length a general rise in the level of the inundated land compelled abandonment. Where the deeper strata have been exposed one can see the remains of towers standing up like factory chimneys (Plate 15). What lies beneath this stratum, perhaps one containing yet older buildings, has been found inaccessible because of the sub-soil water.

A number of small household articles and other objects are pre-served in a well-equipped museum which has been established close to the ruins. The best comparison with other ancient civilisations is afforded by the numerous seals and amulets, most of them carved out of talc-granite. Among them we find swastikas, some with the arms directed to the left, and others to the right. Among animal carvings are those of the elephant, the ox, and the buffalo, but neither camel nor lion. Elephants, the aurochs, the tiger, and the crocodile, seem to have been regarded as sacred. The buffalo drew carts as to-day. A remarkable discovery has been made from a study of these relics in talc and clay, that the religious ideas which prevailed in this early civilisation on the banks of the Indus must have been very much like those of modern Hindus. The ancient inhabitants worshipped a Mother-Goddess, and also Shiva. We likewise find plenty of evidence of phallus-worship, in the shape of lingams like those that crown Hindu temples as emblems of fertility.

It is plain, therefore, that the roots of the confused religious and more or less animistic ideas of the contemporary Hindus date back

10

five thousand years, having changed very little since those remote days, notwithstanding the Aryan invasion of a thousand years later.

CROSSING HINDUSTAN

Everyone who goes to India wants to visit Delhi, the capital. But we could not " do " Delhi thoroughly, for it is a big place and we were pressed for time. Although our friendly fellow-countryman Steiner of the Swiss Hotel lent us his motor to make the rounds, it was impossible even to attempt to visit a tithe of the ancient monuments, fortresses, mosques, and towers of Old Delhi. For above all we wanted to see New Delhi with its magnificent modern governmental buildings, and to present our recommendations from the Swiss Academy, from the Political Department of Berne, and from the London Foreign Office. I had expected the friendly reception to which my experience of other lands under British rule has accustomed me, but in Delhi the authorities seemed to have little interest in our scientific aims, and we came away bitterly disappointed.

By rail, or in four hours by automobile, the traveller from Delhi can reach the much-visited town of Agra, where he will see the finest known Mohammedan architectural monument, the Taj Mahal, built of white marble three hundred years ago by Shah Jahan in memory of his favourite wife. One who, entering by the main portico, sees this splendid structure for the first time will be amazed by its beauty.

We were keen on seeing Benares, the holy city beside the Ganges, the cradle of Brahmanism and Buddhism. It is on a loop of the great river where it has turned temporarily northward again towards the Himalayas, after a long flow S.W. on leaving the glaciers in which it takes its rise. Already in prehistoric days Benares was a holy place. The habitations are on the left bank, for the right bank is a desolate, sandy steppe. About a million pious Hindus of all castes go on pilgrimage to Benares year after year. By dozens the sick, clad in rags, lie in the streets and many die there. But those who are well enough descend the stone steps to wash away their sins in the waters of the sacred stream (Plates 22 and 25).

The dust-storm which had darkened the skies overnight had happily cleared away. The rising sun appeared behind the farther bank (Plate 21). Hundreds of black-skinned and brown-skinned pilgrims of both sexes were already bathing in the Ganges, rinsing out their mouths with the water, and actually drinking it, although the corpses of little children, and even of the victims of smallpox, are flung into the

Ganges. Hiring a row-boat we had ourselves taken along the river-front of houses, temples, mausoleums, palaces, and towers to contemplate its wonders and take photographs in the morning light (Plate 23). Upon the stone steps corpses were being burned on open pyres. We watched a half-burned body flung into the water, where it was torn to pieces by crocodiles, fish, or giant turtles. Not deterred by this, Gansser suddenly resolved that he, too, would become a Sadhu, and the pilgrims were astonished to see a white man take a header into the foul but eminently holy water (Plate 24). Only after he had safely had his dip did we notice fine, slowly moving ripples travelling across the water-line, made by the eyes of the crocodiles.

Strange was the landscape over which we continued our journey by express train. Whereas hitherto in the plains we had seen little but the fields of dry stubble where rice had been grown and cut, livened only by a few green mango-trees, there now came into view fragments of the skeleton of the Indian peninsula, consisting of granite and gneiss with veins of pegmatite, which shone brightly in the sun. These kinds of rock form a hill-country bedecked with jungle and forest which gives the impression of a winter-garden in full bloom. Just as during spring-time in Siam or in the African Sudan, owing to the dryness and the increasing heat few of the deciduous trees as yet bore any leaves. Some, indeed, were green, but most were leafless, though fire-red and canary-yellow blossoms sprouted abundantly from the dry twigs ; [1] but also trees with siskin-green blossoms, such as the mango. At Sitarampo station we suddenly entered a large coal-basin. The seams outcropped at a very gentle inclination and some of them were being worked in the open.

The temperature was more than 100° in the shade. The farther we got to the S.E., the damper and hotter was the atmosphere. The plain was greener and was dotted with ponds. The clay huts of the villages, huts with quadrangular thatched roofs, stood among coconut palms and banana trees. We had entered the tropical zone of Calcutta.

The kindly Swiss Consul, Max Staub, put an automobile at our disposal, and this enabled us to despatch our business in the largest town of India. The office of the Geological Survey was our first objective. There we procured all the books and maps we needed in order to carry out our plans, and we shall never forget the ungrudging helpfulness of the director and the State geologists.

---

[1] Professor S. P. Agharkar, of Calcutta, has been good enough to inform me that the red-flowering tree is *Buta frondosa*, and the yellow-flowering one probably *Cochlospermum gossypinum*.

CHAPTER THREE

PRELIMINARY STUDIES IN THE FOOTHILLS

NEIGHBOURHOOD OF DARJEELING

AFTER an oppressively hot night in the hotel, we were awakened by the deafening clamour of crows and kites. Having finished our business on the ensuing day, next evening we set out by train for Siliguri. There are no sleeping-cars on these railways, but even the second-class provides couchettes with leather pillows. Every long-distance traveller in India takes his bedding with him in a roll.

At Siliguri, though we were close to the Himalayas, nothing was to be seen of the mountains, which were hidden behind heavy storm-clouds, frequently illuminated by flashes of lightning. Instead of continuing our journey by the tedious narrow-gauge railway, we took an auto, which in a few hours, on a road with countless elbow bends, brought us to Darjeeling. Here, at a height of 6500 feet, it was deliciously cool after the plains, the temperature being only 60°. The high mountains, Kinchinjunga and Everest, which are part of the regular view from Darjeeling, were still hidden in the clouds.

I do not propose to say anything about this famous hill-station, which so many travellers have already described, beyond referring briefly to its natural surroundings. Except where the steep mountain slopes have been terraced for tea plantations, the hills are thickly covered with an evergreen coat of ilexes, rhododendrons, and bracken. Wherever the hillsides have been deforested, they show a strong inclination towards landslides. In a Baby Austin, we drove along alarmingly steep curves into the deep gorge of the Tista, where we obtained our first glimpse of the geology of the foothills. We could see how the more recent Siwalik strata, with their sandstones and conglomerates, have normally been overlaid by the older mountain formations, like the nagelfluh or gompholite of the Alpine foothills.

As in the little open car we were driving along the riverside through the damp, dark forest, we saw in front of us something that stood up from the road like a telegraph pole. Not until we were quite close did we realise that this was a huge king-cobra in the fighting attitude. The chauffeur, a Nepalese, in his alarm could find nothing better to do than to step on the gas, so we flashed past the monster which faced us with its hood outspread and well within striking distance (Fig. 1). The king-cobra is one of the most dangerous of all the venomous snakes. Most of these flee when threatened, but the hamadryad or king-cobra, trusting in its size and its poison fangs, is always spoiling for a fight.

FIG. I.   OUR EXPERIENCE ON THE TISTA ROAD.   (H)

Jungle-fowl are common in the Indian jungle. The hens are inconspicuous brownish-grey birds, somewhat smaller than the hens of the domesticated species in the West. The cocks, on the other hand, have a brilliant rust-coloured throat and a gorgeous green tail. When you hear the bird without seeing it, you may be apt to think that you are listening to an ordinary chanticleer, but really there is a trifling difference in the crow, as I became aware when I first listened to this bird in northern Siam. The note of the jungle-cock is not so long-drawn-out, but ends staccato, thus :

k= harshly ; 2 × 8 means two octaves higher

Even more typical of the forest-calls in the tropical and sub-tropical regions of south-eastern Asia is the call of a black bird about as large

14

as an ouzel, which utters a succession of accelerando sequences on a rising note with very short but diminishing intervals, the call being repeated about seventeen times in 40 seconds. It can only be represented in tone-curves, upon the diatonic scale, thus : [1]

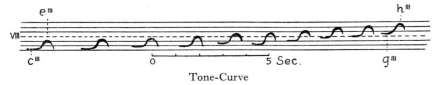

Tone-Curve

Wishing to follow the foothills farther to the east, we crossed the Tista in a primitive ferry-boat, which also carried the Baby Austin, to reach the chief tea-growing district in this part of the world, having passed the frontier into Assam. Since, when night was falling and we had reached Matelli, we could find no house of entertainment, we called on the manager of Samsing plantation to ask his advice. He himself was not able to put us up, but kindly referred us to the house of a native who, said the Englishman, would certainly provide us with tea, rice, and a shake-down. Here we enjoyed a stormy night such as I am not likely to forget. I have known a great deal of heavy rain in the tropics, but this, in what is reckoned the rainiest region in the world, exceeded all previous experience. It began with a few heavy drops—one, two, three. Then came a devil's tattoo upon the corrugated iron roof, as if, not buckets, but baths were being emptied, and it felt as if the roof must inevitably be staved in. The average annual rainfall is 400 inches, and as much as 480 inches has been recorded.

Next morning we were fully prepared to find that our retreat was cut off by a spate, but the river was scarcely swollen. The primeval forest had sucked up the water like a sponge. The adjoining principality of Bhutan is closed to the western world, and has not been deforested. Here is an example by which civilised countries might profit, for the devastating inundations of China and the Mississippi valley are due to the reckless way in which catchment areas have been stripped of their trees.

We carried away with us another interesting memory of these rain-drenched forests—the amazing beauty of the orchids which were parasitic on the tree-trunks ; above all, one species from which hung masses of golden yellow umbels.

[1] Cf. Arnold Heim, *Vogel- und Insektenstimmen aus den Tropen*, " Schweiz. Musik-zeitung ", 1923, Nos. 1-4, and separately printed by Hug and Co., Zurich.

ACROSS THE LOWER SLOPES OF MUSSOORIE

Having now glimpsed the forbidden kingdom of Nepal from the east, we returned to Calcutta and travelled thence about 800 miles to Tehri Garhwal, which lies to the N.W. of Nepal. Here the experts of the Geological Survey have made considerable progress with the issue of special maps, from which we could learn a great deal.

In two days the express conveyed us to Hardwar. This is another holy town, an important place of annual pilgrimage, on the right bank of the Ganges where the river breaks through into the plain. Since there was to be a considerable wait here, we got an Indian to guide us through narrow alleys and a dark gateway to the shrine where hundreds of men and women were bathing. Failing to see a prohibitory notice, and ignoring shouts of protest, I took a snap of the impressive and colourful scene. Instantly we were mobbed by a fanatical crowd, beaten up, and haled before the authorities, while the negative was seized and spoiled by exposure when undeveloped. Never have I had more occasion to regret my ignorance of Hindustani. After two hours' arrest, search, and proceedings in court, we were released with a caution, on swearing that we had taken no other views in Hardwar. We missed our train, which had departed without us, but were luckily allowed to keep the cameras. We had seen the " holy of holies " once, and were never to see it again.

The next train, that by which we were to continue our journey, brought hundreds of new pilgrims of various races and castes. Their clothing was richly coloured ; they wore turbans, had caste-marks painted on their foreheads, and were heavily laden with baggage. As we fought our way to the train against the stream of passengers leaving it, we could see monkeys disporting themselves on the roofs of the carriages and inquisitively contemplating the strange behaviour of their human brethren.

Now the train conveyed us to Rikhikesh, the terminus on the Ganges. Here the geologist J. B. Auden was awaiting us, ready to accompany us for the first six days of our journey, and to help us in securing porters and tents. This was to initiate us into foot-travel in the high mountains.

The first stage was made in carts, for we drove by a zig-zag road to Narendranagar, the new capital of the " independent State " of Tehri Garhwal. Thence we journeyed on foot over hill and dale and terraced slopes with primitive villages amid pine-forests. It was now that we began our intimate acquaintance with the structure of the Himalayas and caught our first glimpse of the distant peaks, which loomed for a few minutes at sunrise as a serrated ridge showing above the nearer mountains as a rose-pink and then yellow glory beneath the pale blue sky (Plate 26). Soon, however, as the day drew on, little white clouds began to appear, speedily coalescing to veil the mountains. Rarely at this season are they visible at eventide.

When it could be seen, however, the range extended more than 125 miles, from Nanda Devi (Goddess Nanda), 25,584 feet, the highest mountain of the Central Himalayas in the E., to the place where the Sutlej breaks through the chain in the N.W. Seen through field-glasses, the boldest of all the peaks is one that shows between Gangotri and Kedarnath. According to Auden, it is a granite tooth, which has hitherto been unnamed, but is now to be known as Sonero Parbat.

I must say a word or two about something which remains extremely vivid in my memory, the indescribable glory of the rhododendrons here (*Rhododendron arboreum*). This tree has a rugged stem which may be more than three feet in diameter, and it has ruby-red flowers as large as a man's open hand. The blossoms and the leaves constitute a matchless foreground to the snowy mountains. Our porters had a ruthless way of tearing off large branches, not because they admired the beauty of the growth, but because they wanted to chew the flowers, which have a tart taste like that of sorrel.

We must have looked like tramps, being weary and travel-stained, when we entered the fine health-resort of Mussoorie, with its luxurious hotels and bungalows, clinging to the mountain slopes at an altitude of over 6000 feet, surrounded by ancient cedars and ilexes. It remains a puzzle to me why this was not chosen as the hill-station of the Indian government in preference to Simla, for Simla is a desolate place with a poor outlook, whereas Mussoorie overhangs the garden-city of Dehra Dun and commands lovely views.

CHAPTER FOUR

THE MOTOR ROAD TO ALMORA

WE had once more to brave the heat of the plains, that we might take train to Kathgodam, the terminus of a branch line farther to the S.E. On April 19th, amid heat and clouds of dust, we were busily engaged in studying the tertiary foothills of the Siwaliks, when the third member of our party, Werner Weckert (who had telegraphed to us from Bombay) arrived, tired, thirsty, and looking more than a little shop-soiled, but glad to have ended forty disagreeable hours of railway travel. By the same train, luckily, arrived the three " tigers " we had engaged in Darjeeling — Sherpa porters, who were to prove our shock troops. The Sherpas are a mixed race from south-eastern Nepal, half Mongolian in blood. They have been found uncommonly useful as porters during expeditions to the high mountains, and these three fellows — Alis, Paldin, and Kirken by name — had done good work on the Everest and other expeditions.

On a well-made tarmac road, we drove swiftly to reach a higher altitude and a cooler atmosphere. The hot plain was left far below in the haze. On the curves amid the pine forest the chauffeur had to drive carefully to avoid running over the monkeys which sped heedlessly across almost under the bonnet of the car. Soon we had passed the sandstone region of the " molasse ". Towering above this were cal-careous crags, ranging up to 7700 feet. The road turns away to the right over a saddle, and suddenly the traveller finds himself in the Naini Valley, where there is a lake at an altitude of 6330 feet. The garages and sheds that decorate the entrance to this " happy valley " are hideous with their rusty corrugated-iron roofs ; but the quiet, greenish waters are most picturesque, whether ruffled by a breeze or tranquil enough to reflect the banks with their weeping willows, the bungalows and the hotels, and the rocks of China Peak.

We were in search of inexpensive accommodation, and found a well-situated boarding-house which charged only four rupees a day, all found, inclusive of bed-bugs which were extremely active at night. From here we could get in touch with the Allahabad Bank, where we opened an account, and received a cheque-book, which greatly simplified future payments.

Next morning we could not resist the chance of climbing China Peak, 8500 feet high, the best view-point in the neighbourhood. We had a lovely walk through the aromatic forest of cedars and cypresses, but it was hazy, and we could not catch so much as a glimpse of the distant mountains.

From Naini Valley we had to retrace our steps for a considerable distance to reach the point where the road branches off to Almora, seventy miles away. Eastward of Naini Valley we entered the valley of the Bovali, a shady stream fed by effluents from the north. Amid ilexes and red-flowering rhododendrons was a small forest tree with snow-white blossoms. So formidable were the geological complications disclosed along this winding road that we decided to postpone investigating its problems until our return. We had to make our way quickly into the high mountains if we were to get through the most important part of our work before the monsoon broke. But even in this casual journey we could make out that the formations grew more crystalline as we ascended, so that they must obviously be inverted.

Farther north we entered open terraced country which was extraordinarily beautiful. Three different stages could be recognised. First of all there were the great terraces, the vestiges of earlier valleys created by a river which no longer flows in its old channel. Secondly there were the much smaller terraces laboriously constructed by the hand of man, suitable for wheat-growing, or, where sufficient water is available, for rice-growing. The large terraces were of a rich green, from foliage ; the smaller ones were yellow in colour, from stubble, or brown where the earth had been recently ploughed. Thirdly one could see goat-tracks, marking the steeper heights with rhombs, which from a distance had the aspect of a network (Plate 27).

Continuing our northward journey, we reached Ranikhet. This is a place of considerable size, 5900 feet above sea-level, commanding a fine view. It is surrounded by extensive pine-forests, is well provided with hotels, hospitals, clubs, offices, bungalows, barracks, tennis-courts, golf links, and race-courses, with a big park — these quarters for the ruling race being well separated from the Indian bazaar and from the garages of the transport companies.

From Ranikhet we drove another thirty miles to the east, at first through thin pine-forests, then over the bridge across the Kosi, to climb thence, past custom-houses, to Almora, where the road for wheeled traffic ends (Plate 28).

CHAPTER FIVE

BEGINNING OF THE TRAMP

OUR first business in Almora was to visit the chief British official in the district, Deputy Commissioner Finley, whose office was in the highest part of the town. For while everyone is free to visit the outer precincts of the Himalayas, a special permit or passport is required before crossing the " Inner Line " to the Tibetan frontier. The young commissioner, who gave us a cordial reception, told us he was about to leave Almora on business, and that while he was away his native subordinate, the tahsildar, would attend to our affairs, and this man promised to make arrangements for obtaining porters. Now we were held up for some time, while impatiently awaiting our heavy baggage, which was being forwarded by Cook's of Bombay. Telegrams of enquiry proved fruitless at first. Still, we were by no means idle. We were admirably entertained in the dak-bungalow or rest-house which was provided for foreigners. They kept a good table, and we lived on vegetarian food with plenty of fresh vegetables. But the visitor had to provide his own bedding.

Indeed, we had more time than we wanted in which to explore the old town. It has 7000 inhabitants, 3000 of whom are Mohammedans. The white residents can be counted on the fingers. Although beautifully situated, at an altitude of well over 5000 feet, Almora is far off the beaten track, and has therefore thoroughly preserved its original Indian complexion. To the N.E. of the forest-clad ridge lies the bazaar. The street is well paved with quartzite flags (Plate 31). One shop or craftsman's booth follows another. The edibles, as usual in India, are black with flies. Here we made our purchases, rice, flour, maize— not forgetting sugar. Not for us the insipid castor sugar of civilisation, or refined white lump, but dark-brown crystals of raw sugar, with an aroma of honey, not deprived of its valuable constituents. For about three shillings we bought a sack containing 60 lb. How absurd it is that in Europe one has to pay more for raw sugar than for highly refined sugar which has lost its virtues. As far as canned food was concerned, except for a few small tins of delicacies, we bought only butter. Even in these very early days we were struck by the friendly attitude of the natives (Plate 32). An old man named Rai Bahadur invited us to tea with fruit and Indian sweetmeats in his fine house looking on the bazaar, a house whose front was adorned with wood-carvings (Plate 31). One evening a Brahman merchant, R. D. Bhatt, took us on a round of the temples, of which there are several in Almora. We climbed up to the Nanda Devi temple, adjoining which is the temple of Shiva with the holy lingam, Shiva's phallus, which is worshipped as an emblem of fertility. The reliefs, obscene according to western taste, have been hidden away with plaster. The result is that the temples, although seven hundred years old, appear dazzlingly white and new (Plates 29 and 30). Then we went up a flight of steps to the fortress, which was taken by the English in the year 1814. Farther to the S.E. we left the street through a gate leading into a garden of flowers where is the white temple of Sri-Krishna, adorned with images of the gods. At length, in a yet more remote spot, we reached, on a steep slope, the habitation of the orange-clad monks of the Ram-Krishna Mission, some of whom greeted us as fellow-Europeans. They were glad to converse in their almost forgotten mother tongues — German, Danish, and Dutch. Now the sun had set, so that it was after dark when we got back to the rest-house.

There are hospitals and large higher secondary schools in Almora ; and, to our great astonishment, we encountered a famous scientist. This was the Indian plant physiologist Sen, a pupil of Sir Jagadis Chandra Bose of Calcutta, the famous author of *Plant Autographs and their Revelations*, etc. Sen took us over his laboratory, where he has up-to-date microscopes and delicate instruments able to measure the electrical processes of the isolated living cell. Thus day by day we found ourselves more at home in Almora.

CHAPTER SIX

APPROACH TO THE HIGH MOUNTAINS

SWITCHBACK WORK

ON the evening of April 25th, after we had waited five days in Almora and when the sun was disappearing in a dust-storm, a lorry rattled in bringing our heavy baggage. What a relief! The coolies were ready to unload, and we ourselves were in high fettle. Over and above the large crates containing the main equipment, including the Attenhofer jointed skis, there were seventeen smaller cases, all numbered, and made ready for the porters before being sent from Zurich. Each was marked SHE. An Englishman who caught sight of these cases asked us where the " she " might be. We replied that, to our regret, we had had to refrain from any such companion, and that they were the initials of the " Swiss Himalaya Expedition ". Besides the cases there were half a dozen reddish-brown sailcloth gunny-sacks. These were quickly unpacked on the lawn in front of the bungalow.

The tahsildar had arranged for the hire of forty coolies. They were men from Nepal, brown-skinned, beardless Dhotial porters, of whom there are always plenty on the look-out for a job. They receive 12 annas (approximately a shilling) per day, and out of this sum have to provide their own food. We agreed with the tahsildar that they were to get every month 10 rupees in advance. The government, which acted as middleman in their engagement and was in some measure responsible for their good behaviour, was to receive 1 anna per man per day. Each porter was pledged to carry baggage weighing 60 lb. in addition to his private requirements.

The porters assembled ready to start early next morning. I still had some letters to write, but Weckert and Gansser were busily packing. On none of my previous journeys had the preparations gone off so smoothly, although the loads were a little too heavy. The ten rucksacks were full to bursting. Coolies, even of the lowest caste, are loyal and cultured after their own fashion — far more so than proletarians

22

1. The twin-engined "Douglas" of the K. L. M. on which we flew to India. Gaza
Aerodrome, Palestine. March 20, 1936.   (H)

2. "Dendritic Erosion" threatens the wheatfields of Western Palestine.
March 20, 1936.   (H)

3. Crossing the Sandy Desert in North-Eastern Egypt. From the south in the early morning, at an altitude of 5000 feet. (H)

4. Isolated settlements behind the Dunes in the Sandy Desert of North-Eastern Egypt, seen from the south at an altitude of about 6500 feet. (H)

5. Bethlehem from the south at an altitude of 6500 feet.
March 20, 1936. (G)

6. Jerusalem with the Mosque of Omar (above and to the left), from 6500 feet.
March 20, 1936. (G)

8. The Jordan near its mouth, surrounded by desert. March 20, 1936.

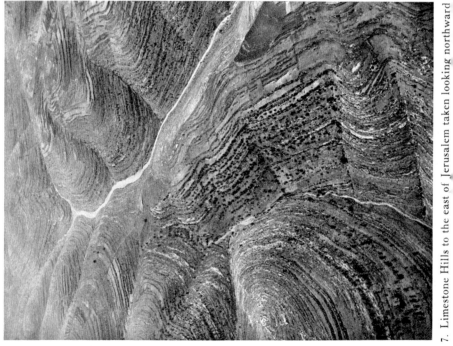

7. Limestone Hills to the east of Jerusalem taken looking northward

9. "Zebra Landscape" of the Syrian Desert in the eastern part of Transjordania. From an altitude of about 10 000 feet. March 20, 1936. The ribs in the sand are presumably strengthened by low scrub. (H)

10. Above the Tigris near Baghdad, showing modernised date-palm orchards. March 20, 1936. (H)

11. Arched ridges on the shore of the Persian Gulf to the south-east of Bushire, seen from about 8000 feet, looking east. Each mountain ridge corresponds to a young anticline. (H)

12. Diaper central mass with radial lines of outflow, near Lingeh on the Persian Gulf. From about 10 000 feet. March 20, 1936. (H)

13. Waterworn Desert Range near Ormuz, where the Iranian Mountain chains dip beneath the Persian Gulf to re-emerge in Arabia, March 20, 1936, from a height of 10 000 feet, looking north-eastward.   (H)

14. The Indus eastward of Karachi and its irrigated plains, March 20, 1936, from 6500 feet. (G)

15. In the excavations of Mohenjo-Daro, the oldest city in India, showing many-storeyed buildings. Valley of the Indus.   (H)

16. Sacred crocodiles being fed. Karachi.   (H)

17. The Maharajah's ancient fortress, built upon a block of red sandstone. (H)

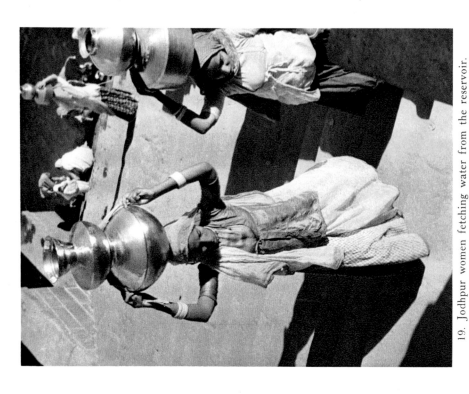

19. Jodhpur women fetching water from the reservoir.
March 23, 1936. (G)

18. Maharajah Ajit Singh's Mausoleum, built of red sandstone.
Mandore, near Jodhpur. March 23, 1936. (G)

20. The famous Taj Mahal at Agra. The memorial of a great dynast's love, built of white marble three hundred years ago. (H)

21. Sunrise over the Ganges near Benares. (H)

22. Old Sadhu nudist at Benares. (H)

23. The holy city of Benares on the Ganges. To the right a ruinous temple tower. (H)

24. Gansser among the pilgrims, ready for a header into the
dirty (but sacred) water. (H)

25. "The three wise men of the East." Benares. (H)

26. View from Dhanaulti, eastward of Mussoorie upon Bandar Punch, 20 000 feet, to the left, and Gangotri, 21 650 feet, to the right. In the foreground deforested foothills. April 15, 1936. (H)

27. Goat-tracks and wheat-terraces to the south of Ranikhet. April 21, 1936. (H)

28. Almora in the foothills, 5260 feet, from the north-east. The bazaar lies to the left, behind the crests. (H)

29 and 30. Whitewashed ancient Hindu Temple in Almora, crowned with lingam stones. (H)

in Europe and a great many of the so-called intellectuals. I never heard them speak roughly or abusively to one another, or say spitefully, " Don't try to foist part of your load on me ". To hear such terms you have to live among people who believe themselves to stand in the forefront of civilisation.

A farewell telegram to Zurich : " Starting with thirty porters, excellent spirit "— and we set out.

In addition to the Dhotials (Plate 33) we had three Sherpas, each carrying a rucksack. The tahsildar had also provided a man who was not to carry any burden, but to act as headman. He could speak a little English, and would be able to interpret. At the last moment we decided, after considerable doubts, to take along a " boy " as well, a servant who could cook, a very dark-skinned Indian of twenty, named Kali. He was the only one who stuck to us faithfully until the last. Most of the porters walked barefoot. Some of them had spent part of their advance in the purchase of cheap rubber-soled slippers (mules), but took them off whenever they came to a patch of sharp stones lest the rubber should be cut.

The heat was intense. In the dust and on the rocks in the blinding sunshine the scales of the crystalline schist glittered. The road led N.W. along a forest-clad ridge, then dipped into a valley, after which it ascended through an aromatic pine-forest to Bari Chhina, where we settled down for the night in the forest bungalow near the village, at an altitude of nearly 5000 feet. These bungalows, built of stone and wood, are as a rule charmingly installed, being provided with bedsteads, long chairs, tables, bathrooms for the usual tropical douche, and a certain amount of table furniture ; often, too, the windows are covered with wire netting to keep out mosquitoes.

Next morning at dawn, after a refreshing drink of sport-ovomaltine to wash down some " four-corn " biscuits, we continued our march along a lovely forest path. The stems of the fir-trees (*Pinus longifolia*) are spirally twisted beneath the bark, most of them having been incised and many of them scorched. Beneath each incision is tied an earthenware pot to collect the resin that exudes. Then this is transported in kerosene tins to Almora, where it is an important article of commerce.

Now we had to climb 2000 feet through the forest to reach the saddle of Dhaul Chhina at an altitude of 6060 feet, where we took a noonday rest in the shade of mossgrown oaks. This was the first place from which, above the haze, we got a plain view of the icy peaks with which we had still to make acquaintance. Then came a long and steep descent to Kanari Chhina. The forest bungalow here was beautifully

D

placed near a few poor huts (Plate 35), and a deep eddying pool in the adjoining stream invited us to a bathe. The forest was alive with birds. As usual in tropical Asia there was an abundance of common starlings with brown-white-and-black plumage. Also there were plenty of distinguished-looking hoopoes, with tits, woodpeckers, crows, turtle-doves, jays, falcons, and small black-and-white scavenger vultures somewhat resembling gulls in appearance (*Neophron ginginianus*). The elegant drongo (*Dicrurus macrocercus*), a shining, blue-black flycatcher with a long bill, sitting on a branch, would snap up insects as they passed in full flight. The dayal or magpie robin (*Copsychus saularis*), a fine black-and-white bird with a sweet voice, was also present, being almost invariably found among the foothills. In China this bird is highly prized as a song-bird, being taught to sing by a master as canaries are with us.

A GREAT MISFORTUNE

While we were enjoying a glorious evening and the magnificent view, a shadow fell on our happiness. Weckert complained of feeling very ill. He had throbbing pains in the right iliac fossa. This was most alarming, being the region in which the pain of appendicitis is usually felt.

Next morning, alas, there could be little doubt. Only one decision was possible; we must retrace our steps instantly.

Gansser summoned the porters, who were already starting, and we promptly unpacked some of our cases. Here was luck. We had a carrying-chair, and found six men, four of whom, relieved two by two, could carry the patient on their shoulders (Plate 34). While I went back with Weckert, Gansser slowly proceeded on our route to continue his geological observations.

With tears in his eyes, Weckert looked back on the mountains of fairyland, which he had so greatly longed to visit, but would probably never have another chance of seeing.

After nightfall we reached Almora. I went at once to the house of Mr. Finley, the Deputy Commissioner, which lay to the S.E. of the town, and found him eager to help. With his wife he took me to the quarters of the army surgeon, who made an immediate examination. Yes, it was unquestionably appendicitis. He telephoned to Ranikhet, and arranged for Weckert to be taken in at the army hospital there. Since, however, motor-cars may not drive on the mountain road by night, we had to stay for the time being in Almora.

When we got to Ranikhet, the operation was successfully performed in my presence. But the surgeon decided that there could be no question of the patient's rejoining us after a brief convalescence. When he was well enough to travel, he would have to return to Switzerland. For this journey, at any rate, we had lost our good comrade, who was the best alpinist of the party and an experienced cameraman. I was deeply moved when I had to say goodbye. The one consolation to us both was that the attack had occurred soon enough to get him quickly into hospital, for had we been a day or two farther on the journey, he would almost certainly have lost his life. Perhaps it was an advantage, after all, that our start was delayed by the tardy arrival of the baggage.

We two remaining Swiss, who had now to shoulder all the work and responsibility, were ruefully aware, as we made for the wilds, that we were both " happy " possessors of an unremoved appendix.

As soon as I got back to Almora, Mr. Bhatt procured a horse for me, and thus I was able without undue fatigue to overtake Gansser in a couple of days.

BY FORCED MARCHES TO ASKOT

From Kanari Chhina, the bridle-path runs for a few leagues eastward down the valley, then crosses the Sardju by an iron bridge, to climb the opposite rocky slope of limestone and barite, where, high above the stream, magnificent palms wave. In a shady spot we prepared a packet-soup. I was concerned about the porters, who had now to make long stages, and suffered from the heat. Not until evening was there any coolness in the air. For a while the path led beside a shady mountain torrent. Then came a tremendous climb, up zig-zags to the big village of Beringo. From the saddle where the houses stood, we had to climb another 300 feet to the dak-bungalow. It was finely placed on the top of the ridge, commanding a view of the snow-peaks, and was surrounded by pine-forests interspersed with horse-chestnuts, which were swarming with insect life. But the bungalow was locked. When the caretaker (called in India the chokedar) at length arrived to open the house, we were still without water and light.

I can hear in imagination, even now, the long-drawn-out chanting of the cicadas in C

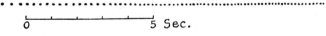

the rhythmic calls of a pigeon

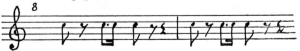

25

and the loud, fluty note of another bird, repeated hundreds of times
until far on into the night :

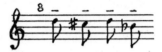

Facing the dak-bungalow was the sharp serrated edge of the still
untrodden Panch Chulhi (the " five caps "), the loftiest peak of which
pyramidal in form, attains an altitude of 22,600 feet (Fig. 2).   Before

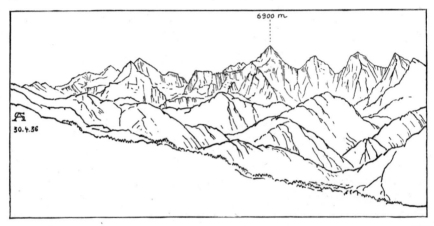

FIG. 2. PANCH-CHULHI GROUP, SOUTHERN ASPECT, FROM EASTERN GIRTIA.   (G)

sunrise, it stands out darkly in front of the clear sky, but is soon obscured
in the glare, whereas the more distant Nanda group lying to the left of it
now becomes more brilliant (Fig. 3).

The track now led downwards to a tea-plantation and past wide
terraced wheatfields, to reach the river Ram Ganga. On the other side
of the rope-bridge, half hidden in greenery, was an old Hindu temple,
where a strange-looking naked sadhu, his caste-marks picked out in
white, posed in front of the camera. His hair was dyed brown and plaited
into slender tails. The native huts ran a little farther along the valley
and there was a schoolhouse with a pent roof opposite the post-office.
There we lay down under cover on the stone flags, although it was not
yet noon. It was necessary to cool off for the rest of the day, since there
was a steep climb coming, the way was shadeless, and at a temperature
of over 100° it would have been too much for the porters.

But directly the heat began to subside, we were fiercely attacked by
mosquitoes, bugs, and fleas, until our bodies were covered with great

weals. I was much annoyed to find that I had forgotten the insect powder.
Of what avail was it, in the light of an electric torch, to kill a dozen bugs
and half a dozen fleas, when new blood-suckers continually arrived
presumably from the schoolhouse ?

Wishing to be beforehand with the heat, we started at peep of day to
escape from this place of torment. The magpie robin was the first of
the forest denizens to awake, and began his song rather sleepily.

By six-thirty we had climbed from 4200 feet to 5900 feet. At this
altitude there was a luxuriant growth of wild roses, and the red rhodo-

FIG. 3.   NANDA KOT, AS SEEN THROUGH FIELD-GLASSES, SOUTHERN ASPECT
(EASTWARD OF THE VALLEY).   (G)

dendrons on the shadier side were already blooming. The forest was
redolent of flowering trees.

A few hours later, when we had turned eastward again, and were
going downhill, I heard a cheerful hail. It was Gansser, coming to meet
me, and bringing good news. I was only one day late. He had sent on
some of the coolies. Others were returning with two tents and various
articles which we should not need now that Weckert had been left behind.
Soon we reached the bungalow of Askot, standing amid a group of ancient,
lancet-leaved white oaks. The table was already laid for dinner, and
decked with roses.

Towards evening, heavy storm-clouds gathered, and the rain we had
long desired began, accompanied by wind, thunder, lightning, and hail.

Darchula

The air now felt splendid, the storm having cleared and cooled it. In the glow of dawn, the distant peaks of Nanda Devi and Nanda Kot stood out plainly.

Our path led through the little village of Askot and its fields, past the loftily placed house of the absent Maharajah, and down into the mighty gorge of the Gori Ganga, by a descent from 4600 feet to 2100 feet — for the last time into tropical heat. The rocky walls stood in violet shadow, and grew steeper as we descended, this being a phenomenon we were to observe again and again later. The convexity of the walls of such valleys is the outcome of the increasing erosive power of the rivers, this in its turn being due to the steady increase in the height of the mountains.

Instead of proceeding up the Gori Valley, our path first crossed Gori Bridge, and then led downstream for more than a mile to the confluence of the Gori with the Kali Ganga, the river which borders Nepal. Upon the sparkling waters there had settled a flight of venturesome ducks, which allowed themselves to be carried round and round until almost engulfed by the whirlpool. In the neighbouring jungle were disporting themselves crested tits, blue tits, green parrots, and lively monkeys. Another surprise was our first encounter with Tibetans, encamped here in tents. Sweating profusely, they had stripped to the waist. On the caravan road we met four Nepalis, who greeted us with salaams. The people seemed to grow more friendly the farther we got from civilisation.

The deforested, desolate slopes of the Kali are made remarkable in places by terraced screes, some of which rise to as much as 800 feet above the river. They are relics of ancient stone-falls in days when the force of erosion was less. In the noon heat we reached the village of Balwakot, a forlorn place with miserable huts, the roofs being of slate. The porters, who are not usually inclined for a dip, followed our example, in water which was fairly cold, the temperature being only 60°. It had the milky look of glacier water, and was spotted in the sunlight. We put up our tent for the first time, on the lowermost terrace close to the river. Before we had got it firmly fixed, there was a heavy rainstorm, so there was no question but that we should have to spend the night there.

Next day, traversing several prettily placed villages, we became acquainted with the Mongoloid mountain tribe of the Bhotia (Plates 40 to 44). They have very prominent cheek-bones. Their skin is brown, their hair deep black. The women and children were washing clothes in a mill-race. Among them were pretty, laughing girls wearing garments of their own weaving, red and black, trimmed with silver thread. Their hair was plaited in numerous fine tails. The mother, who reminded us of a Moorish woman in North Africa, was giving her baby a bath.

For a while the bridle-path led along a limestone cliff high above the river, facing the Nepalese bank with its irrigation channels. Then we reached an expansion in the valley. Here there was a big village, whose huts and houses were embowered on the slope among mangos and banana trees. It was Darchula. A little farther on, close to the river on the lowermost terrace, a dak-bungalow awaited us.

We had learned that the Maharajah of Askot was staying in Darchula, so we sent him a letter of introduction which had been given us. The messenger brought back a typewritten acknowledgment, and an hour afterwards the friendly Indian ruler called on us. He came mounted on a magnificent black horse, and was dressed in the European style, riding-breeches, etc., except for a white Nepalese cap. His slender, sharply-cut face was characteristic of the cultured natives. It was a great pleasure to converse with him in English and to learn his views about India and its inhabitants. As a memento of this agreeable and instructive meeting, he gave each of us a Gurkha jungle-knife in a leather sheath.

To the Village of the Women Weavers

Continuing our journey upstream, three days after leaving Askot we came to a place where communication with Nepal was possible, not by means of a bridge in the ordinary sense of the word, but by a travelling chair hung to a couple of ropes which crossed the torrent. As we went by, we watched a man making this seemingly perilous traverse, pulled along by means of a third rope, and almost dipping into the stormy waters (Plate 36).

Slowly the bridle-path continued to rise from an altitude which at this point was 2800 feet. The Bhotias, with their flocks, were on their way into the mountains. The sheep and goats were laden each with a couple of cloth bags strengthened with leather, looped over the animal's back and kept from slipping fore or aft by attachment to a collar and a crupper. Most of the transport of goods through the Central Himalayas and into Transhimalaya is effected in this way by sheep and billy-goats, the load ranging from 20 to 40 lbs. per beast.

The creatures have fine horns, being more powerfully built and having a longer fleece than the lean, long-legged animals of the plain. Rice, wheat-flour, and sugar are the staples which are carried to the mountain villages and on into Tibet. Occasionally we encountered dzos, the hybrid offspring of yaks and ordinary cattle ; also zebus, humped cattle which draw the plough in these parts ; less often, ponies and mules. The water-buffaloes that flourish in the hot plains do not thrive in the hills.

The Bhotia mountaineers, old and young, taking their women with them as well as their flocks, go on trek year after year, some of them seeming fairly well off, for the wives wear silver chains adorned with

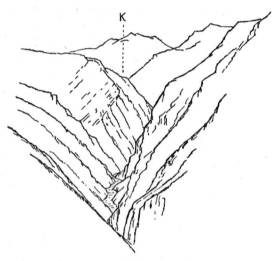

FIG. 4. KALI GORGE IN THE GNEISS HILLS ABOVE DARCHULA. THE VILLAGE OF KHELA (K) IS BEHIND THE SALIENT. (H)

red coral, and often have silver rupees fastened together into chains. We also met some Tibetans, who had a distinctly weather-worn aspect. These must have been the firstlings of the year, who had come over Lipu Lek with their flocks bringing salt and borax, also hides and fleeces, from the dry steppes of their lofty uplands to exchange them in northern India for some of the necessaries of life. During the mid-day heat they slumbered in the shade of their tents, old and young lying higgledy-piggledy, among them kids born by the wayside.

Since leaving Askot we have divided forces in the matter of geological studies. While Gansser enters our joint observations in the maps, I sketch the profile of the hills. One important point has already emerged. When we had crossed a much convoluted limestone ridge, we unexpectedly came upon the gneiss of the central chains, which was superimposed upon the limestone.

Delighted by this discovery, we climbed steeply for another 3000 feet to reach the end of that day's journey. It was the little village of Khela, the word meaning banana. In actual fact here, at an altitude of close upon 5000 feet, the last somewhat dilapidated fans of this tropical fruit-tree were flourishing on the arid slope among huge blocks of gneiss and half-concealed huts. Here we had another surprise. Not only did we find a post-office, but letters for ourselves, forwarded from Almora. This gave us our first glimpse of the admirably managed postal service maintained by the government of British India throughout those parts of the Himalayas that are under its rule. " Runners " are sent out daily from Almora, and carry the post by day and by night, with relays. Besides the post-bag, each postman carries a spear, having four little brass bells attached by rings immediately below the head (Fig. 5). The ringing of these bells scares away serpents and other wild beasts — and also keeps off evil spirits during the night.

The postmaster of Khela made us heartily welcome, and was proud to show off his three pretty daughters, who were clad in woollen garments made out of cloth hand-woven by themselves, and wore enormous brass nose-rings. They made no bones about letting themselves be photo-graphed (Plate 37). Here we found quarters for the night in the upper storey of a hut, but soon took refuge upon the veranda to escape the fleas, and also to enjoy the glory of the landscape beneath the full moon.

FIG. 5.
SPEAR WITH
BELLS. (H)

For the last time we had to descend to the level of 3600 feet, where a narrow bridge led across a tributary of the raging Dhauli Ganga. Then, in zig-zags, we climbed for hours over the gneiss rocks.

At 6200 feet we reached a terrace beset with pine-trees, oaks, and rhododendrons ; and soon afterwards at 6900 feet, we reached Panghu, a clean, pretty, and prosperous village. It was surrounded by magnificent shade trees—walnuts, horse-chestnuts, and ancient oaks. Wheat was growing vigorously on the surrounding terraces. The inhabitants greeted us smilingly as we went by. Soon we met a man whose appearance seemed as strange to us as ours may have seemed to the villagers. He was a bearded, naked sadhu, with white paint-marks on his face,

31

who looked quaint, as did Gansser, while the pair conversed by means of signs. This was by no means the first time when my comrade and I must have seemed queer fellows to the natives, for we wear shorts, with the white caps proper to the Nepalese and the Bhotias, while we are nude from the waist upwards like the Tibetans, and each has a hammer in his hand.

Once more we climbed by zigzags to a mountain ridge at 7000 feet, where the huts of Soso or Shosho stood. An idyllic spot in pure, cool air, with a splendid outlook. We seemed to have dropped into a small industrial centre, for, under the open sky in a little public square, about a dozen women and girls, red-cheeked, were engaged in hand-loom weaving (Plate 38). They were singing a labour-lilt, of which I here record a few bars :

The second air, in the minor key, resembles an Eskimo labour-lilt.

The men, meanwhile, sat on stones in the sunshine, looking on, spinning, or netting. Sometimes a bearded vulture (*Gypaetus barbatus*) soared overhead, the orange-coloured throat standing out in strong contrast to the blue sky. Bengt Berg has rightly called it the king of the birds. Its gliding flight strongly recalls that of the albatross. In fact the bearded vulture is as characteristic of the high mountains as the albatross is of the South Seas. But there are other birds to attract attention in the mountains. For instance, a few male cuckoos were disporting themselves among the sacred ancient trees and pursuing their mates. Their call has the same tones as that of the European cuckoo.

Towards night, as the sun passes behind the mountains, the goat-herd drives his goats to the village and into the shed where they spend the night. Some of the women stick to their looms for as much as three-quarters of an hour after sunset. Then the sexes dance together for a while to the accompaniment of Nepalese folk-songs, until, as if at the word of command, everyone goes to bed.

32

To Camp in Shankula

In the morning cool of May 9th we sent the porters ahead while we two geologists, taking the Sherpas with us, climbed the nearest mountain, since it seemed likely to afford a good view. During the night the temperature had fallen to 54°. The grassy slopes on the sunny side emitted an agreeable odour of pink thyme. There were also many small mountain asters ; and on the rocks of sericite and chlorite schist, shrubs of white-flowering cotoneasters were abundant. In most respects, however, there was little characteristically alpine vegetation here, because of the frequency of fires. It was otherwise on the shady side. Unless they had been destroyed by fire, wherever we got above an altitude of 8000 feet we found a virgin forest of cypresses with trunks 3 feet 6 inches thick, often hung with beard-moss. There were also foliaceous trees, such as sycamores, a pink-flowering rhododendron, a species of willow, guelder-roses (*Viburnum*), raspberry canes, bamboos, and the smaller plants that grow closer to the ground, such as wild strawberries, Solomon's seal (*Polygonatum*), thistles, ferns, and ivy.

At eight o'clock we reached the summit, at a height of 10,230 feet. The view was magnificent, but the mountains were not so clear as they had been the day before. To the N.W. we saw peak after peak of an unnamed chain of mountains ranging up to 20,000 feet. About twenty miles away, N. 25° E., was a sharply pointed ice-crowned tooth — manifestly 62 B on the map — a peak 20,270 feet high. But the highest mountain in the panorama was a snowy cone to the east, projecting above the mighty dark wall of the nearer hills. This must be the one marked Api, 23,399 feet, on the map, but its correct name is Nampa, as it is called on the older map.

While we stood on the mountain-top in the dazzling sunshine, to make sketches and take photographs with the camera fixed upon a tripod, fritillaries and other butterflies fluttered round us, while overhead were numberless swallows.

A steep descent through the cypress forest, rendered difficult by the bamboo-canes, brought us back to the path, which led through villages surrounded by walnut trees and wheat-fields. But hereabouts rye seems to be the favourite cereal. When we had passed a lateral gorge, we began to climb once more. For the first time we traversed a forest of indigenous horse-chestnuts, which gave place at a higher level to oaks. Gradually the skies became overcast, it grew dark and drops of rain

33

fell. We quickened our pace, to reach the top of the pass at four o'clock, tired and dripping with sweat. The altitude was 9840 feet. Then, on the N.E. declivity, we walked for several miles among huge heaps of detritus with gigantic blocks of micaceous gneiss, like those near Darjeeling. This was the site of an ancient landslip, which could only be recognised as such close at hand, being overgrown with old oak trees, the finest we have yet seen. Trunks as thick as five feet were common. The gnarled branches were hung with brown mosses and lichens, and beset with epiphytes. Crowds of monkeys with their young, scared by us strange 'intruders, raced through the tree-tops, making a noise like that of a storm.

At length, when the sun was on the point of setting, we reached camp at Shankula. Here we pitched our tents among similar habitations of Tibetans, mostly lamas, and of Bhotias making for the high mountain pastures with their flocks. Among them we made our first acquaintance with two men who were to play an important part in our subsequent journey—men on their way to summer quarters. We saluted them Indian-fashion by raising both hands with the palms joined. They were : Nandaram, the wealthy patriarch of Garbyang, who wore a white turban ; and Chandru Singh (the meaning of the former name is " moon " and of the latter " lion "), a young merchant who spoke excellent English, and was therefore able to give us much useful information about our route.

As we sat down on boxes to enjoy a warm drink, we were surrounded by a crowd of interested spectators. One of them was a young Brahmin, who described himself, not as a sadhu, but as a boy scout, and had been living for a month alone in a straw hut to pray the livelong day beside the murmuring torrent. He subsisted exiguously upon the alms given by passers-by, slept on the stones in front of his tiny hut, wrapped in a blanket, and every morning took a bath in the ice-cold stream. His intention was, as soon as the high passes were no longer snow-bound, to cross Lipu Lek into Tibet and make for the sacred mountain of Kailas.

This friendly pilgrim, who looked upon us as pilgrims, insisted upon our entering his hut, where he gave us some of the marvellously aromatic wild honey he had gathered in the woods. In return we presented him with a packet of our four-corn biscuits. Then, with the aid of a glowing brand from the fire, we found our way back through the darkness across the little bridge and over the stony encampment to our tent.

34

" We can make Garbyang in a couple of days now, can't we ? "

" Yes, if you put your best foot foremost," replied Chandru.

But at this juncture our geological work became more interesting than ever, and took up a great deal of time. Besides, we should not be able to make good progress until the track was freed from the migratory flocks.

After we had spent two days upon a wide detour to the west because we could not get across the Kali Gorge, we now had to make our way back to the main valley along the left side of a lateral gorge. Soon we were standing on a ledge of rock commanding a magnificent view down the valley (Fig. 6). For about 1500 feet above the stream,

FIG. 6.   INACCESSIBLE KALI GORGE NEAR SHANKULA IN GNEISS AND MICA-SCHIST. (LOOKING DOWN THE VALLEY).   (H)

the average slope was 60°. But the grandeur and savagery of what we were contemplating excelled anything we had ever seen in the Alps. No photograph can give an impression of it. The rocky walls of the valley are very sharply cut, the strata having an inclination of 45° to the N.E. and they are made up of micaceous schist and quartzite. Once more they were convex declivities which showed not a trace of glacial action (Plate 39).

Gansser rushed headlong across the rocks to a vantage-point from which he could take a movie picture of the porters as they passed along a particularly striking part of the trail. Simultaneously, from much farther back, with a second apparatus, while I gradually depressed the bearing of the lens from the skyline to the raging stream, I took a different shot.

The path now led down to the torrent, and then climbed steeply past a waterfall in a lateral gorge—a gorge that reminded us of the Staubbach. Next we reached a plateau named Malpa or Malipa, where we camped among the Bhotias. We were now only a stone's throw from the cliffs on the Nepalese side of the gorge.

During the night I awoke from pleasant dreams, overpowered by the roar of the rushing water. The moonlight on the rocky walls was wonderful. Even in the Grand Canyon of Arizona I was not so greatly impressed by the working of the mighty force of erosion.

It seemed incredible when, at the first glimmer of dawn, I heard a high-pitched voice overtopping the thunder of the stream. After a little search we discovered the singer. It was a small bird, apparently a water-ouzel, sitting close to the stream upon a besprinkled boulder.

Shortly after five o'clock we overtook the Bhotias with their flocks, who had broken camp before daylight. When we meet these migrants it involves considerable delay, for we have to watch out lest the sheep should thrust us over the precipice.

" The terminal moraine ! " exclaimed Gansser at this moment. Yes, with the eyes of a hawk he had from afar made an important discovery, which subsequently I was able to confirm. We were about to pass from big rocks to detritus. Beyond question it was a conglomerated terminal moraine clinging to the slopes. In the conglomerate were deeply scored blocks, bearing witness to the ice-age.

On the cliff facing us, not far above the terminal moraine, a bearded vulture had built her nest. Usually one can recognise these nests from the white droppings wherewith the rock beneath is spotted. The hen bird sat composedly upon her solitary nestling, paying no heed to our shouts.

We were now at an altitude of 7000 feet. In the present epoch the main valley is free from ice, and the glaciers in the lateral gorges end at heights ranging from 12,400 to 13,800 feet. This shows that the quaternary ice-age in the Central Himalayas was much colder than I found it to have been in the Chinese-Tibetan frontier regions of Minya Gongkar, but not nearly so cold as in the Alps where, at this date, the glaciers extended far down into the foothills.

The interesting spot we were now passing also gave valuable indications as regards the amount of erosion that had taken place since the retreat of the glaciers from 15,000 to 20,000 years ago. For on the Nepalese side of the valley, a little lower down the stream, just above the bearded vulture's nest, could be seen the traces of an ancient river-bed which had been filled up with moraine deposit. The bottom of this bed must have been at least 160 feet above the present river.

A few hours later we came to a large inner moraine wall, extending up to a height of 8800 feet.

Before reaching Malpa we noticed some pegmatite veins sparkling with black tourmaline crystals, cutting across the stratified hills of micaceous schist and quartzite independently of the stratification and convolution of these. Up here such veins are distinguishable from a distance, owing to their lighter tint, and are distinguishable also from granite. From contact with them, new minerals have originated under the influence of the ancient flux—such as red garnet, greenish limestone-silicate, and bluish disthene (cyanite). We had, therefore, plenty of hammer-work, chipping off, labelling, and packing specimens, to gain materials for subsequent chemical and microscopical investigation.

At the edge of the expansion of the valley where there are screes, and where two lateral valleys debouch, on the northern slope at 8500 feet is the village of Budhi, consisting of about fifteen stone huts, and reminding us of a mountain village in the Ticino. One of the porters pointed at a distant cliff. I could not understand what interested him until I had examined it through the field-glasses. It was not a vulture's nest, for the spots beneath the overhanging rocks were brown. They were bees' nests, built where they would be safe from men or beasts with a taste for honey.

After an hour or two's rest in the village whose summer population had not yet arrived (cortals, as such villages are called in the Pyrenees) our strength was recuperated. It was only six miles, we were told, to reach our first aim. Only six miles, but they were mountain miles, the first two of them being a very steep climb in zig-zags. The sun was blazing, and the rocks like an oven. We were drenched with sweat when, at 10,460 feet, we reached a green plateau, bestrewn with boulders, but mainly carpeted with flowers : violet iris, carmine primulas (*Primula denticulata*), small pale-blue gentian, odorous violets, flowering shrubs such as daphne, barberry, and cotoneaster. Behind were groups of tall fir trees, and in the background the snow-peaks : the ice-encrusted summit of Nampa, which we were rapidly approaching, and nearer, to the left of Nampa, a mountain like the Silberhorn. They were resplendent above the dark forest of a Nepalese lateral valley (Plates 45-47). Shall we reach them ?

Our goal was in sight only three miles away, and we reached it in a couple of hours—the village of Garbyang.

CHAPTER SEVEN

IN QUARTERS AT GARBYANG

AT home, before coming out to India, I often studied the maps of the Himalayas, and was always attracted by the name and the position of Garbyang. That, I thought, must be a wonderful centre for excursions in the high mountains. Now we were actually there. But to begin with we had to give the porters a day's rest.

We took up our quarters in the dak-bungalow. It was about a furlong behind the village, on a terrace at an altitude of 10,330 feet, and consisted of two whitewashed stone rooms, each with a little window, whose panes were broken. Anyhow there had once been glass here, and glass is a great rarity in the uppermost parts of the Himalayas. In each room there was a table, a bedstead, and a few still usable chairs. Within the walled enclosure, close to the bungalow, stood a second stone house for the coolies, and here our cooking was to be done.

Not only had we got above the region of the heat, but, with an average temperature of 42°, we found writing in the early part of the day so cold that we were glad to accept the friendly offer of some of our men to light a wood fire on the open hearth. We immediately had warmer clothing unpacked. How many months were we likely to wear an " Everest rig-out " ?

For our mid-day dinner, Kali cooked us risotto. Supper consisted of rice boiled in milk with some dried fruit soaked and stewed, and sport-ovomaltine as beverage. The coolies were now to have what for them was a rich diet. During the fortnight's march hither they had lived on an exclusively vegetarian diet, consisting mainly of rice and unleavened bread which could be bought on the road. Now they expressed a wish to have some goat's flesh, so we gave them five rupees to buy a goat, of which soon nothing but the skin and bones remained. The porters were always keen on cigarettes. Although we geologists did not smoke, they regarded it as a privilege to get cigarettes from the

38

sahibs after a heavy day's march. Aware of this expectation, we had
provided ourselves with a supply. They were not pleased, however,
by our decision to send back more than half of them to Almora next
day with our collection of stone specimens. The sorting-out of the
favoured " survivors " was a difficult problem.

The village rose from the same terrace as the bungalow. Having
no less than two hundred houses, it was a large place for the inner
Himalayas, the only other settlement of that size in the Almora district
being Milam, far away to the N.W. Seen from close at hand, Garbyang
was " not so dusty ". Besides the primitive huts, there were some
fine-looking old two-storeyed houses with lovely wood-carvings on the
door- and window-frames. Being painted reddish-brown, they stood
out in splendid contrast with the deep blue sky. This Bhotia settlement was obviously under Tibetan influence, the staircases in the
two-storeyed buildings were cut out of a tree-trunk, and near by some
prayer-flagstaffs had been propped against the wall (Plate 49).

It being only the middle of May, many of the houses were still
empty, but people were coming up daily from the valley, and families
settling in. Among these newcomers was the postmaster, a lean old
fellow, a relative of the Maharajah of Askot, as was plain enough from
his wizened, sharply-cut features (Plate 54). He could speak a little
English, and his intentions were excellent. He brought our correspondence to the bungalow. Being well-informed as to the currency
he knew that 1 rupee = 16 annas ; 1 anna = 4 pice ; and 1 pice = 3 pies :
also that a letter to India cost 9 pies = 3 pice — and he had an ancient
pair of scales, but the carriage of mails seemed slow here after Switzerland
and the air-service. We had to tell him as much. When we handed
to him a sealed packet containing exposed films which were to be
developed in Zurich and registered to an address in that town, he did
not know what to make of it. We squatted beside him for hours,
I doing sums in the hope that the letter would not be understamped.
In the end we relied on the belief that the native postmaster at Almora,
who was also a friendly fellow, would make up any deficiency.

The post-office was built over a goat-stable, and access was gained
by a narrow staircase. It was a dark and dusty room with a very small
window. The floor was of clay, on which were scattered a few mats
for the visitors who squatted there. The whole stock of this office,
consisting of stamps, a few official forms, and a post-marking outfit,
was kept on the floor wrapped in a cloth.

Such primitive institutions have another aspect which is characteristic
of Bhotia villages. Whereas the Chinese begins his house by digging

E

a privy, and looks askance at the guest who does not use it and therefore deprives him of precious manure, the Bhotias eased themselves early in the morning by squatting in the street. The result was that we sometimes brought in stinking tokens from the unsavoury village.

Our coolies settled down on the grass-plot in front of the bungalow, where they lay about in the sun stripped to the buff, rubbing oil into the skin and doing massage to one another. This gave us something to think of. Surely someone had told me years before that the eastern Tibetans are accustomed, as a protection against cold and the weather, to smear themselves with rancid butter — though many of them never dream of washing, while being marvellously energetic and hard as nails? What, on the other hand, does the civilised European or American insist on whenever possible after a fortnight's march? A hot bath, of course, in which he uses plenty of soap. But surely this must deprive the skin of its natural fatty covering, and make the body more sensitive to wet, cold, and bacteria, instead of protecting it. We Swiss geologists were reminded by the coolies of something we had forgotten, and henceforward we practised inunction like our men.

On this day of rest I took occasion to study the feet of those of the porters who had not yet deformed them with cheap rubber shoes. The chief thing we noticed was that the inner side of each foot was straight, or even concave, so that the great toe turned towards the mid-line of the body, and broadened at the end (Fig. 7), whereas our great toes were compressed and distorted by the pressure of shoes. When will our shoemakers adapt their wares to the undeformed foot, instead of, the world over, making shoes of the " civilised " shape, pointed in front and with unduly shallow toe-caps which mutilate the feet and cause all kinds of foot-trouble?

I need hardly say that we could not rest until we had solved the geological puzzles of Garbyang.

As if cut with a knife, the upper border of the terrace runs along the side of the valley, not only in the village, but for several miles above Garbyang. On the opposing, the Nepalese, face was the village of Changru, also upon the terrace, which ended down-valley towards the S.W., in the transversely disposed plateau (marked 10,809 feet on the map) about two miles from Garbyang. A further visit showed that the lower part had the aspect of detritus, of moraine, but the upper part the aspect of landslip. Vainly did we seek a place from which the landslide had come. Had it fallen upon the glacier which was once there? This much was certain, that the river had been dammed up by the transversal plateau. This gave rise to a lake, which extended

40

more than six miles down the valley. Gradually this lake was filled up with fine silt which now forms the fertile soil of the terraces of Garbyang, through whose deposits the river has once more cut deeply. On its new course, deviating to the left of the wall, it reached rock-bottom under the moraine, and is now cutting into that rock-bottom

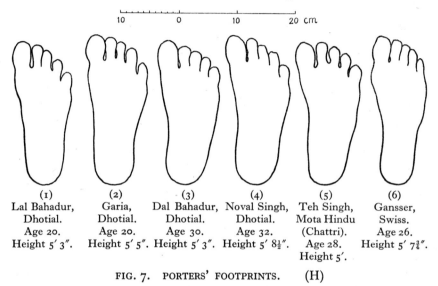

	10	0	10	20 cm.

(1)	(2)	(3)	(4)	(5)	(6)
Lal Bahadur,	Garia,	Dal Bahadur,	Noval Singh,	Teh Singh,	Gansser,
Dhotial.	Dhotial.	Dhotial.	Dhotial.	Mota Hindu	Swiss.
Age 20.	Age 20.	Age 30.	Age 32.	(Chattri).	Age 26.
Height 5′ 3″.	Height 5′ 5″.	Height 5′ 3″.	Height 5′ 8½″.	Age 28.	Height 5′ 7¾″.
				Height 5′.	

FIG. 7.   PORTERS' FOOTPRINTS.   (H)

yet more deeply, instead of taking the old more direct valley towards Budhi. It has cut down about 800 feet into the transversal plateau (Plate 47).

Every day a bearded vulture patrols the valley. In its wonderful soaring flight it is able, without beating its wings, to glide as close to the ribs of rock as an albatross glides almost touching the crests of the waves in the South Seas. At Garbyang there are some of the carrion crows and kites (*Milvus migrans*) which enliven the lower levels. As for the red-billed Alpine crows (*Pyrrhocorax pyrrhocorax*), huge flights of these settle down on the flowery meads. Their call reminds us of that of the European jackdaw.

On the second day after our arrival, since I had still some writing to do, Gansser made the first excursion to higher altitudes, accompanied by Paldin. They scaled the rocks immediately behind the village, but alas, after we reached Garbyang there was a change for the worse in the weather. I anxiously noted that the clouds were gathering overhead, and was somewhat disturbed as to the possibility of their being lost in the mist. At length, as twilight was falling, there came a hail.

They returned with noses blistered by the sun, but in enthusiastic mood. " Through a rift in the clouds I saw all the way to Gurla Mandhata in Tibet. Magnificent peaks, white horns with fluted icy encrustation, are pretty close to us in the S.E., in Nepal, whereas the twenty-thousander above Budhi, which had seemed attractive to us on the map, is less interesting, and probably unclimbable." (Plate 79.) After a long scramble over the ridge, Gansser reached an altitude of 16,467 feet, at a point where the Indian topographers erected a cairn long ago. He brought me back a big spray of foliage. The specimen stands on my table as I write ; it is vigorous and tough — rhododendron from 13,000 feet, with white, violet-bordered trumpet-shaped flowers in spherical tufts. I have never seen anything of the sort in a garden. (It was, presumably, *Rhododendron lepidotum*.)

CHAPTER EIGHT

ENTERING FORBIDDEN NEPAL

MEANWHILE Nandaram had reached Garbyang, being the first member
of his family to arrive, and we had a talk with him in his broken English
and our broken Hindustani—with Kali's help having quite a long pow-
wow (Plate 50). His view was that we should find no serious difficulty
in getting across into Nepal. The north-west corner of this kingdom
is separated from the rest of Nepal by impassable mountains, and
except from Tibet can be reached only from the British side. Besides,
this region contains no more than a few little villages inhabited by
harmless people. This news helped us to make up our minds.

Two decidedly unsafe bridges, which are occasionally swept away
by floods, lead from Garbyang into the forbidden realm. Close to the
upper one, near the village of Changru, is a stone cabin for a sentry.
We chose the lower bridge, 500 feet below the terrace (Plate 59).

ON THE API GLACIER

Our first objective was the glacier on the western side of Nampa.
Since the main arms of this glacier obviously came down from Api,
we called it the Api Glacier. Over and above our geological work,
we wanted to find out whether Nampa could be climbed from that
side. A shepherd guided us across the Alpine pasture. After crossing
the bridge, we took a narrow track which first led downwards beside
the river through a wonderful landscape. Small brooks flowed from
beneath the rocks, and on the green areas that lay between odoriferous
ferns and pines spring was in full bloom with a glory of carmine
primulas. Tits were twittering among the trees, busied in building
their nests. After this, the path rose steeply.

At 10,820 feet we emerged from the pine-forest carpeted with
needles on to an alpine pasture which, like the others, was covered
with carmine primulas. With the commonest and most luxuriant

43

Primula denticulata was associated another, smaller and short-stalked kind (*Primula minutissima*, which resembles *Primula viscosa* of the Alps). Sparkling yellow anemones and a star-shaped yellow flower (*Oxygraphi, glacialis*) also grew in this meadow. For the first time we came across a large, dark-violet primula with lancet-shaped leaves (*Primula nivalis* var. *macrophylla*).

Now our mountain path petered out. The climb on a steep ascent over an ancient conglomerated moraine was risky for the porters. The needle-shedding pines were replaced by juniper bushes. Then, at 11,970 feet, we emerged on to a lofty moraine terrace, which reminded us of an alpine rose-field in our homeland. Here, however, the flowers were not red, but pale yellow, with a scent like that of fruit-essence. There were a few butterflies, the first of the year at such a height — an Apollo and a little Bear. Then, from a thicket burst out two barking dogs, and two men, one carrying a musket, the first Nepalese we encountered. At about a hundred paces distance our parties faced one another. Would they seek to arrest us ? Slowly we approached them, noting as we did so that they were more afraid of us than we were of them. We inferred that they must be poachers. Remarkable-looking fellows, in clothes that were little more than rags which had been patched and darned again and again. When they saw that we did not intend to do them any harm, they became thoroughly genial. We all sat down together, for our men needed a short rest. The old fellow who had the musket, which was a muzzle-loader, laid it down with his tinder-box, and began a savage sword-dance, of which Gansser happily took some movie pictures (Plates 61 and 62). The other fellow sucked away at a bamboo tube the lower end of which was inserted into the earth. What was he doing ? He had put tobacco and embers into a hole in the ground, thus making a sort of pipe.

At 13,100 feet the carmine primulas were still growing, but were as small and stunted as if they belonged to a different species. " Why should you poor creatures grow here so high up on the rough mountains, when your kindred in the warm valley below can thrive and enjoy life ? "—" We would not change with them ", they might answer. " What do we care for luxury and an easy life ? No doubt we have to endure hardships. But when the sky is blue and the sun drenches us with ultra-violet rays we have just as good a time as those can have who live on the lower slopes."

Now we reached a recent moraine, with an icy coat in which were puddles here and there. For another hour we continued to climb over detritus and snowfields until, on the lateral moraine of the Api Glacier,

44

at an altitude of over 14,100 feet, we found an open space where, with our ice-axes, we could level the surface sufficiently for a camp. It was hard to induce the porters, most of whom walked barefoot, to climb over the snowfield, though they could return for the night to the shelter of an overhanging rock.

Next morning there was fog and sleet when we awoke, so that we could only make a late start, roped and using our ice-axes. As we were nearing the upper edge of a steep snow-slope, Kirken, who was not roped, slipped, and slid down on his back, the instrument bag with him, for more than 300 feet into the valley. Luckily there were no stones in the way, so that he got off with a few trifling excoriations.

It was plain enough to us that, although the Sherpas are used to ice and snow, they have had no experience as alpinists, and are not fitted to serve as guides.

From a terrace at an altitude of 15,250 feet we got an extended view of Nampa. Although its form was partly veiled, we were able to sketch and photograph it, and, with the field-glasses, make out a route by which an ascent might be possible. Only the central split portion of the ice-cap seemed likely to offer difficulties. Above this was a broad and gently sloping snowy surface which rose to the very summit. It would be admirably suited for skis, and seemed to have been made for Gansser and Weckert. Of course the climb would be impossible unless the weather improved (Plate 60).

Since the mist thickened once more, we had to renounce attempting the climb of the peak opposite to Nampa. For the first time we put on the jointed skis, made for us by Attenhofer for use in the Himalayas. When opened, they are locked by a key, the hinge being for convenience of transport. This short ski-run on the Api Glacier is certainly the first in northern Nepal, perhaps the first anywhere in Nepal.

On these skis, we pressed a few miles on up the Api Glacier, whose surface was covered with a fresh fall of snow. But the excursion proved unsuccessful, for the peaks were completely hidden and the weather grew worse. On arriving back at our encampment, we had an agreeable surprise. While we were away, the porters had brought up some wood. Kali had cooked a tsamba soup (tsamba, roasted barley meal, is the staff of life in Tibet) and made us some tea. In addition we had a dessert of grape nuts with cane-sugar and rhubarb fool, made from wild rhubarb gathered on the way up at an elevation of 11,500 feet.

On the second morning we spent here our tent was encrusted with frozen snow. The weather was so threatening that we decided not to waste any more time at this altitude, but to return down the valley to a lower level. While Gansser was still working with his geological hammer to secure a unique mineralogical specimen—a cyanite crystal eight inches long embedded in a moraine block—Kirken, who was on the snow-field, suddenly vanished from sight, rucksack and all, having broken through the ice into a glacier rivulet. However, no serious harm was done, and he soon climbed out of his icy bath, more frightened than hurt.

The weather got steadily worse during our descent. Rain followed the snow, and we were wet to the skin before we reached the dak-bungalow at Garbyang, and were able to dry ourselves in front of a roaring fire.

During our absence, the mail had arrived. One of our letters was from Weckert, and it extinguished our last hope that he might be able to rejoin us. " For some time I was pretty wretched, sweating profusely by day and it was still worse by night. Now, I am glad to say, they move my bed every day out into the veranda, where I can see the mountains. I feel battered and shipwrecked. But everyone here is most kind, and I must make the best of things. The doctor says I must stay in hospital for another week, and there doesn't seem to be any chance of my following you".

When poor Weckert was able to get about again, there was nothing for him to do but travel home, in the hot season.

There were also letters from home, which had taken only twelve days to reach us. It seemed almost incredible. Nowadays, thanks to the air mail, we are not cut off from our dear ones even in a remote corner such as this.

To the villagers, who had been joined by reinforcements, we were no longer strangers, and we went freely to and fro among them. We also had a distinguished visitor. Nandaram came to call, bringing us spinach, parsley, onions, and potatoes from his garden lower down the valley. We had only one thing to give him in return, but a rather precious gift, namely an unopened bottle of brandy, which we had brought as antidote in case of snake-bite. This was the only alcoholic drink in our baggage. Now that we had got beyond the region of venomous serpents, we could get along without it.

THE CAVE OF THE DEAD AT CHANGRU (GANSSER)

I was still licking my fingers, having used them, Indian-fashion, to eat rice with, when Chandru Singh arrived, and, in fluent English, told us about a burial cave in the cliffs above the Nepalese village of Changru, facing us. I promptly decided to visit this cave. A rickety bridge led across the roaring border torrent, Kali Ganga.

No-one tried to hinder us. Through a pine forest on a steep slope we reached Changru, situated on the terrace about 330 feet above the river. Its stone houses had been built in a most picturesque situation. Between the prayer-staffs there was a good view of the savage ice-peaks crowning the Nampa Valley.

The village chief was an elderly woman with finely cut and intelligent features, Himeti Padani by name. According to local belief, she had sprung from the legendary family of the Boro. She invited us to tea. In the courtyard of her house, we squatted tailor-fashion on a carpet and were served with tea in saucers of wood rimmed with silver. The tea was disgustingly sweet and full of floating hairs. At least half the inhabitants of the village had assembled, and stood round us staring. Apparently I was the first white man most of them had ever seen. Himeti Padani told us an ancient legend in a low-pitched melodious voice, and Chandru translated it into English :

" Long, long ago there was a path leading to the village of Marma which lies to the S.W. over the ice ridges of the Nampa Valley which are now unscaleable. In those days flowers bloomed where to-day there is nothing but a wilderness of ice (Plate 98). The men of Marma came to Changru, where they found wives and returned with their families to Marma. Thus sprang to life the race of the Boro.

" Once a Boro woman came with her child to Changru and wanted to build herself a house here. The child was playing with sharp stones and cut one of its fingers. Out of the blood which dripped from the wound, the walls of the house grew of themselves. The inhabitants of Changru, seeing the miracle, supposed that there must be supernatural forces in the child's blood and slew it, hoping to see more miracles. But nothing happened. The heartbroken mother cursed the village, prophesied that it would be smitten with black smallpox, and departed. Owing to her curse, the pass became ice-bound, and the flowery alps were transformed into savage glaciers. No longer could anyone from Changru come to visit Marma."

I looked across to the savage icy ridges of the Nampa chain. In truth this north-western part of Nepal is completely shut off from the rest of the country, with which it can only communicate by way of British India or by way of Tibet (Plates 97 and 98). Is it not strange that one of the principal themes of our Swiss mountain legends — that which concerns the disappearance of flowery meads owing to a curse — should exist also in these little-known regions of the " Himalayan Switzerland " ?

Such were my reflections while the old Boro woman served me with a large basin of rice. Her intentions were most kindly. Drawing her white coif over her forehead, she resumed her tale.

" A few years later, on the night of the full moon, two men went down to the mill by the river. Their faces were whitened by flour. Since the mill was running badly, one of them went to look at the mill-wheel. Some of the foam splashed into his face. When he came back to his friend, the latter did not recognise him, but fancied himself to be looking at the smallpox demon. Terrified, he ran back to the village with the dreadful tidings. At that moment, black smallpox broke out. The Boro woman's curse had been fulfilled. At Changru, the Boro families fled with all their possessions into the rocks, and disappeared into a cave. Since then nothing more has been seen or heard of them. The village was completely depopulated until, many years later, new inhabitants occupied the ruined huts. Having heard that the Boros had had immense riches, they sought a long time for the cave and at length discovered it. But when they were about to carry off some of the treasure, a voice shouted from the deep interior that a dreadful fate would befall them if they did not leave all exactly as it was. Greatly alarmed, they fled from the sinister spot."

Among the gaping populace who had listened, as well as myself, to this recital, no-one would admit knowing anything about the cave, except for a man who declared that ten or twenty years ago, during a violent earthquake, the roof of the inner part of the cave had fallen in. He had been there once. Though clad in rags, he seemed a good sort of fellow enough, and, at my request, promised to take me to the cave.

A dense thicket of junipers, wild roses, cotoneasters, and gorse barred our way. Our hands were badly scratched when we had forced our way through the scrub, the little thorns of the gorse sticking in the skin like those of certain cactuses. Large multicoloured lizards vanished into the fissures of the rocks as we passed. Though we were at so great an altitude, I could not feel sure that there would be no snakes.

About 1600 feet above the village, the cave was over 12,000 feet above sea-level. My companion peered anxiously as if afraid that someone might be spying upon us. It was a difficult climb over the last rocks to reach the cave. The sun was blazing from the zenith. We climbed round a shoulder of rock, and suddenly happened upon a skeleton in a crouching posture. On the ground beside it a couple of skulls were lying, and grinned at us out of the black orbits. Several plaits of hair still clung to the vertex of one (Plate 96).

A narrow aperture led steeply into the interior of the cave, which soon opened out into a great space. My companions followed me

48

timidly, covering mouth and nostrils with their rags so that the evil spirits might not find entrance. We made what light we could in the interior with a candle and a torch of resinous wood. The whole place was crowded with human bones. The skeletons were enveloped in parchmenty skin, and in some cases still bore rags of clothing (Plate 95). Among the skulls and the fallen rocks stood two long wooden cylinders adorned with bamboo fibres — such as are still used to-day by the Tibetans when brewing their tea flavoured with rancid butter. In the back of the cave we found wooden cases that were crumbling to dust, but still contained the bones of children. We could not get any farther because, as my Nepalese guide declared, the roof had fallen in during the great earthquake. Beyond this point he said, there had been a still larger chamber, and many more boxes filled with the bones of children had been piled around a hearth. There were also many weapons and trinkets. He also insisted that a threatening voice from the far interior had demanded the restoration of whatever anyone wanted to carry away. I myself had to refrain from carrying away any mementoes, not from superstition, but because I was so scrupulously watched by my companions when I was examining the various objects.

As we were clambering down the rocks and pushing our way through the thorny thicket on the way back to the village, I was wondering how whole families, cumbered with little children, could ever have reached this cave. Besides, what was the meaning of the boxes filled with the bones of children ? My guide said that the children must have been put into the boxes alive, hoping to ward off the infection, and had there perished miserably.

Having returned from the gloomy cavern, I was again the guest of the old Boro woman, who set before me another bowl of rice. She had sent for eight of the prettiest girls in the village, who were dressed in their best and adorned with a wealth of silver ornaments to perform a dance, which did not amount to much more than a hand-clapping performance. From one of the uppermost steps where I sat, I watched the dancing girls and the gaping spectators, feeling like a king of old in whose honour a popular festival had been organised. I was sorry to part from these kindly Changru folk, whose lively youth is over-shadowed by so gloomy a past.

TO THE HIGHEST VILLAGE IN NEPAL (HEIM)

On May 20th, after a night of storm and rain which covered the mountains with new-fallen snow down to an altitude of about 18,000 feet, we made a fresh inroad into Nepal, this time with a more important objective. We wanted to explore the unknown mountains lying to the north of Nampa and also to visit the border regions towards Tibet. This time we had to cross the upper bridge. Immediately before us, along a cliff above the raging torrent, the path which had been hewn out of the rocks was safeguarded at dangerous places with threads which were supposed to keep off the spirits of the dead. Beyond the bridge, which was unwatched at the time of our passing, a narrow track below the village of Changru led through an untroubled forest of aromatic fir-trees which, in clear weather, with its background of ice-peaks must present a wonderful spectacle. Then, on the advice of a shepherd, we went up the right bank of a tributary coming in from the left, for it would lead, he said, to the little village of Tinkar.

Soon, however, the path ceased to exist. It had been destroyed by the rock-falls and snows of the previous winter. Then we came to the remains of an avalanche, blocking the valley for more than two hundred yards, but the debris had formed a bridge to the other bank. Higher up the valley, on the northern declivity, we once more found traces of a path leading through a scrub of flowering daphne and various kinds of wheat, amid gnarled birches and lofty pines (*Abies webbiana*). Not until we were considerably higher, close upon 13,000 feet, could we make out through the field-glasses white-flowering rhododendrons.

Now followed a descent into the gorge, which was risky work for our porters, especially when they were clambering over another avalanche-bridge. Then we climbed the opposite slope where, upon an ancient moraine wall a few miles farther on, we could make out a group of houses. Chandru Singh, who accompanied us, said that it was Tinkar.

Here, on the sunlit face, at an altitude of about 12,000 feet, the mountaineers have made terraces where the land is cultivated with the plough. Indeed before long we saw two pairs of black yaks harnessed to ploughs. They are handsome, long-haired beasts with arched necks and bushy tails, being indigenous to the Tibetan plateau in the wild state, but are also domesticated for farm work. This was the first time that I had seen genuine yaks used to draw the plough (Plates 65 and 66).

It was with considerable excitement that we entered Tinkar, being probably the first white men who had ever done so. A woman whom we met on the road, and whom I saluted, returned my greeting by putting out her tongue, which in Tibet is a reverential gesture. The population of the village consisted of over two hundred persons of the

50

Bhotia race, who had arrived for the summer about a fortnight before. But a few families, we were told, actually wintered in this lofty spot, braving the snows.

Chandru, in addition to Hindustani and English, speaks Bahari, Nepali, and a little Tibetan. He walked into the fields in search of the village headman. This man turned out to be small and unimpressive. It was he who assigned us a hut. On the ground floor we found a stable for farm-beasts. Out of this a stone staircase led into a dark attic, where we could spread our sleeping-sacks and store our baggage.

The huts and houses of Tinkar are massively constructed, with low-gabled roofs, which are tiled. In some cases, too, the roofs, which rest on heavy wooden beams, are covered with earth to keep the interior warm. The " fireplaces ", made of blocks of stone, are cumbrous, and mainly ornamental. Here and there the houses were surmounted by a lingam, as among the Hindus, while the numerous tall staves with festoons of prayers fluttering in the wind and also the dried pine-trees in the " fire-places " are purely Tibetan. Thus the religion would seem to be a mixture of Hinduism and Lamaism, as is appropriate to this frontier region which separates India from Tibet (Plate 64).

As was the case in Garbyang, so here some of the houses are decorated with fine wood-carvings, painted reddish-brown. The inhabitants live by agriculture, growing buckwheat, root-crops like turnips and radishes, potatoes, and two varieties of barley. Occasionally they indulge in fresh meat, and brew themselves beer from barley.

While Gansser went to explore a lofty path to the north, I was kept indoors by a feverish cold which I had caught at Garbyang while writing. However, though unfit for much exertion, I did not stay indoors long. On the terrace in front of the headman's house I found a place sheltered from the wind where I could lie in the sun on a stone bench and watch the doings of our good-humoured hosts. They were not at all inquisitive, and up here in the heights seemed to have no inclination to beg. We felt safer in this remote upland spot, part of the Forbidden Land, than we should have felt anywhere else in the world. Here was the oldest inhabitant, eighty-six years of age, a man with an almost black skin, a friendly grin on his face, who was content to spin woollen yarn the live-long day while looking after one of his great-grandchildren, perched on his back wrapped within the folds of the old fellow's blanket (Plate 63). The women went on spinning busily, whatever else they might be engaged upon. Their husbands, squatting on the stone flags, stitched transport bags for the sheep and the goats. The women came back from field work with baskets on their backs. Then it was turn and turn about at having a draw from the great family pipe. This was a curiously wrought wooden instrument with a heavy foot of German silver and a clay bowl, similar to those which, varying slightly from place to place, are used throughout the central Himalayas (Fig. 8).

The bowl is filled with tobacco which has been moistened with sugar-cane sap. Then it is closed above by a stone disc on which red-hot cinders are piled. At the bottom, just above the stand, is a water chamber, for the pipe is a hubble-bubble. The aromatic smoke is drawn through the water by means of a long bamboo stem, and is deeply inhaled. The pipe passes from hand to hand, but not from mouth to mouth, for the smoker does not touch the mouth-piece with his lips, using his hand curled to form an intermediate tube.

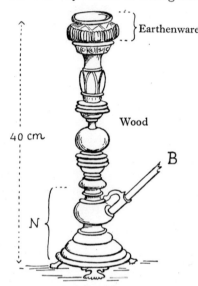

Now the housewife appeared on the roof. What was she up to there? She scattered grains of rice, and, as I learned afterwards, also a piece of bacon as offering to the gods, for a month ago her daughter had died.

Tinkar, like Garbyang, was visited every morning by one or two bearded vultures, which swept by only just over our heads. We had obviously been mistaken in supposing that this bird of prey, unlike the carrion-kite, feeds only on living animals.

FIG. 8. TOBACCO-PIPE FROM TINKAR, NEPAL. N, GERMAN SILVER FOOT; B, BAMBOO STEM, WHICH IS 28 in. LONG. (H)

As we had expected, the Nepalis of Tinkar were thoroughly friendly. One may have the same experience anywhere in the world where the natives have not been given cause to dread the whites, and when neither religion nor politics come into play — even among the South-Sea cannibals, who are by no means so black as they are painted.

CROSSING THE FRONTIER PASS

During a few hours one morning we obtained a good view of the "new mountains" in the background of our valley — twenty-thousand-foot snow-peaks standing out boldly in relief against the deep-blue sky.

It certainly seemed improbable that anyone ever came over that way. The natives told us, however, that more to the left was a path leading into Tibet and often used by caravans, Tinkar Lipu by name. We decided to try it. Although the weather was again cloudy, we left at early dawn with half a dozen of the porters who had come with us from Almora. A man from Tinkar acted as guide.

About two miles E. of the village, where we turned into the left lateral valley, upon a green moraine was standing a mass of rock with a cairn and a prayer-flag after the Tibetan fashion. Here our Sherpas kneeled in prayer. They pointed to a stone on which there was a mark like a human footprint, concerning which there is a legend which relates also to the foundation of Tinkar.

" A hunter once came through this valley. With his dog, he pursued a wild sheep. This creature made a gigantic leap across the torrent. The dog followed, and so did the hunter." The narrator showed us, with a wave of his hand, the site of the jump, which must have measured more than a hundred yards. " The hunter wanted to camp here. He had some grains of barley with him. He planted them. If they sprouted within a few days, he would stay there. After a few days he came back to see, and the barley was sprouting vigorously. That was the origin of Tinkar."

Such was the story of the oldest inhabitant. The impressions in the rocks were those made by the hunter, the dog, and the wild sheep when they jumped. They had become sacred.

A league farther, at an altitude of 13,000 feet, up a side valley on the right, we caught sight of the dome-shaped mountain, 20,330 feet, which we had already seen from Garbyang at the head of the valley, and which was called, our guide said, Kacharam. Nowadays the glaciers descending from its flanks no longer reach the main valley, ending at a height of about 13,500 feet. The alpine pastures were beginning to show their spring green. Except for two yaks grazing, we saw no beasts on them as yet, and the primitive stone huts of Donyang were unoccupied. Since the edge of the forest on the shady side was at from 12,500 to 12,800 feet, we, at about 13,500 feet, must be near the upper limit of the wooded area. However, there were still some small junipers of a kind (*Juniperus recurva*) which grows at great altitudes. Far higher than this, up to the snow-line, the mountains are peopled with birds. Sometimes we encountered swarms of merry yellow-billed mountain jackdaws ; sometimes graceful wild pigeons with steel-blue and white plumage — birds that build their nests in rocky fissures. For the first time we now saw specimens of a large game bird, akin to the

53

mountain-cock, coloured white and grey, kongma by name, a specialist in A-major four-six song :

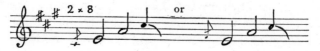

From the moraine we walked on snow, and since the porters were far behind and snow was beginning to fall we decided to camp. We found a suitable place at 15,580 feet on a thick dry grass-plot where the humus was deep black. It was at the foot of a steep moraine rampart made of white quartzite blocks.

Next morning, though the weather continued bad, we made for the pass. I must certainly give a good word to our porters for having marched many miles barefoot over the snow. There were only four pairs of old mountain boots left to distribute. We did not start until about ten o'clock, when it cleared a little. Without much enthusiasm, I followed in the footsteps of my more experienced comrade through detritus and snow. Then, at noon, I needed to stir my stumps, for the wind lashed me. We stood awhile on the top of the pass, for we had reached the Tibetan frontier. Our aneroids showed an altitude of 17,050 feet. Suddenly a rift opened in the clouds, disclosing in the distance a brilliant, richly coloured landscape in yellow and red and blue — the Purang district, where the highest isolated mountain in Tibet, Gurla Mandhata, flings its summit 25,355 feet into the air. The huge, broad snow-peak on the left of our observation point, rises steeply to begin with, then gently to the top, from which a rocky wall falls away to the S.E. (Plate 82). This was one of our objectives, but we had to renounce it at the request of the government of Delhi.

I was taking our bearings when a surprise diverted my thoughts. A little while before I had dreamed of magnificent fossils, which we had been able to pick up like gold and silver on Tom Tiddler's Ground. Now Gansser called to me : " I say, come here ! " He had happened upon a stone plate full of the most wonderfully preserved ammonites, and held it up to show me (Plates 67 and 68). Among these spirally rolled cephalopods, there were straight ones having a trumpet shape. They are akin to cuttle-fish, and their presence sufficed to show that the spot on which we stood had once lain at the bottom of the deep sea. Closer investigation showed that we were on the Trias, belonging to a geological period dating back more than 100 million years. Through the field-glasses we made out strata of black clay, up-ended, which could be followed to a height of over 19,000 feet. Surely this must be

54

31. Old Indian House, the residence of a man of quality, in the bazaar at Almora. (H)

32. Schoolchildren at Almora. (G)

33. Dhotial porters from Nepal; on the left, Yogi, a headman.   (H)

34. Our patient is carried back to Almora. April 28, 1936.   (H)

35. In the pine-forest beside the Dak-Bungalow at Kanari Chhina.
April 27, 1936.   (H)

36. Crossing the Kali into Nepal by a rope-bridge. May 7, 1936.   (H)

37. The three daughters of the Khela Postmaster.　(H)

38. Weaver women of Soso. Altitude 8000 feet.　(H)

39. Among the gneiss rocks on a path through the formidable Kali Gorge. (H)

41. Bhotia man with tobacco pipe, on the caravan road. (H)

40. Bhotia girl with a necklace of musk-deer teeth. Balwakot. (H)

42—44. Bird's-eye view of Bhotia youngsters.   (G)

45. Bhotias on the March in the mountains. The sheep are laden with rice. Taken 1¹/₂ miles south-west of Garbyang, looking south. May 11, 1936.   (H)

46. The ice-encrusted peak of Nampa in Nepal, to the right of the plate, altitude 23 339 feet. The view-point is 1¹/₄ miles south-west of Garbyang.   (H)

47. The Kali, the stream that borders Nepal, has cut its way through the Garbyang ridge formed by moraine and landslip, which formerly dammed up a lake. Looking S.S.W. May 12, 1936. (H)

48. Old Bhotia shepherd near Garbyang. June 12, 1936. (H)

49. Old house at Garbyang, with wood-carvings.   (H)

51. Woman of Garbyang carrying dung to manure the fields—an

50. Nandaram, Patriarch of Garbyang. (G)

52. Women dancers of Garbyang, in full dress, with silver trinkets. (H)

53. Beside the fluttering prayer-flags the women of Garbyang assemble to watch the dance. (H)

54. The friendly postmaster of Garbyang. (H)

56. Cobbler at work. (G)

55. Two dancers at Garbyang. (H)

57. Aged Mongolian mendicant lama with fantastic headdress. (H)

58. Mendicant Tibetan monks with drum and bells. Garbyang. (H)

enough to convince even a layman that the Himalayas were forced up out of the sea by the shrinking of the earth's crust?

To secure somewhat more protection from the S.W. wind, we climbed half a mile down the pass on the Tibetan side, and pitched our tent on a dolomite and quartzite (Silurian) crag at 16,730 feet. The white cross on a red ground fluttered wildly in the wind. Meanwhile the clouds had parted. For the first time we realised the full glory of our position. Above us, to the right, clung a huge ice-crest with an overhanging slope, which formed the boundary between Nepal and Tibet. Our man from Tinkar calls it Phung-Di (Plate 71). Farther to the right, near the mighty Gurla, is a serrated ridge of unnamed Tibetan peaks, but one of them, a horn which towers over the rest to a height of 24,064 feet, is called Nalkankar.

Who or what gives us the first greeting in the grey of dawn on the Tibetan side of the pass? A redstart, perched on a boulder, chirping. Not the sun, for the mountains are shrouded in mist, so we are in no hurry to start. We take our pulse-rate, to find that, after a good night's rest in our warm eiderdown sacks, it is, despite the altitude, only from 60 to 65 per minute. Our axillary temperatures are in both cases about 97°.

Although May is not yet over, at 16,750 feet close to our tent there are already yellow and blue flowers showing beside the edge of the puddles made by the melting of the snows (*Draba alpina, Ermannia himalayensis, Lagotis, Braya rosca, Ranunculus pygmaeus, Oxygraphis glacialis*).

Since, in the fog, there can be no question of our attempting any higher climbs, we go on down the valley towards Gurla Mandhata across endless old moraines, and, after about four miles, come, at 15,000 feet, to two huts, called Tharedunga, which are empty. A few miles farther on, where our lateral valley opens out, we get a free view of the great Tibetan highlands in front of us, with the distant Kailas to the left. This most sacred of mountains, with an obtusely arched summit, projects like a sugarloaf above a nearer mountain to a height of 21,976 feet. The highest yearning of millions of Hindus and Buddhists is to see it from afar, or if possible to reach its foot.

We seated ourselves on the surface of the desolate moraine and took counsel together. Taklakot, whose lamasery was ahead of us, was forbidden ground. " I don't care what you say," exclaimed Gansser, " I am at least going as far as the nearest Tibetan settlement ". — " You know we were told we must not enter Tibet. If you go, you do so at your own risk."—" All right ", replied Gansser cheerfully. " Goodbye and good luck until to-morrow evening." Having watched his departure, I turned back with Alis and Kirken to march four leagues over stones and snow in a biting head wind. Meanwhile heavy clouds discharged their waters over distant Lake Manasarowar, and ere long the storm reached us. Wet, tired, and chilled to the bone, I got back to our tent just before nightfall.

Next morning the weather cleared for a short time, so that I was able to clamber up a slippery mass of rocks and from the top could take a photo of the magnificent Phung-Di with our camp in the foreground (Plate 71). From the gap to the left of this peak there descended a broad glacier with green crevasses, while beyond this and still farther to the left there towered the somewhat less lofty brother of Phung-Di, which our man from Tinkar told me was called Sabu in the Gurkha tongue or Ramupanga in Tibetan (Plate 73). Just as I was about to take the view, a bearded vulture soared high above my head, the yellow plumage of the bird's breast standing out sharply against the dark-blue sky.

The mist soon gathered again. However, there was plenty of geological work close at hand to occupy my time during this spell of bad weather. My first business was to study the scale-like repetition of the strata, and then to pick out specimens of the rock where another seam outcropped. Soon, however, the drizzle, sleet, and wind became so heavy that I abandoned the task and sought shelter in the tent.

At half-past five Gansser hailed me as he was climbing out of the valley. He was very thoroughly drenched, after a long fight with the wind and rain, but most enthusiastic about his experiences.

EXCURSION INTO TIBET (GANSSER)

" Before me stretches a broad, pebbly steppe. Among the rounded stones, withered edelweiss trembles in the icy wind. But the sun strikes down hot, for the rays plunge almost vertically. For many miles ahead, nothing but stones to be seen. Then rusty brown hills, red and ochrous mountains come into view. If my gaze travels farther to the N.E., it discovers the glaciers of Gurla, whose summit of 25,355 feet strays into the clouds (Plate 82 — but this view was taken by Heim on a comparatively clear day). Then the clouds break up into an army of little cumuli, which hang at an immense distance, yet as it seems almost within grasp, in a crystal-clear atmosphere. Picture this, and you have a fragment of Tibet, whose plateau is at a level of more than 13,000 feet, while its mountains tower far above the 20,000 mark. Not a bald and chilly landscape, but warm with colour in this clear upland air.

" What did that great black beast that ran past us think of it ? Paldin, my Sherpa, shows his teeth and growls a word which means ' Wolf '. The Nepalese from Tinkar tramps along solidly behind us. About five miles ahead lies Taklakot upon its terrace of rubble. The red and yellow buildings of the lamasery can be plainly seen. But I must be on my guard. The presence of sahibs in the frontier region may already be known to the local prefect, or whatever he is called. Still, we three approach so close that we can make out every detail. In the steep walls are rock-dwellings, most of them abandoned. Below, in the plain, where the broad Humla-Karnali flows, a few houses stand amid green fields. Yaks draw ploughs, to break up new ground in the previously untilled and barren region. My aneroid registers 12,800 feet."

Gloomy clouds gathered meanwhile. Heavy rain began as we descended into the broad valley. Then we struck the great caravan route leading from Khojarnath to the Nepalese frontier beyond Taklakot and as far as Gartok. Two horsemen advanced along it from the south upon their agile Tibetan mounts, regardless of the rain. We drew a little aside from the road and I dropped my head into my raincoat so that I should not be recognised as a white man, for I did not wish anyone in Taklakot to know of my presence so long as I was still on Tibetan soil. These savage-looking riders were sturdy fellows, who did not take the slightest notice of us. We turned southward along the caravan route. Here and there we passed yak-teams ploughing. " Hooo-eeh " called the Tibetan ploughmen melodiously when the powerful beasts were to turn at the end of a furrow. The colossal creatures did as they were bid, slowly and majestically. Barley, the staff of life in Tibet, will be harvested here in due course. Isolated houses stood like fortresses on the stony steppe. The surly, barking dogs and the nearness of Taklakot decided us to make a slight detour. We continued on our course, hungry and tired, having been afoot the whole day without pause.

Once more an icy rain stung our faces. The dark was falling. Then, from the direction of Taklakot, three riders galloped after us. They had long Tibetan muskets slung across their backs. I looked at my companions, who were obviously disquieted. Unfortunately I found it difficult to converse with them. My fragmentary Hindustani was of little help so far. I was glad that Paldin was an intelligent fellow, and spoke Tibetan fluently. We understood one another by signs, without speech. " I think they are only intending to pass us ", was what I wanted to indicate. I did not turn my head, but I heard the clatter of the horses' hoofs drawing nearer. Then, suddenly, three savage, brown faces stared at me from beneath dripping headgear. My geological utensils were not obvious anywhere, so that our aspect was not particularly striking. They must have recognised me as a sahib, since on this short detour I had no longer wrapped my head in the raincoat. Yet they passed us with little attention, galloping ahead on their three nimble Tibetan ponies. My sigh of relief sped down wind.

The night was well advanced when we knocked tentatively at a house to ask for accommodation (Plate 90). The place we believe to be called Dhogang, and Gombu the name of the family. The people were not a little astonished to find themselves so unexpectedly in contact with a white man. Across two outer courts, peopled by yaks and sheep, we entered through a small and low doorway into the innermost court, the sides of which were roofed, but the middle open to the sky, forming the main abode of all the inhabitants. Gombu (Plate 87) was a fine-looking old fellow. His silvery locks fell almost to the shoulders. He was squatting cross-legged on a hide mat. In his right hand he held a prayer-wheel. My arrival must have disturbed the inmates at their occupations. They spread a dirty sheepskin for me beside the old man. Here I was to sleep, then. Gradually I became accustomed to the dim interior, which was lighted by flickering tallow dips, and was able to make out a considerable number of inquisitive spectators. In spite of their keen inspection, not one of them seemed to notice that we were ravenously hungry. However, Paldin got to work with his explanations, and soon there was placed before me a saucer of salted rancid-butter tea, which presumably contained tsamba. I set about kneading some tsamba dough with my fingers, and then conveying it to my mouth with the same utensils. Hunger is the best sauce, and the tallow dips gave so poor a light that none of my hosts were likely to be critical about minutiae. I was sharp-set enough to find Gombu's supper extremely tasty.

A little girl, who could not have been much more than three years old, served her grandfather. When she had relieved him of his little wooden saucers, she climbed into his lap and stared at me. I made a funny face at her, and she laughed. She would have been quite a pretty child if she had not been so frightfully dirty. The old man turned his prayer-wheel unceasingly, and murmured monotonously in a nasal tone, " Om mani padme oom ". While he was praying, the little girl caught a moth on the wing and held the fluttering creature over the burning tallow dip. The old man looked on indifferently, continuing his prayer. Slowly the poor moth was roasted to death, and the prayer-wheel went on turning. . . .

58

The privy was apparently on the other side of a wooden door. Chained within this place of public resort was a Tibetan puppy-dog, which howled mournfully when the old man visited the retreat. On the inner side of the doorpost a large prayer-drum was fastened. As he went in, the old man set it turning, and did so with renewed energy as he emerged. This formality was conscientiously attended to by every member of the family that had occasion to answer the calls of nature, so the attention of God the Father in Heaven was automatically called to his poor creatures here below many, many times a day. One must be practical in all things.

The two smallest members of the family were disposed of together in one hide sack, and promptly went to sleep. We were tired too. I lay down close to the old man on my dirty sheepskin. His " Om mani padme oom " seemed to recede into the farther distance. From above the stars shone down on us.

It was a long, long night. The grandmother had a hacking cough, and the puppy-dog kept in the aforesaid retreat howled unceasingly all through the night. From time to time Gombu murmured his prayers even in his sleep. There were other drawbacks. The very air felt far from clean, and I had two undesirable visitors during the night. We hastened to make our escape at peep of day. When we left, the whole company was contemplating with much satisfaction a small marbled vulcanite goblet which I left them as a memento.

Along the valley farther to the S.E. about a thousand feet above the level of the caravan route was a gompa or lamasery, Jitkot by name. It was in a commanding position (Plate 91). For a long time we stood at the door vainly seeking admission. A savage Tibetan, the janitor, was as forbidding as Cerberus. Then a lama with a shaven head espied us from the roof. I stood there and raised beseeching hands, while Paldin negotiated. When admitted, we entered cautiously, for we could hear Tibetan mastiffs barking somewhere close at hand.

However, I was granted access to the sanctum. A huge gilded Buddha stared at me. At his feet were burning small butter-lamps. I kneeled, said my " Om mani ", etc., and laid a silver coin upon the altar. For this I was allowed to kindle a new lamp at the foot of Buddha. With a few red lamas I climbed to the roof of the monastery. Then a wonder met my eyes. The memory of it will never fade. The present lamasery was surrounded by the ruins of a much older building, which must have been of enormous size. Eastward the walls, built of the prevailing rubble, descended perpendicularly into the valley. A long series of rose-tinted peaks led towards the unknown giants of the

Nepalese frontier, from among which glaciers flowed into the plateau. The lamas stood in silence as they contemplated the crystalline distance (Plate 86). Over the Himalayas behind me, dark storm-clouds were creeping, invading Tibet with an aspect like that with which we are familiar in Switzerland when the föhn rages.

The visit was a success. Sitting upon a little stool, I sketched the gompa. Then I became aware that someone was behind me and turned. The head-lama or abbot stood there smiling at me.

Leaving Jitkot, we marched across the wide expanse of steppe to regain Tinkar Lipu. On the way we passed a group of tents, surrounded by a wall which made an enclosure. Some nomads were engaged at the moment in milking their sheep. The beasts stood in pairs facing one another, their heads tied together. As soon as the rope was loosened, they departed at a gallop. Every evening they had to be rounded up and driven into the walled enclosure to save them from the wolves and the ounces or snow-leopards.

We faced a raging storm as we remounted to the pass. So fiercely were we lashed with the ice-needles that we could scarcely get along. Stiff with cold and almost frozen were we when, in the evening, we reached the tent, which had been pitched at an altitude of 16,728 feet. Gradually we were thawed and revived by a cup of hot ovomaltine. Then we slipped into our sleeping-sacks. As I drowsed, I could fancy myself watching a prayer-wheel turn, and an unhappy little moth being burned alive. . . . Om mani padme oom. . . .

A JOINT FIRST ASCENT IN TIBET (HEIM)

The storm lasted most of the next day, so that we could do very little geological work. Towards evening, the sky cleared and the whole sierra to the right of Gurla was disclosed.

Then, on May 28th, came a cloudless morning. As we were preparing to start for Sabu, there mounted out of the valley a huge caravan from Tibet, the first of this season to cross Tinkar Lipu. The sheep were heavily laden with salt and borax (Plate 69).

The snow was crisp, being frozen hard. With unexpected speed we crossed the snowfields and then climbed up along the edge of a glacier to reach a gap in the rocks where we had an unrestricted view of Gurla, which already seemed much closer. But now the sun was high in the heavens, for at mid-day it stands almost overhead, and, since it had thawed the surface of the snow, walking again became difficult. At 18,368 feet (by aneroid), in the saddle on the N.E. of

Sabu, we were exactly opposite Gurla, and the unknown Nepalese mountains thickly coated with snow stood before us in dazzling splendour (Plates 72 and 75). The Cimbrux photometer shows $\frac{1}{30}$th second exposure to be suitable with F/25 stop, and even so the plate was over-exposed. Our eyes suffered from the glare though we were wearing our darkest smoked spectacles.

Gansser roped us for fear of hidden crevasses. Then, with him leading and making ice-steps, we went straight up the snow-slope which stood at an angle of 38°-40°, reminding me of the summit of the Jungfrau, and in an hour we reached the top. The aneroid registered 19,024 feet, which was probably rather too humble an estimate since the barometer was low; but we can hardly congratulate ourselves as yet at having touched the 6000-metre level (19,680 feet). The view was magnificent. Three-fourths of the panorama consisted of an army of peaks covering more ground than the entire range of the Swiss Alps, most of them unnamed and unclimbed. Still, we hoped to conquer some of them. North by east stood Kailas, and a trifle to the right of this were the great lakes of Raksas and Manasarowar, as a dark-blue line; then, farther to the right the mighty Gurla massif with its numerous glaciers, and a horn which was probably Nalkankar (24,064 feet = 7500 metres) on the map 62 F of the Nepal-Tibet frontier. Then, still farther south, bearing E. 39° S., far distant Nepal, a vast massif, one of the peaks, we suspected, rather to the left, being Dhaulagiri, a virgin eight-thousander (26,240 feet). The nearer peaks of Nepal are all unknown and unmeasured except for the mighty head of Nampa, whose bearing was S. 33° W. (Plate 81). We could also recognise the acute pyramid bearing W. 4° N. as the topmost summit of Panch Chulhi in Kumaon, and more to the right, still farther away, Nanda Devi, 25,584 feet, the highest mountain in the central Himalayas. Finally, to the right of Phung-Di, on the Kumaon-Tibet frontier, bearing N. 54° W., was the highest peak of the border chain, known locally as Zaskar. This peak is marked on the map as 21,262 feet.[1]

On this glorious day the air was absolutely motionless, even on a mountain-top open to all the winds, and the sun was so warm that the rocks, though chilly, invited us to sit down. They were free from snow, for what the wind had not swept away had evaporated or melted. But we had no time for a rest. While one of us was sketching and taking photographs, the other was busily engaged in recording the bearings of all the important peaks (Plate 76). Our cheerful company (with the three Sherpas there were five of us) was, to our astonishment,

[1] We learned later that this peak lies above Kuti, and is there called Shangtang.

joined by some other living creatures : a kite and two butterflies. These last were Vanessas enjoying a sun-bath.

We made a slow and careful descent, for there was a risk of starting an avalanche in the softened snow. Having reached the saddle, we took our skis out of our knapsacks and opened them at the hinged joint (Plate 74). Although the snow was in fine condition, when ski-ing I now became aware for the first time of some difficulty in breathing at this great altitude, whereas Gansser, having the advantage of youth, raced ahead of me in a sinuous course down the declivity, while the Sherpas, amazed at the novel spectacle, stamped laboriously along behind us (Plate 78).

In the first light of evening we had another entrancing view of the brightly coloured Tibetan mountains with their valleys now of a dark violet shade. Thus a magnificent day came to an end. This wonderful day in the mountains will remain vivid in memory as long as I live.

ON OUR FIRST TWENTY-THOUSANDER

After what we called a day of rest, during which we were engaged only in minor activities, such as picking flowers to press, and when we even found time for a sun-bath, stormy weather returned, and raged throughout the night, so violently that I was anxious lest our tent might be carried away. What sort of a monsoon are we going to have, I wondered.

To our surprise, the weather cleared before morning. Was it only a local gust or two, and not the monsoon at all ? After a further doze, we were awakened by strange visitors, four untamed Tibetans, who pulled open the door of our tent and stared in shamelessly. Then we saw that the camp had been invaded by hundreds of sheep. The men were not police-agents, after all, but only inquisitive fellows who knew no better. What could be the meaning, they wondered, of those long curved pieces of wood that stood outside leaning against the tent— our skis ? Gansser offered them some cigarettes, and immediately we were all on the best of terms. Then they departed towards the other side of Tinkar Lipu.

Our stores of food were running low. What could have become of the porters we had sent back down the valley ? Well, there was nothing to do but to break camp. Each of us carried what he could to the top of the pass, where we cached a few loads, for, though provisions were scarce, we were unwilling to renounce our next objective—Phung-Di.

Among the three coolies still with us, Yogi is the best. We have always called him " Number One ", because he generally leads the way, and during the early days he carried case no. 1. He is willing and cheerful, and among dozens of workmen of our homeland it would be hard to find one so perfectly behaved. He also has the advantage of belonging to the lowest caste, so that he can eat anything, even what we can spare him from our own food, whereas the others may not take anything from a person of a different belief — not even from a sahib.

With these three coolies, and the Sherpas, with Gansser in front, we climbed a steep snow-slope to the rocky ridge on the west, by which we hoped to reach the summit. But now, notwithstanding the mountain boots we had given them, the porters could get no farther. We therefore sent the men back with Kirken in charge, to Tinkar, to fetch some more tsamba. Then, going to and fro, we conveyed our equipment in small loads as high as possible, clambering across the ridge until we found a spot at an altitude of about 17,700 feet where there was just room for our two little tents — a hard bed upon angular stones. While we were thus engaged, a bearded vulture soared inquisitively close above our heads. We have enough meta fuel left to cook the soup with snow, and the water does not take long to boil, since here the boiling point is 176°.

After an unexpectedly quiet night, when the alarm awoke us at four-thirty, we were distressed to find that it was misty, with sleet falling. But an hour later Nampa showed up in a wonderful light beneath a greenish sky and above rolling mists that filled the valleys to a level of above 16,400 feet (Plate 80). Since the wind had now changed, and was blowing from Tibet, we broke camp at seven o'clock. First we climbed a rough slope, and then, clambering on all fours, made our way over the craggy quartzite spine. Alis panted and lagged behind. Since the weather went wrong again, I decided at 18,860 feet to return with Alis, while Gansser with Paldin still hoped to get across the ice-bound ridge in spite of the mist. Now there was another mishap. A stone as large as my fist, which I must have dislodged, hit Alis on the thigh. He screamed, blubbered, and refused to move. But it was soon obvious that he had sustained nothing worse than a slight muscular contusion. Carrying my rucksack I went slowly ahead, and he followed at a crawl. Just as we got back to the tent, Gansser came rattling down the slope. Yes, he had done more than make a reconnaissance. Continually using his ice-axe on new snow and ice he had managed to climb the ridge and, with Paldin securing the rope, to creep up to within seventy feet of the top, where the icy crust was as sharp as a knife and overhung. It was a first climb, but no view was secured.

PRISONERS

That evening Kirken and the three porters got back from Tinkar. For one rupee he had purchased a sack of tsamba, which would last us for several days, and the coolies had brought some wood along. But they were all moody. So far as we could make out, one of the Maharajah's lieutenants with seven privates had arrived at Changru, and the bridges were watched. A report had been sent from Garbyang that two sahibs without passports had entered Nepal. By the fire we held a council, three coolies, three Sherpas, and two Swiss geologists (Plate 93). It did not seem likely that we could escape over a pass leading northwards, since probably soldiers had been sent to watch there also. Besides, at Tinkar we had left baggage it was essential to recover. Our men said that perhaps we should be able to get across the lower bridge unnoticed after dark. Maybe time would solve our difficulties. Anyhow we must be ready to start early next morning. Now we had an additional disaster. Paldin, usually the most vigorous of the Sherpas, complained of severe headache and abdominal pain. Was he suffering from mountain sickness ?

The night on our hard and angular couch of stones was not very refreshing. But what a sunrise we saw once more over Nampa ! Having packed our traps, we scrambled down a steep slope of snow and ice. The coolies had hard work, but they made a good showing. The two invalid Sherpas followed in the rear, unladen. On Mount Dongang, since we had last seen it, the spring had advanced, with the appearance of violet gladioli. Shepherds came to meet us, driving their flocks. The men nodded to us as old acquaintances. They were the savage Tibetans we had already seen, now on the return journey.

By one o'clock we reached the holy place (the hunter's leap). Gansser, who had gone on ahead with Kali, and hitherto had been quite cheerful about our prospects, now returned to say : " Things look rather nasty ". The lieutenant was already at Tinkar. We were prisoners, then. When we reached the village, we saw a man wearing a white turban. We gave a friendly salute, to which he responded, and let us pass. Our first step was to prepare and eat our soup. Then, with Kali's aid, we did our best to come to an understanding with the lieutenant. He entered our hut attended by a soldier who carried a double-barrelled musket. Our conversation was difficult, for we know only a few words of Hindustani, and Kali can speak very little English.

64

As far as we could make out, the lieutenant's orders were, if we had no passports, to keep us under arrest until the Maharajah sent permission for our discharge. This would take about a month, more or less. The man from Tinkar who had acted as guide was to be imprisoned. Vainly did we protest that we were perfectly harmless people, that our camp was not in Nepal but in Tibet, that it was out of the question for us to waste a whole month, as we were scientific investigators who could do no-one any harm. Without any harsh words on either side, we had a first conference, and then a second one. The officer would not accept tea from us, but did not refuse a cigarette.

We spent the afternoon in great depression. Of what use would it be to write up our diaries if they were going to be impounded, and our whole expedition frustrated? Then Kali reported that, after supper, the lieutenant would like to have another talk.

I had already gone to sleep in my sack. Gansser called to me: " Here he comes ". In our hay-loft we quickly lighted two candles and stuck them on a food-box. We offered the lieutenant the only chair, on which he sat down. We squatted on the floor. Kali, as interpreter, was close to the lieutenant, and behind him sat the guide, who was the chief culprit. The man who held us under arrest seemed in a queer mood. He spoke in a tone that was hardly above a whisper. As far as we could make out, the officer could do pretty much what he pleased in his own district, and his salary was very small. Gansser and I exchanged glances of relief. In certain circumstances, said the lieutenant, it might be possible to arrange for a passport.

SAFE AGAIN

Early next morning we had another conversation with the lieutenant, a short one this time. Terms were arranged. We put our best foot foremost down the valley. The mountains were hidden in the clouds. The bridge was unguarded, and shortly after noon we re-entered the dak-bungalow at Garbyang with all our luggage. Wind and rain could not mar our high spirits at the way things had turned out. Besides, at Garbyang we had news from home. The first films had been developed and were all right. We had plenty to read, and a lot of letters to write. In the morning the temperature was 42°, and by noon had risen to 56°. The time hung rather heavily on our hands, except when Kali provided us a good meal. At length the sun shone brightly once more. The belles of the village assembled for a dance. Wearing almost all their worldly goods in the form of a wealth of silver trinkets, they emerged from their houses and huts. Silver chains weighing as much as a couple of pounds each hung down over the black and red-brown garments. They even had chains of rupees fastened together by little rings. (Plates 52, 53, and 55.) There were pretty red-cheeked girls among them, with spangles and red chains round their necks. Cheerily they assembled on the edge of the terrace, where the great cairn with the prayer-pennant stood. At length the dance began. The chief dancers, wearing anklets of bells, advanced in a half-circle, shyly at first. Then came mazy movements keeping time with a strange drum accompaniment. A little man who stood among the women seemed to be master of the ceremonies. A lively picture, but it left us somewhat disappointed, for after all it was insipid, lacking fire.

INTO THE UNEXPLORED NAMPA MOUNTAINS (GANSSER)

From Garbyang two bridges lead across the Kali into Nepal. The upper and larger one, on the road to Changru, was now watched, while the narrow and rickety footbridge about half a mile lower down the stream, the one we crossed on our first expedition (Plate 59), was probably still unguarded. Anyhow this was of little moment, since I now owned a passport, or rather a scrap of chequered paper torn from a little block, and bearing a sentence or two in Hindustani which (I was told) allowed me to spend five days in Nepal. Five days would certainly not suffice to explore a large and unknown mountain region. I hoped to be back in nine days, and since I intended to exceed my time, it would be just as well that no-one should note my entry into Nepal. Here and there, between the thickly set fir-trees, we caught a glimpse of the little stone sentry-box, in front of which two soldiers were stretched on the ground, fast asleep. With Paldin and Number One I set out, all three of us being heavily laden (Plate 94).

For hours we climbed through the densely forested lower Nampa Valley. " Sahib, it is very hot to-day and Number One is a long way behind." Paldin, the Sherpa coolie from Darjeeling, pulled up, thrust the handle of his ice-axe between the heavy rucksack and his back, to ease the weight for a moment, and adjusted his forehead-strap. Number One was the best of our thirty Dhotial collies from south-western Nepal. He was always the leader, and that, as has previously been explained, was why we had nicknamed him " Number One ". Though his amiable, complacent, rather indifferent grin never varied, one could see that he prided himself on this name. To-day, however, he was no longer in the fore-front. We had to wait a long while for him. When he turned up, I said: "We shall camp soon, Number One" —"Yes", he answered, in his usual tone of absolute conviction. With the back of his hand he wiped the sweat from his brow, and also dried his nose as best he could. "We shall need some firewood, you know" — "Yes", he answered again, without budging. If I had said to him: "You are a moon-calf", he would have answered in the same way — for he does not understand a word of English.

At 13,000 feet we camped among flowering rhododendron bushes (Plate 100). We had reached the lower end of a glacier about six miles long, a place where the ground was strewn with moraine blocks. Among these blocks, wild rhubarb was growing, looking very fine with its huge leaves and shining red stalks. I took off my rucksack with a sense of great relief. When anyone carrying a heavy pack has to take observations all the time, make sketches, and peck out stones for specimens, the weight on his back is not always agreeable. Of course we divided forces, but selfishly, I had chosen the better part (better for me, though not for the others), and in a trice I stripped and plunged into the lovely glacial brook which rippled among the rhododendrons and the boulders.

My part in the "work" consisted of a luxurious bathe, followed by a complete inunction. Next I had to write up my geological notes, and make the appropriate entries in my diary. Then there were some new botanical specimens to label. Meanwhile Paldin came down from the moraine, bringing an ample supply of lovely rhubarb. One corner of a great stalk protruded from his mouth, and was gradually disappearing into the interior as he made chewing movements with his brilliantly white and grinning teeth. Also chewing rhubarb to stay my stomach, I went in search of Number One, whom I met labouring along with a huge dried rhododendron root for fuel. Together, we soon got it to camp, and quickly had a fire ablaze. The rhubarb stalks were simmering in the big saucepan which was part of Paldin's load. With distended cheeks, Number One blew the fire, which scattered sparks. Tsamba and rhubarb soup was our main dish. While we were eating, night fell. Cross-legged, we squatted round the fire, each wrapped in his blanket. The huge white blossoms of the rhododendron bushes showed up well in the flickering firelight. Gradually the fire died down. Paldin and Number One crept beneath an overhanging rock. I lay down under the rhododendrons in my sleeping-sack. We did not bother to pitch the tent. The stars sparkled amid the ghostly white blossoms as I looked up. I slept like a dormouse, a solitary white traveller in unknown Nepal.

We were at the end of another day's journey. Below us, on the

67

moraine-strewn surface of the glacier, was our provision-store, a cairn surmounted by a fluttering Swiss flag. In the background was Nampa, 23,399 feet, and to the left a gap in the sierra. The precipices here were encrusted with savage-looking ice. This was the site of the flower-bedecked pass about which we had heard the legend in Changru (page 47 and Plate 98).

"Sahib, Sahib!" Paldin was holding his arms like horns above his head, and pointing towards the right moraine on the soiled glacier.

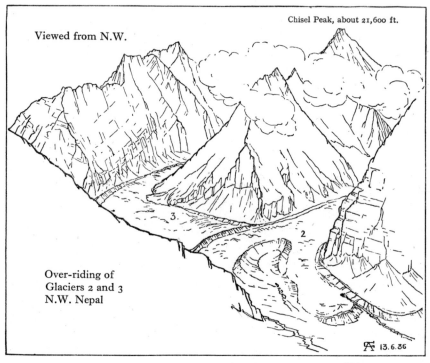

Viewed from N.W.

Chisel Peak, about 21,600 ft.

Over-riding of
Glaciers 2 and 3
N.W. Nepal

3.

2

13.6.36

FIG. 9. NAMPA GLACIER, N.W. NEPAL. (G)

A flock of wild sheep was rushing down the steep slope. Above, two bearded vultures were planing down beside the perpendicular cliffs. They passed behind a projecting crag, and then reappeared a little higher up. Never could I detect a wing-beat. Once only, one of the birds stooped with folded pinions, but speedily reopened them without touching the ground and resumed its soaring flight. False alarm! The breast shone orange-yellow in the evening sunlight. This bird was apparently the male. I could easily make out the little black beard under the beak.

Paldin and Number One went down to our provision-store to fetch firewood. I made an excursion into the lateral valley. This opened to the south of us, and almost perpendicular ice-covered rocky walls rose from the glacier on either side.

On the southern side of Nampa Valley are four lateral valleys, indicated by numbers in Figs. 9 and 10. Out of each of these lateral valleys, a glacier flows northward to join the main glacier. A study of the confluence showed a remarkable fact. Each of the lateral glaciers

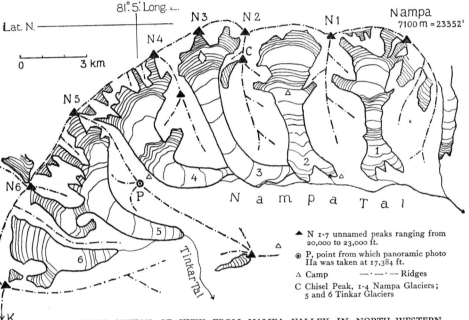

FIG. 10. ROUGH SKETCH OF VIEW FROM NAMPA VALLEY IN NORTH-WESTERN NEPAL, MADE BY A. GANSSER IN JUNE 1936. K POINTS TO KACHARAM (20,270 FEET), WHICH LIES 2½ MILES TO THE NORTH OF N7.   (G)

overrides the main glacier, until, as it continues its course down the main valley, it is, in its turn, overridden by another lateral glacier. Thus the ice becomes superposed in layers like tiles, and the main glacier seems to consist of a number of successively overriding lesser glaciers. I took up my position high above lateral glacier Number 2, to sketch the interesting results. While I was doing this, my two companions came slowly down the glacier carrying wood. We were camped where the little triangle is placed near 2 in Fig 10. There were numerous crevasses in the glacier, round which we had to make frequent detours. On the morrow we intended to continue our course up the main glacier, but to-day we were engaged in exploring Number 2. Wood and a little food were left in a new dump. We were compelled to ration ourselves, since we had an ambitious programme. As evening came on, mist-wreaths rose out of the main valley. The omens for the night were unpropitious.

Paldin and Number One were chopping up wood. I had to finish my notes quickly. There were rock specimens and plants to label. My sketch of the glacier was not yet finished. Although a storm was brewing, I had to push on with my work. The time allowed for this expedition was too scanty for us to be fastidious about the weather. Tiny ice-needles began to pester me ; presages of the monsoon, and this when May was only just over. Paldin and Number One went on chopping vigorously. Now they were using their ice-axes to carve a weather-proof shelter for us beneath the ice. I wondered whether they would not soon bring the rocks tumbling about our heads. However, it was all right. " Ready, Sahib ", said Paldin and we crept into our places.

" To-day we hope to camp near the upper end of Nampa Valley, surrounded by new, unknown peaks (Plate 97). Slowly the white ridges show up over the dark rocks. Even the steepest places are ice-coated, and the face of the ice is covered with fine corrugations. We hurry on, enticed by the glory of the ice-clad peaks. ' Oh, Sahib, look at that one ; it is finer still.' Paldin is quite enthusiastic. Number One has hung his mountain boots over his back, and comes slowly over the sharp moraine crest. ' They're too heavy, Sahib, and I can walk better without them.' That may well be true. Even this sharp-pointed detritus cannot penetrate his elephantine hide. Weckert's heavy boots wobble grotesquely above the dirty gunny-sack. It was typical of our Dhotial porters that their admiration for our hobnails was unstinted, and each of them wanted a pair of his own. They wore them in burning heat on well-made paths, when one would have thought it a delight for them to go barefoot. But when they had to climb over rocks or on a difficult snow-slope, they preferred to take them off.

" Towards the head of the valley, near the great crevasse in Nampa Glacier No. 4, we made our finest camp. This is shown in the sketch by a small triangle. We were surrounded by steep, ice-encrusted peaks, ranging from 20,000 to 23,000 feet (Plate 99). They are all unnamed. Even the natives had never been in these remote but extraordinarily beautiful regions. Paldin cooked our general supper of rice. Throughout this journey we ate with our fingers out of the same saucepan.

59. We enter Nepal by crossing the Kali near Garbyang. May 14, 1936.   (H)

Nampa (23 339 feet) and the Api Glacier. Looking S. E. Altitude 15 000 feet. May 15, 1936.   (H)

61 and 62. First encounter in Nepal: Poachers among alpine roses. (G)

63. The oldest inhabitant of Tinkar, spinning. On his back is his great-grandson. (H)

64. Lamas saying mass. Tinkar, Nepal. (G)

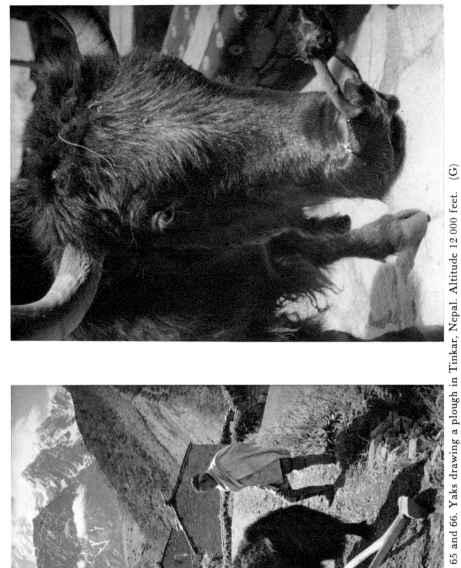

65 and 66. Yaks drawing a plough in Tinkar, Nepal. Altitude 12 000 feet.   (G)

67. First find of fossils at Tinkar Lipu on the frontier between Nepal and Tibet. Altitude 17 000 feet. (H)

68. Lump of limestone as picked up on the above spot. Contains ammonites of the noric trias. Two-thirds natural size. 1, parajuvavites sp. n.; 2, placites; 3, steinmannites sp. n.; 4, celtites; 5, small mussels. (Species identified by Professor A. Jeannet.)

69. The first Tibetan flock of sheep of the year passing our camp at Tinkar Lipu on May 27, 1936. Tibetan side of pass, at 16 728 feet.   (H)

70. Safely housed at Tinkar Lipu, on the Tibetan side, at 16 728 feet.   (Kali)

71. In dazzling splendour, there towers over our camp (+) the peak of Phung-Di on th
Nepal-Tibet frontier. May 27, 1936. Gansser was the first to climb this mountain. (H

72. Gansser with our three Sherpas ready to climb Sabu, Tibet. In the background is Gurla Mandhata, 25 355 feet. Looking north-east. May 28, 1936. (H)

73. Sabu, 19 024 feet, the first view-point climbed in Tibet, seen from the west. May 27, 1936. (H)

74. From the Sabu Saddle, 18 368 feet, we return on skis. May 28, 1936. (H)

75. The Nepalese Mountain Chain seen looking south from the
Sabu Saddle, 18 368 feet. May 28, 1936. (G)

76. From Sabu, 19 024, the bearings of the peaks in view are taken for
topographical purposes. May 28, 1936. (G)

77. The ice-encrusted mountains of Nepal, as seen looking south
from Sabu. May 28, 1936. (G)

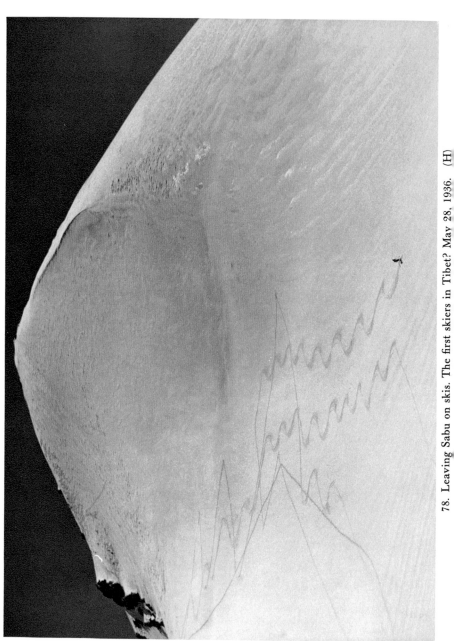

78. Leaving Sabu on skis. The first skiers in Tibet? May 28, 1936.   (H)

79. The Nampa Group in Nepal, from the 16 400 feet ridge overhanging Garbyang, looking south-east. May 13, 1936.   (G)

80. Nampa (23 399 feet), to the right, and Chisel Peak, to the left, seen from the Phung-Di Ridge, 17 712 feet, in Nepal, looking S. S. W. May 31, 1936.   (H)

81. Nampa, 23 400 feet, in Nepal, seen from Sabu 19 024 feet, looking south-west. May 28, 1936.   (G)

82. Gurla Mandhata in Tibet, 25,355 feet; to the left, in the distance, Kailas; in the middle distance, the Rubble Terrace; on the left, beneath Gurla,

83. Tsamba (baked barley-meal) is the staff of life in Tinkar. May 22, 1936. (G)

84. This youngster leads Yaks harnessed to the plough. Tinkar, Nepal. May 21, 1936. (G)

85. Gombu's grandson, in a leather coat. Purang, Tibet. May 25, 1936. (G)

86. The Lamas of Jitkot on the tower of their "Gompa", with the cloud-capped Gurla Massif

" Number One has a contused wound on the heel. It looks rather angry, and I have had to bandage the foot, after applying a thick layer of our cure-all antiseptic ointment. He can stay in camp for a day or two, since, on the rather difficult explorations in the immediate vicinity of our camp, Paldin and I can get along without him.

" Paldin is by no means a bad mountaineer, but the rock here is of a tricksy character. We turn together along a ridge. Slowly the dreaded mists are gathering on the topmost peaks, and soon we shall be wrapped in them. Still, I feel it is absolutely essential to take pictures of these new heights. We scramble along the ridge at well over 17,000 feet, snorting like racehorses, as we look for a good place from which to take photographs and sketches (Panorama II a). While I fix the camera on the tripod, take the bearings of the surrounding peaks, and draw a hasty sketch (Fig. 10), Paldin builds a cairn. On a big plate of stone he scratches in Tibetan writing ' Om mani padme oom '. This stone prayer is put on the top. As he stands beside the cairn praying and looking at the white peaks, I recall the Buddhist mass I watched a few weeks ago in the little Nepalese village of Tinkar. I was strolling there alone one fine morning. Heim was getting over his cold and I was making local explorations. I stood in front of the little temple and watched, while the lama, in the clear morning sunlight, conducted his poojah. An octogenarian Nepalese held the great prayer-drum, on which the lama punctuated the ceremony (Plate 64). The dark-brown wrinkled visage of the old man holding the drum was uplifted towards heaven ; as if transfigured, he stared at the dazzling sun, the ice-clad mountains — the home of his gods.

" For my part, too, I had to lay aside my work and look at the frozen peaks, trace the course of the ice-flutings up to the snow-white ridges. Far beyond the peaks and ridges my gaze plumbed the dark blue sky, and, to my imagination, the whole firmament was ablaze with the holy words of the prayer ' Om mani padme oom '."

In camp, a fierce storm was raging, and our tent was almost carried away. In the interior, the little primus was singing its monotonous song, while outside the avalanches of new-fallen snow thundered.

We squatted on our sleeping-sacks, huddled together. Waiting was the order of the day. We had to wait in this little tent, which hardly had accommodation for two men. I had just wrapped the botanical specimens in impermeable paper, using the back of Number One as table. On the primus water was boiling for tea, while my companions were thawing their icy limbs, and chatting about their homes. Seldom

G

did a sahib deign to show interest in their family life, and they were obviously flattered by mine. Of course the conversation was restricted by the lack of a common vocabulary, and we had to help ourselves out with gesticulations. Number One had a wife in Southern Nepal, and not long ago she had given birth to a baby. It was months since he had seen her, and it was many months more before he would see his family again. Pulling up his right sleeve, he showed his naked forearm, explaining that the baby was just that long. " Your forearm is extremely dirty," I thought, " and your baby is by no means of an outsize ". Paldin was more advanced in fatherhood. Two children were awaiting him at home, in the wild valleys of Eastern Nepal, on the southern slopes of Mount Everest. One could already walk. Paldin ran a pair of fingers up and down his tattered trousers, looking affectionately at the imagined stripling. The other son had not yet acquired this difficult art, being in an earlier stage of development — and Paldin sucked his own forefinger. Immediately afterwards, he thrust it, unwiped, into the saucepan, to see how the water was heating.

We seemed likely to be snow-bound if we stayed much longer. There was little food left and we must make tracks for home. At dawn next morning, when we got out of our sleeping-sacks, we found the walls of the tent stiff with ice. There was even a thin layer of hoar-frost upon the sleeping-sacks. With stiff fingers I managed to untie the tent-flap and thrust my head out. Instead of a morning wash, I received a discharge of fine frozen snow in my face. An icy wind was whistling across the desolate scene, and one could see the snow-dust streaming downwind from the peaks and the crests. Still, the weather was clearing. Slowly the summits lighted up in the first rays of the sun. A whole range of hitherto unknown peaks formed part of the golden display. No white man before me had seen these mountains, and no-one knew their names. (In Fig. 10 and in the Panorama II *a* they are indicated by N 1–7.)

Heavily laden we made our way down Nampa Valley. The food had been transformed into rock specimens, and the expectation of a light return journey had been frustrated, as it always is on geological excursions. During the days of our visit to the high mountains, a large flock of sheep had entered the lower part of Nampa Valley. A fine-looking Tibetan mounted on an unkempt pony stared at us with astonishment. He could not understand how human beings could come down from among these desolate glaciers, and almost took us for mountain demons. Suspiciously he watched the three men (likewise unkempt) who walked slowly past carrying heavy burdens. While his beast pawed the rubble impatiently, he continued to gaze after us until we had vanished among the luxuriant rhododendrons. As we were about to disappear, he wrinkled up his eyes, glanced at the setting sun, and galloped off to his black tent.

CHAPTER NINE

IN NORTH-EASTERN KUMAON   (HEIM)

THE MOST POPULOUS OF THE FRONTIER PASSES

It was June 5th when, despite wind and rain, we left Garbyang :
Gansser, after exploring the unknown mountains of Nepal at the head
of Nampa Valley, a journey of which he has given his own description ;
I, after my visit to the busy frontier pass of Lipu Lek. Our main
purpose had been to acquire a complete picture of the geological
cross-section of the Kali.

Around the mountain village the fields were being ploughed, sown,
and harrowed. The women were carrying dung to the fields, using
for this purpose baskets on their backs (Plate 51). Among the fir-trees
beside the bridle path golden-crested wrens were trilling notes so shrill
as to be barely perceptible to human ears. The shrubs on the right
bank of the Kali were now in flower : a white prune, yellowish-white
and pink wild roses. Whereas the red rose normally has five petals,
almost all these white-flowering roses had only four petals (*Rosa sericea*).
This seemed most wrong-headed of them, for have we not all been
taught at school that the rosaceae bear five-petalled blossoms ?

After two hours' march we reached the spot where the Kuti,
emerging from a longitudinal valley in the N.W., debouches into the
Kali. Really it is the other way about. The Kuti ought to be called
Kali, for it brings down from its extensive catchment basin six to eight
times as much water, and can only be crossed by making a long detour.
We had to walk upstream as far as Gunji to find a bridge and a path
back into the Kali Valley.

We had passed from the monotonous schists and quartzites to the
overlying reddish calcareous schists of the Silurian, and beyond them,
still descending south-eastward, we followed the more recent strata as
far as the upper Trias, but they were so much complicated by folds
and scales that they were hard to trace. Not until it was nearly dark
did I reach our goal for that day, the stone huts of Kalapani, which

74

means " bad weather ". They are at an altitude of 12,450 feet on the left side of the valley, but still in Kumaon, for now the border-line between British territory and Nepal took a turn to the S.E. Not far from the huts there were a few firs, this being the highest point at which we have met them, whereas outlying isolated cypresses extend three or four hundred feet higher.

To my surprise, the Kali woke me early next morning, this being a sign of good weather. A huge rocky tooth rose above the valley wall to the left. One caravan after another met us on the march, piloted by Tibetans inured to the uncertain climate of these regions. They all had their hair plaited in pigtails, many of them wore ear-rings (turquoise), and comical-looking felt hats (Plate 108). From a considerable distance one can distinguish Tibetans from Bhotias by their skin-coats with long sleeves which serve instead of gloves, and by their multi-coloured boots which remind one a little of those worn by the Eskimos. Among their beasts were magnificently horned, long-haired goats, and also rams with huge curved horns. Often the shepherds have a hard job to get their flocks together when the creatures wander off among the rocks to graze. In such cases the men pelt the sheep with stones until, bleating, they rejoin the flock. Trained sheep-dogs such as our shepherds use, are unknown in the Himalayas and Tibet. The Bhotia shepherds were also at work, going in the opposite direction to the Tibetans (Plate 48).

A terribly thorny scrub-gorse with with yellow flowers was abundant here, climbing among the sun-kissed rocks as high as 14,760 feet. There were black-and-white birds looking like wagtails, but with a song like a lark's; also, besides the familiar redstarts, there were bramblings, mountain jackdaws, and (as everywhere along caravan routes where sick and injured beasts are left to die) carrion-kites and bearded vultures (Plate 101). Among the former there is often to be seen a gull-like black-and-white carrion-vulture (*Neophron ginginianus*) usually known as the Indian scavenger vulture.

We were continually crossing old moraines, but could see no trace of the main glacier which extended at one time from 20 to 25 miles down the valley : nothing but snowfields, though these were rapidly disappearing beneath the vertical rays of the sun (Plate 102).

At three o'clock we reached Lipu Lek, 16,800 feet. A cairn, surrounded by prayer-staves to which were attached tattered fragments of cloth, stood on the summit of the pass leading into Tibet.

Facing us was Gurla Mandhata, 25,350 feet, having from this outlook almost the same shape as from Tinkar Lipu (Plate 103). So fierce

75

was the wind from the west that we had to go about 160 feet down the Tibetan slopes to find a more protected camp. Not until night was falling did the porters arrive, chilled to the bone. Nevertheless their religion forbade them to accept so much as a little snow-water which we had heated. All they had to eat was tsamba slightly moistened to form a hard and unappetising dough, without salt. I felt quite ashamed when I was enjoying my own supper which Kali had prepared for us in the tent with the aid of the primus stove : barley soup, rice, and some stewed fruit. This time there were six of us in a tent only eight feet square.

The next two days were devoted to geological work. Accompanied by Kirken I made a tedious and difficult climb northward over the rocky ridge to a saddle where we got specimens from a new fossil bed in black clays (Permian). Then we climbed higher still to a ridge at 18,000 feet where we had an unrestricted view northward towards Kailas and southward towards Phung-Di and Nampa. Next came the turn of the southern side of the pass ; dangerous scrambling with very little result since the clouds lowered as the afternoon advanced. We hurried back over the steep snow-slopes to the tent, and the same day went down the valley as far as we could, to reach the stone huts of Darum Sala. As at Kalapani, these are huts which any traveller can use for shelter at night, and to accommodate his beasts as well as himself. The largest hut, roofed with flat stones weighing as much as a hundredweight each, has four rooms, each with a low entry through which we had to creep on all-fours to sleep upon a thick, soft pile of goatskins. The fleas were troublesome, although not so voracious as those of eastern Europe.

Sheep and goats, one flock after another, shepherded by Bhotias (many of them goitrous) and Tibetans encountered us. There was also a long string of ponies, laden with gaily embroidered carpets, and their harness decked with red tassels and jingling bells. With this caravan, which came from India, were not only traders, but many pilgrims on their way to Kailas.

I spent two more days clambering alone among the rocks on the declivities to gain a general idea of the geological structure of the mountain range and to sketch its profile.

In many places the ground was so thickly covered with thorny thickets of barberry and wild roses, interspersed with a growth of two kinds of juniper, to say nothing of cotoneaster, box, currant (Ribes), and various other shrubs, that it was impossible to get through.

76

GOODBYE TO GARBYANG : MORTUARY FESTIVAL
AT GUNJI

On June 15th we bade farewell to our quarters at Garbyang to establish ourselves at a new base, Kuti, the highest village in Central Himalaya (12,300 feet). We set out at ten in the morning and, making good time of it, shortly before one o'clock we reached the bridge for which a huge rock fallen from the heights served as central pillar. Then we climbed 160 feet to the fluvio-glacial terrace of detritus. Original Gunji was a Bhotia settlement, but now the inhabitants are largely of Tibetan type (Plates 104 and 105). We secured quarters in the main street, in the central portion of a house adorned with fine woodcarvings, big enough for three families, for we were guests of the mayor. He was the richest man in the village, Kusal Singh Gunjial by name, and, in his hemispherical leather cap he reminded us of an Appenzell shepherd. In the middle of the dwelling-room was a stone hearth round which mats were spread on the floor. No chimney, no furniture, no glass in the windows, no privy. The roofs of the houses are pointed at an obtuse angle, or some of them practically flat like those of Tibetan houses, covered with flat stones plastered with clay.

The streets were thronged, for the festival in honour of the dead was at hand, and people had flocked in from neighbouring villages. The relatives of those who had died during the year provided rice, rice-beer, tsamba, and meat — not only for the human beings who were celebrating the occasion, but also for the beasts that participated in the ceremonies — some of them as objects of sacrifice. First came two yaks, their horns adorned with silver tips. Bells were hanging round their necks and Persian rugs encircled their bodies. They had been gorged with tsamba till their bellies were as tight as drums. In addition, liberal doses of arrack had been poured down their throats. They were marched in the procession, in front of them women keening. The tune may be thus rendered :

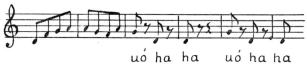

uò ha ha   uò ha ha

The women had their heads wrapped in black cloths from which black veils fell. The procession visited by turns the houses of the deceased. A sacrificial sheep decked with a white shroud was handled even worst than the yaks, being so much crammed with tsamba and rice-beer that it almost died of distension before being slaughtered. Bottle after bottle was opened, the street being splashed with it and sprinkled with barley-flour. There was also a dzo, laden with the boots, sword, bow and arrows of its sometime owner.

The racket continued till midnight. " Tatschúmatátata — táta " came the drum-taps again and again, more and more furiously. Seizing torches, the drummers joined in the dance, while others rushed along our street waving white cloths to scare away the demons. In the adjoining square, copper and wooden vessels filled with rice-beer passed from hand to hand. The dance was held round a mighty bonfire, and all the drummers joined in it. At length began a brawl among a number of drunken Tibetans, who bashed one another's heads with burning brands until the sparks flew.

The women resumed their keening next morning. The copper pots in the street were full of boiling rice, and little cakes on pewter plates were offered round. When we left to continue our march up the valley we were told that the festival would continue for several days. The way led through a pine-forest which grew on a broad mound of detritus. The four-petalled roses were blooming on all hands. In front of us towered a huge mass of rock more than 3000 feet high, horizontally stratified with quartzite (Silurian) which had weathered white and rusty brown, and was capped by stone of the Trias formation traversed by a black vein of schist. At the foot of this mass was a little village named Nabi, through which our route led. The day, though sunshiny to begin with, was now heavy with clouds which gathered over the valley. Soon the rain came down in buckets so that we were drenched to the skin when we reached Kuti at nightfall. Chandru Singh acted as our guide, and owned a handsome but rather gloomy house in the middle of the village, where we took up our quarters. He had actually spread two mattresses for us on the mud floor, and in the surrounding walls were hooks on which we could hang our clothing and apparatus. Inquisitive youngsters assembled to stare at us (Plate 110).

IN QUARTERS AGAIN

Kuti enjoys an extremely favourable situation. That is why its terraced fields are fertile up to a level of 12,460 feet, and a village containing 40 houses inhabited by 80 families has sprung up. The soil is exceptionally fertile, and the longitudinal valley is well sheltered from the prevailing winds (Plate 109). The dark soil consists mainly of the washings from the Trias clays and the Jurassic cretaceous deposits which stretch above Kuti as far as the Chaga Pass. The tilled area must comprise about 300 acres. Besides two kinds of barley, buckwheat (called here phaper), and potatoes are grown. The grain is ground in mills with undershot water-wheels that have been built on the adjoining torrent. Bread is made from barley meal and tsamba is roasted. From buckwheat they prepared a less tasty breadstuff, for it is somewhat bitter. This is greenish in colour and is baked at an open fire. The potatoes had just been planted when we arrived, and will be lifted in October. During the winter they are stored in pits and used for the nourishment of the three families that stay in the village throughout the cold season. We had some of last year's crops, and found them just as fresh and toothsome as if they had only just been lifted.

We record the temperature day by day, and find it to range between 42° and 56°, which is low for the season. Since the rainfall has been excessive, the people fear a bad harvest. Still, the weather is calm, and bright days are more dangerous than rainy ones, since when there is free radiation the nights are frosty, followed by sudden and excessive heat.

The architecture of the houses is typically Bhotian. The roofs, built in an obtuse angle, are thatched with brushwood and covered with heavy stone plates, these again being plastered with clay. The better houses have fine woodcarvings on the door and window frames, usually painted reddish-brown, but sometimes picked out in various colours (Plates 107, 110, and 111). In the larger houses the gables overhang. As we entered the village, the largest house stood in front of us on the right. It was 130 feet wide and sheltered eight families, each of which had access by a separate door. On the ground floor were stalls for the farm beasts and quarters for the flocks used in caravan transport. The second storey consists of the dimly lit habitations. Every evening, when sunset nears, the shepherds drive their flocks down from the mountains to bring the sheep and goats under cover for the night, for they must be protected from the ounces. Now and again a goat may be milked, but the Bhotias in general drink little milk, and know practically nothing of cheese. Butter, when obtainable, has been scalded, or is rancid and dirty. Sheep are used mainly for transport (rams for the most part) and are seldom slaughtered for food. Their wool is not an article of export, being hand-spun and woven for domestic use.

During the bad weather which prevailed throughout most of our stay at Kuti, we have been engaged in cartography, drying and pressing plants, and making our quarters tidy and comfortable. Each of us has a table in the form of a box placed in front of the window ; and each of us has his own mattress on which to squat. While on the march we have found it rather too cold to write with comfort.

We are well supplied with food, and Kali really spoils us in this matter. Apart from the stores brought with us from Switzerland or from Almora, we can buy in Kuti potatoes, linseed (dal), tsamba, maize flour, wheat flour (ata), and almost daily we have rice, of which we never get tired.

The nights are less agreeable, not because of insect pests, but because of quadrupeds. The rats gnaw at our provisions, run races in the roof until the plaster falls about our heads, or squeak when they have differences of opinion in the walls. We speak of this as a " ratification ". Worst of all are the dogs, which go on barking all night, preferably at our door, keeping up the din for hours twice or thrice a second. Sometimes we can scare them away with a pocket torch, a douche of water, or a well-directed stone. After such a night, we sally forth at an early hour for our daily geological avocations, defying rain and tempest, but seeking a moderately sheltered corner as far as possible from the village. On rare sunny days we put our drenched hobnails to dry on the stones in front of the house, where they seem of interest, not only to the bipeds of the village, but to a snow-white kid, a recent arrival, which comes and licks them (Plate III).

Every morning and evening, Chandru's sister goes out on to the roof of her house which is opposite ours to make oblations of food and water on behalf of her father who died a few months ago. There do not appear to be any congregational religious observances, and there is no temple here. When people die their bodies are burned and the remains cast into the river, Hindu-fashion.

ON FLOWERY ALPS

When the weather was really fine for a day or for a few hours, we found Kuti an excellent centre for excursions, the geological surroundings and the botany of the region being extraordinarily interesting. Chandru has taken us to the nearest mountain pasture, where the villagers have found ammonites. They are in a black clay, like that of Tinkar Lipu, but of much more recent date, being what is known as spiti shale, transitional between Jurassic and cretaceous. Fossils are less frequent here, and must be excavated from gravelly or ferruginous concretions. Like pearl-divers, we feel lucky when we find that one of twenty turns out well. Here and there the fossils are pyritised, that is to say they have been impregnated with iron sulphide, or " fool's gold "—and in these cases the natives naturally suppose that we have found gold. Far more interesting than the fossils of this region are the strata. In our very first excursion we discovered that the black clays are overlaid by a mountain chain whose strata are Silurian or older. This chain, to which the highest peaks above Kuti belong, has also been superposed upon the younger formations from the Tibetan side.

Below the superimposed strata, on the black clays which spread south-eastward through a little valley to Chaga Pass, 15,900 feet, the flora is most diversified. First we came upon meadows covered with golden-yellow sunflowers having strawberry-pattern leaves (*Potentilla argyrophylla*). Another variety, less common, has flowers ranging from orange coloured to brilliant red. Then there are violet-blue or carmine geraniaceae, and various kinds of white anemones (*Isopyrum grandiflorum, Anemone rupicola*). In some places the almost bare ground is occupied by a tiny flower which at the first glance one might take for a violet, but it has pinnate leaves and a long, thick tap-root (*Corydalis*). Another novelty to us is the violet bells of a liliaceous plant (*Fritillaria oxypetala*). On the stony slopes, which sometimes have almost the aspect of a tundra, there flourishes an aromatic daphne which allures the fat bees. In the stony rubble, at a higher elevation, we have found a remarkable plant with large lobate leaves on a stem which resembles that of a small maple, but the flower has six readily detachable pink petals (*Trillium*). Among the limestone rocks ranging from 13,800 feet to 14,450 feet there flourishes a large-leaved saxifrage (*Bergenia stracheyi*). The pink primulas, which have ceased flowering lower down, are still in their glory at these higher levels near the snow-line. Even higher, up to 15,750 feet, we find the most beautiful and largest of the primulas, the dark violet *Primula nivalis*. At these altitudes, too, there is often found a delicate, brightly shining, spurred little blue flower with delicate rootlets (*Corydalis cachemiriana*). In places, at these great heights, the ground looks as if it had been sown to produce interlacing threads like a yarn of some peculiar kind. Among the shrubs there is a juniper which clings close to the ground (*Juniperus recurva*) and grows on the sunny face of the rocks up to a height of about 15,000 feet.

Very different is the flora on the shady side of Kuti Valley. There, at a range of from 12,500 feet to 13,200 feet, we find, mixed with dwarf birches, slopes covered with great bushes of rhododendrons bearing innumerable white flowers (*Rhododendron lepidotum*).

Although we encounter many plants which thus remind us of those seen in the Swiss mountains, we are struck by the frequency of unfamiliar growths, and by the lack of soldanellas, campanulas, and dryads. Gentians and edelweiss would seem to be rather late in appearing.

I must not forget to mention a remarkable plant we have found close to the village. We call it the collar-bell. The flowers are large, violet-black, six-petalled, bell-shaped structures, surrounded at the base by a closed green involucre.

THE MONSOON

While normally in this part of the world clear weather persists well on into June, and on the Tibetan border behind the lofty chains the dreaded S.W. monsoon begins a few weeks later than in the neighbour-hood of Darjeeling, this year we have had bad weather almost persistently since the middle of May, or else, when the mountains were clear in the morning they clouded over before noon. We were reminded by this of the fate of the great British Everest Expedition led by Hugh Ruttledge, sometime deputy commissioner of Almora, and of the first French Expedition to the Karakoram Range. We have learned from the news-papers that both of these have had to abandon their schemes. The inhabitants of Kuti had been much excited by the announcement that the present ruler of the district, the deputy commissioner, would pay them an official visit, accompanied by two ladies and a small army of porters.

But he had to give it up this year, and got no farther than Garbyang, returning thence by way of Askot to Almora. For our part, we have suffered a good deal from bad weather, although sport was not our primary aim, and we found plenty to do even when the weather was unfavourable. But now the monsoon has burst, and will certainly make things much worse. Our hope was to climb Shangtang, the highest mountain in the chain on the Tibetan border, a wonderful white pyramid (the peak marked 21,262 feet in the map). Gansser had already climbed the adjoining ridge of 16,728 feet, from which he sketched Shangtang (Fig. 11). He decided that the best way of climbing the latter would probably be through the valley behind Kuti, and that if the fine weather held we should be able to reach the summit on the morning of the third day. We prepared supplies for five or six days if necessary, greased our faces, and treated our feet with formalin. The evening of June 20th proved most promising, but on June 21st we suffered a grievous disappointment. The dogs had ceased barking towards mid-night and drizzle set in. In these regions bordering on Tibet, when the monsoon bursts it comes, not with storms and a heavy downpour,

82

but with a steady, gradually intensifying rain. The temperature was 46°. That evening snow was lying down as low as 15,750 feet. On the average, in the Himalayas, as one climbs the temperature falls about 1° C. for every 500 feet.

Next day, although the rain was not falling so heavily, it was plain that the monsoon had really burst. This view was confirmed by the fact that I had rheumatic pains in the back. Two Bhotias who arrived after crossing Mangshang Pass on the third day of the monsoon reported that the snow was two feet deep on the top (18,040 feet).

FIG. 11. SHANGTANG FROM THE SOUTH. (G)

To cheer us up a little, the runner brought our mail, which included a telegram. I opened it with considerable anxiety, with thoughts of my aged father in my mind, to read a lively greeting signed, " Hilsener Wegmann, Julianehaab ".

It was a message from our friends in Greenland, dispatched on June 15th to reach Kuti on June 22nd. Probably the first dispatch from within the Arctic Circle to the Himalayas and answered from the Himalayas to the Far North.

Since during the monsoon the weather often improves for a few days we did not propose to abandon our designs on Shangtang, and, on the first day of the monsoon, although it was still wet, we set forth

83

up the steep lateral valley to the N.E. of Kuti. I was encouraged by a memory from Minya Gongar, where, one day, I emerged above the cloud-stratum into bright sunshine although at a lower level it was gloomy, cold, and rainy. Gansser was carrying a porter's load, for we had had to leave a sick coolie at Kuti and one of the others refused to accompany us because no-one but himself in the village was of the right caste to give food to the invalid. To begin with we followed a shepherd's track; then we took the line of a furrow made by an avalanche across a wet and slippery moraine until, at an altitude of 16,070 feet, we could make no further headway and, drenched and bitterly cold, pitched our two tents. After a while, with Gansser's help, the coolies joined us.

This should have been a magnificent viewpoint, but the monsoon would not give us a chance. During the night the gale carried away the flag we had erected on a cairn. We stuck it out amid rainstorms and snow until evening, when we decided to make tracks for Kuti, leaving a tent with a store of provisions there on the heights. Through the mist we could hear the thunder of avalanches. The descent was a rapid affair, for we made a snow-slide of the avalanche-groove, so that in an hour we got down the 3600 feet. The friendly Chandru gave us a warm welcome, providing tea and goats' milk, with a fire in our room at which we were able to dry our clothes.

The following nights were disturbed, even though we were under a roof. The plaster in the ceiling became thoroughly moistened, so that water fell, at first in drops, and then in a steady stream. We had to shift our sleeping-sacks, and even then got thoroughly wet in spite of raincoats and a sheet of tent-cloth stretched over the roof. Under this cloud-pall, the temperature has an oceanic equability, ranging no more than from 42° in the morning to about 48° at night. We kept the fire going, but were almost stifled by the smoke which had no outlet.

The old shaman, who has been treating the sick coolie by cauterising his heels, prophesies fine weather next week, and the whole village is of the same opinion. In the end he proved fairly correct.

Now we formed a plan which we were eager to carry into effect. Two of the most vigorous among the villagers were about to make a dash for Kailas in order to buy sheep and goats for the forthcoming festival of the dead in Kuti. They expected to be back in about twelve days. This gave Gansser an unexpected and unique opportunity of accompanying them incognito. Was I, the responsible chief of the expedition, to forbid this undertaking? Not only did I fully understand and sympathise with my energetic comrade's desire, but I should

84

have liked to go with him, and could not but feel that the bold scheme might prove of good service to science.

"Of course," said Gansser, "should I go, it will be on my own responsibility; and if you veto the plan, I will give it up."

This was June 28th, on the eighth day of the rains. Borrowing a lama's caftan, Gansser disguised himself as a pilgrim (Plate 118), and set off at top speed with the trusty Paldin (who can speak Tibetan), hoping to overtake the Kuti men. He left me the following chit: "The undersigned hereby declares that, on his own responsibility, he sets forth to-day upon a geological excursion which is not to last longer than a fortnight. June 28th."

ON SHIALA PASS

Meanwhile I was going to spend four or five days studying the geology of the district S.W. of Kuti as far as the Shiala Pass (called also the Nama Pass. But now I had trouble with the remaining Dhotial coolies who, though they have had a good rest, are by no means better for it. Yogi declares that he has pains in the chest. We could only take with us the minimum necessaries.

When we had crossed the bridge over the Kuti and were climbing over the flower-clad terraces on the farther side, the sun (after a rainy night) was so hot that I took off coat and shirt, with the result that my back was badly sunburned. The bees were humming, while the swallow-tailed butterflies and the vanessas had fully recovered from the wet. We noticed a few quadrupeds as well, apparently wild goats. In the lush grass flourished long-stalked white or pale-pink primulas (*Primula pargesii*), red orchids, forget-me-nots, crowsfoot, and knot-grass; while here, as everywhere in these regions, potentillas, geraniums, and anemones abounded. But not until we reached an altitude of 13,000 feet did we find any considerable quantity of edelweiss (*Leontopodium leontopodium*). A few miles farther on, at 13,400 feet, we were right above the end of the glacier, from beneath which a considerable stream emerged. Then we reached the ice-covered crest, encumbered with detritus, where we pitched our tent on a small green area. My men were in poor case. Both Kali and Kirken were now complaining of headache, and the three porters straggled a long way behind. I let them all rest in the afternoon, finding plenty of interesting work on both sides of the valley. I discovered another big fault, so clearly marked that I was able to measure and sketch every detail and take photographs as easily as if we had been at home in the Alps.

June 1st began badly. It had been raining since midnight, with a dense mist. Not until noon could we start on a fresh stage of our journey, to reach an altitude of 15,250 feet on the left margin of the moraine. With Dilly, our guide from Kuti, we were seven in the little tent, and the unwashed coolies stank like a piece of carrion so that I could not get to sleep. I took the opportunity to make an early start, being off at the first glimmer of dawn with Dilly and Kirken while the coolies slept out. The skies had cleared, which was better luck than I had expected. The unnamed twenty-thousanders with their sharply marked flutings (Plate 113) were strikingly contrasted with the dark-blue sky when the light came. Dazzling was the surface of the depression in the ice-cap up which we now made our way, to the right of a bluish-green ice-precipice about 4000 feet high (Plate 114). By eight o'clock we reached the top of the pass, 16,560 feet. It forms a deep notch between walls of brown calcareous schist (Plate 112). Southward was a steep descent to the glacier leading down Dhauli Valley, while high above this, more to the west, were seen the lofty peaks of Panch Chulhi, 22,630 feet, with in the middle distance " cotton-wool " masses of cloud. Soon little cloud-drifts began to reach us, driven by the N.E. wind. Thus during the middle of the monsoon there can be a change of wind, which brings fine weather.

As we were returning over the ice-cap a small vanessa fluttered by, and settled on my hand for a long time. What could this butterfly be seeking at such a height ? Sunlight, I suppose. At noon the sun is only 7° from the zenith, and can rapidly melt the upper surface of the snows.

All that remained for me to do was to complete my geological studies and collect fossils. These were brachyopods from a Lower Silurian sandstone.

The north-easter blew for another day, the cloud-veils slowly returning upon the mountain, and Shangtang remained hidden. On the Tibetan frontier a N.E. wind at this season betokens rough weather.

TO MEET THE KAILAS PILGRIM

On getting back to Kuti I determined to pay off the remaining Dhotial coolies and send them back to Almora, hiring (with Chandru's help) men from the village in their place. They want somewhat higher wages, but are familiar with the mountains of the region. The barometer has fallen with the change of wind, and the weather is still very bad.

Gansser and I had agreed that, if possible, ten days after he left I

87. Old Gombu. Purang, Tibet. May 26, 1936. (G)

89. The "Beauties" of Purang, Tibet, made-up with lampblack.

88. Shepherd boys of Tinkar, Nepal. May 22, 1936. (G)

90. Old Gombu's House. Purang, Tibet. May 25, 1936. (G)

91. The new Lamasery of Jitkot has been built amid the ruins
of the old one. May 25, 1936. (G)

92. Women taking an easy at Tinkar, Nepal. May 1936. (H)

93. Council before descent, after receiving the bad news. May 31, 1936. (H)

94. Gansser, with Paldin to the right and Number One to the left, makes a fresh start
into unknown Nepal. June 6, 1936. (H)

95. In the Cave of the Dead, Changru, Nepal. Beside the skulls are Tibetan tea-canisters standing on end. (G)

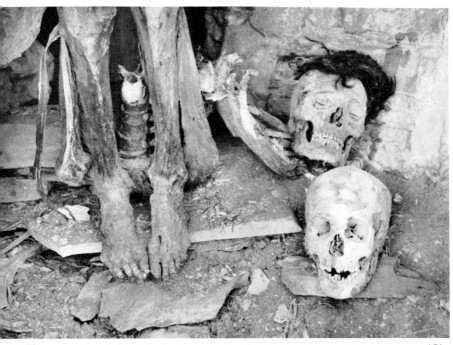

96. The grinning skull with the hairy scalp lay beside the squatting mummy. (G)

97. Behind the Nampa Valley in Nepal we discover unnamed knife-edged icy ridges. June 9, 1936. (G)

98. Here, according to local legend, was once a pass between flowery meads, at the top of the Tinkar Valley, Nepal. (The pass is between peaks No. 5 and No. 6 of fig. 10 in the text.) June 9, 1936. (G)

99. Unknown and unnamed, a peak nearly 23 000 feet high situated behind
Nampa Valley, Nepal. June 9, 1936.   (G)

101. At 16,000 feet bearded vulture soaring. Liang Li ...

100. Rhododendron lepidotum at 13,000 feet in

102. Looking back westwards from Lipu Lek. June 7, 1936. (H)

103. On Lipu Lek, 16 800 feet, the most-travelled frontier pass to Tibet. In the background, Gurla Mandhata, 25 350 feet. June 7, 1936. (H)

105. Guests of the Mayor of Gunji. June 15, 1936.

104. House in Gunji, Kumaon. Tibetan type. (H)

106. Woman of Kuti, Tibet. (H)

107. Wood-carvings on the oldest house in Kuti. 12 300 feet. (H)

108. Drover of a Tibetan Caravan. (H)

109. Kuti, 12 300 feet. Highest village in Central Himalayas, on river Kuti. Looking west. June 18, 1936.   (H)

110. Our second quarters, Kuti. June 1936.   (H)

112. Shiala Pass, 16 560 feet. Calcareous schists of the lowermost Palaeozoic. The plates are vertically disposed. July 2, 1936. (H)

111. Our hobnailed boots, drying in the sun, seem to interest the kid. (H)

113: Lateral glacier moving to the south-east flanked by unnamed peaks ranging to 20 000 feet.

114. A depression in the ice-cap on Shiala Pass. Top of pass on right. Looking south-west. July 2, 1936. (H)

115. Presages of the Monsoon. May 21, 1936. (G)

116. Detailed Tibetan Map of Kailas, the sacred mountain.
A Fresco in Tinkar, Nepal. (G)

was to set out for Mangshang Pass. Meanwhile I had still plenty to do in the upper Kuti Valley. For the time being, however, I was held up, not only by bad weather, but also by a village festival. This (by order of God and the village council) is to continue for a second day, and no-one must work under pain of punishment. It would be an offence to do so much as wash out a pocket handkerchief. What do the men do during these holidays? Loaf and talk themselves hoarse, until even the kids are bored. There is no sign of merriment.

On the ninth day after Gansser's departure, when the rain ceased towards eight o'clock, we set off up the valley. I had with me, besides my two trusty men Kirken and Kali, four excellent porters belonging to Kuti. At first the scenery was monotonous, the mountains being hidden. In the main valley our way led us for the most part over ancient moraines. On the flowery meadows there was not much novelty as regards botanical specimens beyond the extremely abundant ever-lastings (*Anaphalis nubigena*).

After two hours, since it was raining once more, we took shelter under an overhanging rock, and afterwards among some Nepalese on their way to Kailas, who had piled up their sacks of rice, barley, and sugar to make a barrier against the wind. They gave us some roasted grains of wheat to chew, which we found to have a very pleasant taste. Then, having resumed our march, we at length, wet to the skin, reached our objective for the day, a place called Joling Kong, at a height of about 14,250 feet. It was a grass-grown level at the outlet of the Lebong lateral valley, bestrewn with huge blocks fallen from the mountains which offered a little protection from the rain. Although we had a pair of bellows essential to travellers in such regions, the porters found it very hard — with only wet juniper branches for fuel — to make a fire with which they could boil their butter-tea.

Next day we reached a picturesque lake at a height of 14,430 feet, behind the Kailas terminal moraine at the foot of what used to be a much larger glacier than it is now (Plates 138 and 140). The map shows a good many other lakes in this region, but we could not find them, so we supposed them to be no more than occasionally flooded areas at the outlets of the lateral valleys to the south-west. By the detritus of the moraines the main stream has been deviated to the left, where it has cut itself a gorge in the rocks. We waded through the marshes and the outflows from the glaciers barefoot. Higher up, it would have been harder to cross the river Kuti had there not been an arched mass of detritus formed by an avalanche which could be used as a bridge. Once more we had to take shelter from the rain under an overhanging block. Another hindrance to our progress was the raging torrent coming from an eastward lateral valley out of a huge glacier. About 160 feet higher, on the old lateral moraine of this glacier, at 15,750 feet, was a seemingly much-used camping ground, with ruined walls close at hand. The place is called Wilsha. Since leaving Kuti we have passed no permanent habitations.

Despite the rain, at 4.15, before daybreak, the redstarts began to sing as merrily as larks. There is another species, one with a red belly, which gives a shriek in the middle of its song, just as do our black-bellied redstarts at home.

Now we climbed over moraines and masses of detritus, and then, as we made our way to the left past the end of the glacier, amid rocks, the path grew continually steeper. When we were at 16,400 feet, the rain changed to snow, and the wind was biting. We were vainly hoping at 17,400 feet that we must be near the top. Now came the steepest and roughest stretch where, on the zigzags, indications were painted on the rocks. Every twenty paces we had to pause and recover breath. At length, at ten o'clock, Kirken and I reached the Mangshang Pass. The aneroid reading was 18,760 feet, but this was probably too high, and should be corrected to 18,200 feet. Up there, beneath a flat stone, we had a find — a tent which Gansser must have left behind to save weight on his way to Kailas.

Although the rest of the party were far in the rear, we set off without pause. It was too windy and cold to stay on the top of the pass, so we trudged down the Tibetan side of the snowfield, which was extremely steep and where avalanches seemed imminent, in search of a ridge of rock which would protect us a little from the wind. We could neither see nor hear amid the snow-storm. We hallooed loudly every few minutes. One of the men from Kuti who was with the party must know the way over the pass. Being afraid that they were still belated, we clambered back to the top. Then we heard shouts from somewhere higher up on the left. We had missed our way. The proper route from the gap was 160 feet higher along the ridge to the right (S.E.), and then straight down the precipitous snow-slope into Tibet. Below, a huge glacier emerged from the right. At first we followed its left-hand moraine, and then for hours marched along the windswept surface of the glacier, almost as smooth as a stirrup-iron, practically free from crevasses and ending above a moraine at an altitude of about 16,400 feet. Here was a marked contrast to the detritus-covered glaciers on the other side of the great watershed. The stream issuing from the foot of the glacier was pale pink in colour, like diluted milk containing

88

a little blood. We could easily guess where the " red blood corpuscles " came from — from the marly limestone of the ancient red Silurian strata which, on both sides of the valley, formed the mountain slopes in complicated folds.

Although we were all extremely tired, we had to go several miles farther down the valley, crossing rough stone-fields, until at length, on the left side, we reached green plots — the first fuel. This was not scrub juniper but a dwarf heath. While we were pitching our tent there on the left end of a sheet of gravel, at a height equal to that of the top of Mont Blanc, across the valley we caught sight of a magnificent black wild yak which, however, soon departed for loftier regions, following the herd which was pasturing higher up (Fig. 12).

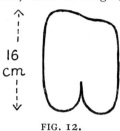

FIG. 12.
WILD YAK'S SLOT.
MANGSHANG.

We are already so far from the water-parting that the clouds are breaking up a little, and we can see blue sky now and again to the north. Amid the detritus round our tent, flowers are blooming — old friends and new. There are tufts of a small edelweiss, a violet-coloured miniature vetch (*Oxytropis*), a tiny red-flowering shrub, violet-coloured alpine asters, and a plant with white spikes and a scent like that of creeping forget-me-not.

CHAPTER TEN

ON PILGRIMAGE TO KAILAS (GANSSER)

CROSSING THE MANGSHANG PASS IN A
MONSOON STORM

" ' PALDIN, look, to the left of that rocky tooth, far away behind the hazy blue mountains you can see Kailas.' Paldin clasped his hands and prayed. He has been on many expeditions before this, but has never yet visited the most sacred of mountains. He and I had climbed together a rather difficult peak above Garbyang, and were astonished at the extensive view. Since then, in the middle of May, we have made acquaintance with a great many new mountains, but cannot forget our glimpse of snow-crowned Kailas in the far distance. But it was in a forbidden land.

" The monsoon burst when we were at Kuti, in our second quarters. During the tedious and gloomy rains of the end of June, we formed various schemes. Kuti was preparing for its festival of the dead, which was to take place in a few weeks. For this, sacred sheep were needed, sheep raised at the foot of Kailas. Two of the sturdiest Bhotias were commissioned to undertake the difficult journey. Two men of Kuti were going to Kailas ! I could find no more rest. At length, on a cloudy morning, June 28th, not two but four of us were on the way to Kailas, the two extra ones being Paldin the Sherpa coolie and myself.

" The two Bhotias have gone on ahead, wishing to collect some wood for use as fuel when crossing the pass. All the better, for in that case my departure from the village with Paldin would attract less attention. ' Bara Sahib ' (Heim) and Chandru accompanied us a little way, and two of our Dhotial coolies helped to carry our loads as long as we were still on Indian soil. Two days' march will take us across the Tibetan frontier. Joling Kong is our first camp. I cook my soup in pouring rain. We have found here a couple of Tibetans beneath the huge overhanging rocks. For nearly a week they have been awaiting better weather before crossing Mangshang Pass. They are father and son, returning to their homeland and bringing all sorts of trade-goods. Among these are white-metal tubes for the nozzles of Tibetan goat-skin bellows, tsamba, and lal (paprika) — some of which latter they are using as provisions on the journey. Decent fellows enough, and I see no objection to chumming up with them. I told them as much as was needful about the purposes of my journey, and I do not think that they will give me away. This evening I am still a sahib, but to-morrow they will find me transformed into a Tibetan lama. The two Dhotial coolies were sent back with a farewell greeting to Bara Sahib — somewhat unpoetically written on a scrap of excellent toilet paper.

" Next morning, heavily laden, we climb the steep ascent to Mang-shang-La, 18,380 feet, the frontier pass between India and Tibet. The new lama does not find his disguise as comfortable as he could wish, for the heavy, red, sheepskin caftan is a hindrance to the free use of his legs. His fur cap is coated with snow, and his beard frosted with icicles. A snow-storm rages on the top of the pass ; we sink deeply into the new fall, which lies upon scattered rocky debris, so that we make slow progress. Still, here we are at the top. From the folds of his voluminous garments the red lama extracts an aneroid, takes bearings with the compass, and, with a little hammer, chips off a few samples of rock. These are secreted within the caftan, where every Tibetan carries his portable goods when on a journey, including pro-visions and the indispensable prayer-wheel. For the moment I still carry an ice-axe under my arm, and beneath the shaggy lower end of the sheepskin caftan my mountain boots peep out. At the next camp I shall leave the ice-axe behind, and march boldly on wearing red leather Tibetan boots.

" Through a thick layer of newly fallen snow we descend the steep rocky declivity on the northern side of the pass. We hear a few avalanches rustling down on to the lower glacier. The old Tibetan has lagged behind, and is lost to sight in the fog. Then a rough voice comes downwind. The mist clears for a moment, and we catch sight of the old man standing on a rock with uplifted arms, praying. The distant prospect having also cleared, a marvellous view is disclosed — a vision grown real. There are endless chains of red, brown, and yellow mountains, incredibly clear. On the far horizon we discern a new mountain range, pastel blue in the distance, with yellow glaciers. This is Transhimalaya. Out of the vast extent of these new peaks there thrusts up a white cone, a mountain of strange shape, Kailas, the holy of holies of the Asiatic religion. My companions are motionless, the snow reaching to their hips, while they say their prayers. Each of us offers up to Kailas a handful of rice, scattered down the wind which blows towards the mountain. On the remoter horizon are ranged white cumulus clouds sharply marked off from the clear blue of the Tibetan sky. But over the Himalaya chains stands a wall of thick clouds, like those which accompany the föhn in Switzerland, these being vapours from the Indian plains. Then we make a speedy descent to cross the level surface of the glacier on the northern side of the pass. From this view-point the savagery of the Himalaya chains has been mitigated. The peaks are covered with rounded ice-caps, from which icy rivers flow sluggishly into the valleys. Between these stand out barren rocks and wide detritus-covered slopes and screes of the most diversified colours. This is a picture which will live in my memory like that of the Greenland glaciers.

" On a wide rubble-covered level, stands a wild yak at gaze. Slowly I approach the beast, camera in hand. The huge animal moves its tail restlessly. Its long, brownish-black hair, which reaches almost to the ground, gleams in the sunlight. Irresolutely the creature paces to and fro, obviously puzzled what to make of this stranger. He suffers me to come within a hundred yards, then snorts, stamps, lowers his head and charges. The other men shout to me to look out, and I leap across a rivulet while Paldin rushes to my support with an ice-axe. The old hermit thinks there are too many of us, stops short, turns, and gallops away at full speed. A little lower down is a large herd of wild yaks, the calves trotting beside their mothers. Solitary bachelors are regarded as the most dangerous of these creatures."

NOMADS

" We camp at 16,400 feet. The last wood we have is used to build a camp fire, which will at least suffice to make tea. We dispose ourselves round this fire in the open, couched on sleeping-sacks or on blankets. On this journey the tent is a luxury with which we shall have to dispense. As I gaze at the starry heavens it seems to me that there are more stars than I am used to at home, sparkling in the icy night.

" Leaving the rounded ice-clad peaks of the Tibetan Himalayas well behind, we cross arid, hilly steppes. The lamasery of Mangshang must be somewhere hereabouts, but we deem it expedient to make as few human contacts as possible. The sun blazes, although we are at an altitude higher than the summit of Monte Rosa. Following the Tibetan

92

fashion, I bared one shoulder. It was already brown, and my hands besooted by handling the charred remnants of the camp fire give my sweaty skin a seemingly natural Tibetan patina. My face would also look genuine enough were not my beard rather unsuitable. Still, perhaps it will give an added touch of holiness.

" Having waded through a broad river, we cross the important trade-route which leads from Purang to Gartok. On the map it is marked as a thick black line, but in truth it is only distinguishable by a few sheep-tracks and skeletons of these beasts that have perished by the way. Except for numerous hares, there is no living creature within sight. We climb once more, up a gorge. Through strikingly green grass a tiny rivulet winds. A number of lousewort flowers adorn the marshy banks. Here, to my surprise, I find a most unusual rock formation. There are large whitish masses of rock many hundred feet across embedded in a dark matrix of eruptive stone. This is the first time we have met with such exotic blocks, which have hitherto only been known to exist in the more northerly regions of the Himalayas (see page 134). Their appearance here gives a pointer concerning their origin, which was hitherto extremely enigmatic. This is one of the most important discoveries made during the visit to Tibet."

While I was studying my find, my companions got a long way ahead, so that I only overtook them when they had already camped at the top of the gorge beside a roaring fire. There was gorse here which provided admirable fuel. But after nightfall the camp was less agreeable, for icy rain, soon changing to sleet, began to fall, and lasted until dawn. The water trickled into our sleeping sacks and we lay in puddles. When day came it was actually snowing, and we could not light a fire. We were wet through and chilled to the bone as we footed it heavily through new-fallen snow to the top of Amlang-La (*la* is Tibetan for pass), at an altitude of 16,400 feet. There we were greeted by a raging snow-storm, and our wet garments began to freeze. My red sheepskin caftan and my Tibetan fur cap, in any case a considerable weight, now felt as heavy as lead, while my Tibetan boots were full of water. I should have been glad indeed could I have dispensed with my incognito, but there was no use thinking of that. I looked down ruefully at my frozen lama-envelope, and my fine red Tibetan boots which squirted water at every step.

That evening we struck an inhabited region once more. The first token of it was a number of tame yaks grazing. With their wet, shaggy hair thickly coated with snow they looked like antediluvian monsters. Then we came to hundreds of yaks, thousands of sheep, and at length a few black Tibetan tents. But we were not to get access so easily to a fire and the food of which we were so much in need. Fierce Tibetan dogs, half a dozen or more of them, assailed us, as we stood back to back, warding them off with sticks. An isolated tramp would have been torn to pieces. The old Tibetan drew his long sword, and I prepared to make the best use I could of my geological hammer. A firearm would have been useful, but then there would have been no chance of hospitality. That was why we took none with us on the journey. Now a little Tibetan girl appeared, and dispersed our assailants as if by miracle. She merely stooped to pick up a small stone and this had more effect than the heavy missiles we had hurled at the furious beasts. They were fine creatures all the same, and thenceforward my great wish was to become the owner of one, at least, in the puppy stage of development.

Soon we were sitting in a big black tent, before a fire at which we could warm and dry ourselves, although the pungent yak-dung smoke was agonising. The top of the tent was open to let the worst of the smoke escape, and the rain-drops fell hissing into the fire. The man wielding the goat-skin bellows did his best, but the nozzle was no more than a charred remnant, and our old Tibetan was able to do his first trade. Our entertainers were a whole family. The grandmother, a withered hag, mixed rancid butter with the tea that had been made in a long cylinder. The mother had a baby at her dirty breast — so dirty that compared with it my streaked and browned visage seemed almost clean. Three men were twisting cords; while those of the group who were too young to work crawled about on the floor among new-born lambs. The oldest of the clan, a man with long, grey hair, toothless, and with seven ragged strands of beard on his chin, was sitting in front of the domestic altar which, decked with purple and bearing brass utensils, is an indispensable article in the tents of these nomads. The old fellow stared at me fixedly, and obviously realised that beneath the Tibetan shell a foreign kernel must lurk. Happily he was not inquisitive, and we tranquilly joined in drinking butter-tea. Attentively I imitated the behaviour of my hosts, until the last drop of the contents of the wooden saucer had vanished into my mouth. I need hardly say that the last but one of the various manipulations made a deep impression upon me, for the hospitable mother of the tribe (Plate 123) with the palms of her grimy hands cleared out of the saucer intended for my use some vestiges of food and then licked the platter clean before pouring out my portion. The lightly salted beverage was at least pleasantly warm.

94

RAKSAS VALLEY, THE HAUNTED LAKE

Next day we went close to several settlements of the nomads and had to defend ourselves once more against their savage dogs. Broad, shallow passes on which isolated gorse-bushes were growing led us from one steppe valley into another, all of them strangely alike. Then, after we had tramped through sand and rubble across an eminence, we suddenly caught sight of a great stretch of blue water beyond some low hills. The sun was shining, and never have I seen a deeper blue than that of Raksas Valley, the " haunted lake ", which, surrounded by violet-brown mountains, looked like a jewel in a lovely setting (Plate 119). We were a little off the track, and a ragged shepherd put us right again. We had to make westward to the shore of the lake and then follow it northward. Jungbwa was the name of the nomads' settlement where we passed the night. The Tibetans provided us with a tent which, like all the tents of these nomads, is open in the middle of the top to allow the smoke to escape — a most desirable thing since the fumes of the yak-dung they use as fuel are extremely acrid.

" A wonderful evening. With the help of the goat-skin bellows our yak-dung burns like straw. We have yak milk and tsamba for supper. I sit in front of the tent. Since the dogs are numerous, and their keen noses enable them to detect me as a foreigner, I dare not stray from the camp. The sun sets behind low hills to the westward. Down these, away from the sunset, comes a huge herd of yaks, with little and medium-sized calves following their dams. The long hair of the beasts has a golden tinge in this light. Two Tibetan women are driving them back from their pasturage to the camp. All the calves are caught and roped to stakes, for they must not be allowed to suck their mothers. The more thirsty specimens have long sticks tied crosswise on the neck, so that they cannot get near the udders. The cows are milked, and then their hind legs are hobbled. This work is done by the women. The sun is rapidly sinking. To the S.E. the distant Gurla Mandhata is resplendent in yellows and wine-reds ; Raksas Valley is violet and green ; the clouds aloft are golden ; and in the west the mountains covered with new-fallen snow have a golden-red tint. Gurla turns dark violet, the clouds red-violet, a moment snatches the glory from the grey, the sun has vanished. A flock of more than a thousand sheep is driven home. The long hair of the great yaks waves in the wind. Near our tent is an altar-stone. An old Tibetan kindles incense and prays ' Om mani padme oom '. I wrap my sheep-skin coat more closely round me, as a big Tibetan dog scrutinises me. Three puppies are playing like kittens, pretty little beasts. I was to own one of them later. On the western horizon there is still a narrow golden-yellow streak. Sheep in an unending series pass by, as little silhouettes. It is blue-grey on Gurla, and blue-grey on Kailas.

" The old Tibetan awakens and shouts ' Chaloo ! ' It is still dark, but we have a long day before us. With empty stomachs we set forth over broad passes on the steppe. Then I find myself sitting in astonishment on a sandy shore. A little dune borders a mirror-surface of water. In this mirror are reflected towering storm-clouds above reddish brown hills, above blue mountains (Plates 124 and 125). Terns shoot gracefully into the picture. I fling a pebble into the water and watch the widening circles. The mirror is disturbed, so that the reflected blue of the sky and the reflected white of the clouds tremble. Waves break and spray flies across the dunes. I look beyond the waves across the wide, blue-shining expanse. A header into the lake, and I awaken from my dream. I am taking an icy bath in an inland sea which is almost as large as the Lake of Geneva and lies higher than the top of Monte Rosa. Raksas, and Manasarowar which lies beyond it, are the two holiest lakes in Tibet. They form the great upland basin out of which the Brahmaputra flows eastward, and the Sutlej, one of the main tributaries of the Indus, north-westward. Or, rather, used to flow. The domain of these mighty lakes is undergoing depression, and it has long been known that the Sutlej has ceased to derive any of its waters from them. They have no outlet now, and I can find plain evidence of changes in the direction of the flow — very recent changes in the course of the rivers that rise in the Transhimalaya.

" Our little group of pilgrims hesitatingly approaches a nomads' camp. Black tents, pasturing yaks and grazing sheep — it all looks harmless enough. But my companions thought it better to go no nearer. These fellows must be robbers, who had camped here for a while with their flocks. An old man approaches me. With his long flintlock, which looks more like an anti-aircraft gun than a modern firearm, with his huge sword thrust obliquely through his girdle, he has an imposing appearance. So magnificent is he in his savagery that I, forgetting my incognito, produce my little camera. The instant the apparatus comes into sight, the old man draws his long sword and rushes upon me. Nothing but a hurried leap aside saved me from the point. He supposed, no doubt, that I was about to bewitch him with this damnable little engine. The whole episode is uncanny, and before he can summon any of his colleagues we make a bolt for it.

" The hilly steppe is swarming with hares and little lemmings. One sees thousands of them in a single day's march. Millions of potential roast hares are running about here unheeded. I should not mind a change in my rather monotonous menu, but a lama must eschew flesh.

" We reach the northern end of Raksas Valley. A wide plain stretches before us. Broad and fathomless bogs compel a wide detour. Here must once have been the outlet of the great lakes. Now the rivers flow in the opposite direction. We reach a sandy steppe. Laboriously we traverse the sand dunes, constantly slipping back. After a while we reach a more gravelly and firmer steppe. Huge herds of wild asses, almost as large as horses, and known here as kiangs, gallop hither and thither, raising clouds of dust. A magnificent picture. The sun shines upon their whitish-brown backs. Black storm-clouds hang low over Kailas, which lies in front of us to the north.

" Gradually darkness falls. We continue to stumble over the wide stony steppe. The full moon peeps from amid the clouds. We wade across a broad river, the water reaching to the hips. We are close to the foothills of the Transhimalaya. It is hard to get along over this stony ground. We have marched more than thirty miles to-day, and it has been rough going. Now dogs bark at us. Half-ruinous stone walls with tent-cloth for a roof loom on us through the darkness. We have reached our first goal, Darchen, 15,400 feet, the place from which pilgrimages round Kailas start. I must watch out. We find harbourage in various tents. Wearily I stumble through the low entrance into a black Tibetan tent. A whole family lies mother-naked beneath heavy sheep-skins. Man and wife, a squalling brat and two older children between them. I lie down close by, listening to the dogs' bark and the infant's squall. Over my head are hanging two long Tibetan flintlocks. Kids (I do not mean human kids but four-footers) settle down in comfort upon the less occupied parts of my sleeping-sack. The father dandles the baby, whose cries cease. A stinking butter-lamp burns for a while in front of the silver image of Buddha, which vanishes from sight as the floating wick flickers out."

KAILAS, THE HOLIEST MOUNTAIN IN THE WORLD

" ' All that is beautiful is sacred.' Though what to a Western eye is apt to seem little better than devil-worship, has been much distorted and veiled in the course of the centuries, the fundamental idea of Asiatic religions is embodied in one of the most magnificent temples I have ever seen, a sunlit temple of rock and ice. Its remarkable structure, and the peculiar harmony of its shape, justify my speaking of Kailas as the most sacred mountain in the world. Here is a meeting-place of the greatest religions of the East, and the difficult journey round the temple of the gods purifies the soul from earthly sins. The remarkable position of this mountain that towers out of the Transhimalayan plateau already indicates that it must present extremely interesting geological problems for solution. Strangely enough, it consists of horizontally stratified conglomerate masses with erratic admixture. In the course of geological aeons, these strata have been elevated many thousands of feet without any change in their horizontal lay-out. Next day, when for the first time the mighty Kailas is displayed to us in its full magnificence, Paldin, my companion, kneels and touches the ground with his forehead. Then he looks round at me questioningly, somewhat anxiously. ' No, Paldin,' I answer the unspoken enquiry, ' this mountain is just as sacred to me as it is to you, for I too am a pilgrim, just as those two lamas who passed a moment ago are pilgrims. Like you, like them, I am in search of the beautiful, the sacred in this wonderful mountain.' I wrestle with my broken Hindustani, interspersed with broken English. But Paldin understands me.

" For nearly three-quarters of a mile, our road is bordered by high walls of conglomerate. This is a genuine road, and is marked out in addition on either side by rows of small cairns. There are more of these cairns on the right, for you must always pass to the left of a shrine, and the pilgrimage round Kailas, like that round other holy places in the East, must be made clockwise. Only the Boen-Po, adherents of the pre-Buddhist, originally animist, religion of Tibet, make their pilgrimage counter-clockwise as a protest against the interloping and more orthodox Buddhism." (Two of the Boen-Po are shown in Plate 121.)

" The very stones of this region are sacred, and to collect specimens is sacrilege. Consequently, though the prospects for geological research are rosy, peculiar methods of work are needed. A gradual adaptation to my surroundings has been produced by exposure to the weather and to the smoke of yak-dung fires. But beneath the veil of dirt and my lama's outer garments, I feel as unreligious as possible, for the geological sketch-books, hammer, compass, small field-glasses, a fair number of geological specimens, a bottle of hydrochloric acid, and a conveniently portable camera, are stored about my person, and give me a paunchy appearance. But in this matter I was outdone by a Tibetan I encountered who, after a deal in which he disposed of four sheep, packed away within his caftan the sugar he received in exchange, thus creating a preposterous bulk above the girdle. Of these hidden impedimenta, the one I use most often is my Bézard compass to help me in making sketch-maps. Fortunately most of the Tibetans wear an amulet round the neck, and the compass is not a bad imitation of one, so I can hang it on a string and have it readily available without attracting too much attention. I have got quite used to the monotonous repetition of ' Om mani padme oom ', this having been my lullaby when the old Tibetan who camped with us a while ago murmured his refrain far on into the night with the assiduity of a perpetual-motion machine.

" The pilgrims' way leads into a lateral valley by which we can reach the northern side of Kailas. Crossing the torrent once more, I enter an area which is highly interesting for a geologist, being the granite pediment of the huge conglomerate mass of Kailas. A little to the side of the track we rested. For a time I was able to divest myself of my lama envelope and climb the opposite slope, from which, while studying the geological structure, I was able to take an excellent photo of Mount Kailas and neighbourhood (Plate 128). There were marmots everywhere, uttering their peculiar cries monotonously. The sound made by these Tibetan beasts was very different from the whistle-like call of the marmots of the Alps, being a ' ft, ft, ft ', like the noise produced by a wheezy, worn-out lorry ; and these marmots are of a foxy-red colour.   45655

" Having washed my socks in a snow-water rivulet, I laid them on a hot stone to dry in the sun and sat down to make a sketch, but was soon interrupted by one of those rapid changes in the weather common in the high mountains. Even before the gloomy storm-clouds had gathered, the thunder was rumbling and echoing in the wild upland valley. Our immediate objective to-day was a gompa or lamasery at an altitude of over 16,000 feet on the northern slopes of Kailas. A few leagues short of this we were overtaken by a storm more violent than any I have seen in the Alps. The rain was quickly followed by snow. Lightning flashed amid the snowflakes, illuminating the rugged granite rocks against the background of a dark-grey sky. We have not been bothered by thunderstorms during our sojourn in the Himalayas, but here in Transhimalaya they are an almost daily occurrence. The dense monsoon-clouds which surmount the Himalayas with a huge wall like that produced in the Alps by the föhn, are not seen here in Trans-himalaya. All the same, we are not free from the influence of the monsoon, but the chief movement of the rain-clouds is from the west towards the east. The discharges take place mainly in the form of thunderstorms rather than in that of continuous rainfall. Of course I can speak only of the regions I visited, where the local conditions in the Sutlej Valley doubtless have something to do with the matter.''

WHERE THE PRAYER-WHEELS TURN

The lightnings flashed from crag to crag, an echoing clap of thunder following each. Night was falling as, amid mighty scattered rocks of granite, we reached the lonely gompa (Plate 130). The walls, picked out with red at the top, were covered with new-fallen snow. As a weary pilgrim, feeling somewhat uneasy, I made my way through the low entry to find myself in a dark, soot-begrimed granite cave, where I could hope that the lamas, however inquisitive, would not notice anything amiss with my aspect. Of course, it was common form for Kailas pilgrims to seek shelter in this monastery, but it was important that my identity as a European should not be pierced. I did not care to let myself dwell on what might happen if it was. The place was lighted by one little candle, which scarcely did more than make darkness visible.

Every pilgrim who considers himself of importance must request the pleasure of an interview with the head-lama. I myself was posing as a lama of importance from a distant region, and must therefore seem eager for an interview. With mixed feelings I stood before the little door leading to the head-lama's quarters. Paldin and one of the Bhotias accompanied me. My other travelling companions had stayed behind at Darchen, for a trade in sheep and goats — always a long business in the East. Paldin, who was familiar with the ways of lamaseries, had given me an hour's private tuition upon the best way of conducting myself in these unfamiliar circumstances. Bare-footed, with folded hands and lowered head, I entered the dark chamber which was lighted only by a few small butter-lamps. Behind a long altar, which looked like the table of a medieval alchemist, squatted the high priest, tailor-fashion. Slowly and reverently I approached His Holiness. He had sharply cut features and an intelligent expression, very different from that of most lamas, who look like self-satisfied materialists. Paldin announced me as an extremely holy man from far, far away, and fortunately sanctity connotes the idea of a discreet silence. My head still devoutly lowered, I handed him two small coloured goblets of marbled vulcanite, a somewhat risky gift here, but we have found them effective and comparatively easy to transport. An attendant rummaged in a small chest, and then, with a solemn gesture, His Eminence handed me a strip of red ribbon, which, according to custom, was im-

100

mediately hung round my neck. I was also given a little bag of tiny pills which would preserve me from every possible mischance. In the dim light, the head-lama evidently had no suspicion that he was receiving a European in audience. Soon we were back in our dark, soot-begrimed cave. Although I was not best pleased to learn that a number of sadhus had arrived during the audience, I soon fell asleep, while from the roof flakes of soot fell upon my face. Every time I awoke from my uneasy slumbers, I heard a peculiar noise as if large stones were being rubbed together. Was this a prayer-wheel in permanent operation, or was tsamba being ground throughout the night? From a furtive enquiry I learned that the latter was the true interpretation.

A glorious morning followed. I was up at peep of day, and, armed with my leica (portable camera), I went out to take what views I could of this remote and inaccessible spot. Hidden behind a big rock, I secured the photo reproduced in Plate 127. Slowly I made my way back to the lamasery. In the rays of the rising sun the head-lama was standing on the flat roof, with folded hands, contemplating Kailas, and bowing before the sublime view. Every morning throughout the year, summer and winter alike, he greets the sacred mountain, praying to his god, and praying also to demons. In a granite cave beneath the monastery the gilded emblems of the gods are kept. They grinned at me unmeaningly, for their symbolism was beyond my power of inter- pretation. We entered this sanctum through a low doorway, after traversing a little library. Everyone who came in had to give the big prayer-drum a turn, and it seemed to me that the head-lama would do well to have the axle greased. If that were done, it would go on turning for a while after being set in motion, and the number of prayers would thereby be greatly increased. Now I stood before the holiest of all the images, that of Kailas. We prostrated ourselves in front of this divinity, who was draped in tulle. Each pilgrim must offer up a little butter-lamp. All around were the strangest figures of demons, whose goggle eyes stared at us from every corner. As was proper to the holiness of the place, on leaving I gave the great prayer-drum an especially vigorous thrust. Drawing a deep breath of relief, I found myself once more in the sunshine. White prayer-flags were fluttering, and Kailas shone down upon us.

FANATICAL PILGRIMS

" Now we are on pilgrimage to Dolma-La, a pass over 18,000 feet high, the highest in the circuit of Kailas. A forest of cairns indicates the holiness of the place. Great piles of human hair are encircled by little walls. A rock is covered with teeth that have been extracted — religious sacrifices made by fanatical pilgrims. Huge and savage granite crags border the pass, which is covered with new-fallen snow. My companions kneel at the tomb of a saint. Hard by is a rock showing what are said to be the holy man's footprints. As usual, in such cases, he must have needed an outsize shoe. Often we have to kowtow and knock the ground with our foreheads, as we get a fresh view of the sacred mountain. A small dust-avalanche rushes down from the peak. The great god up there has smiled.

" Beside Dolma-La is an enormous crag surmounted by a flag-staff from which small multi-coloured streamers flutter. The abundance of cairns give the place its peculiar stamp. Almost everyone who goes by erects his own cairn, for which purpose, since stones are scarce, he often has to rob previous structures. A white stone usually crowns the little edifice. Although the summit of Kailas is not visible from this spot, it is of peculiar importance. When we recall that many of the pilgrims are persons who never before have left the plains of India, we cannot but suppose that a number of them fail to get home again, perishing here from the hardships of the journey. The more fanatical of the pilgrims make the circuit of the mountain crawling on their bellies, thus achieving the highest degree of spiritual purification."

Here is a description of the actual process. With hands crossed, the pilgrim prostrates himself. Then, wearing gloves armoured with metal plates, he makes a scratch as far ahead as he can reach. Rising erect at the point where his feet are, he strides to the scratch-mark — the length of the body with arms outstretched — prostrates himself once more, and repeats the process. Thus performed, the circuit of the mountain takes about three weeks (Fig. 13).

Several times we overtook such fanatics, once just below the pass. Among them were two Tibetan women, who would occasionally drop from sheer fatigue, lying half-dead for a while, and then resume their laborious pilgrimage. In one place a roaring brook poured across the granite blocks, but even here the pious routine was not in the least interrupted. I was amazed.

" Concealed within his garments, our old Tibetan has a reserve of coloured prayer-flags. Again and again I have watched him produce one or more of these on the top of one of the many passes, to weight them with large stones or the branch of a tree ; nevertheless, his supply seems inexhaustible. With astounding tenacity, he climbs a huge boulder, shouting ' Chaloo, sho, sho, sho, chaloo, sho, sho, sho ' alternately with ' Om mani padme oom ' and then a new streamer is fixed. He stands with clasped and uplifted hands, and then kowtows, knocking the ground with his forehead. So great is the power of this mighty religion.

" A little below Dolma-La there is a small sacred lake where the

FIG. 13. FANATICAL PILGRIMS, BELLY-CRAWLING ON THE ROUGH ASCENT OF KAILAS. SKETCHED FROM MEMORY. (G)

pilgrims make their ablutions — as a rule. But this time the lake, being at an altitude of over 18,000 feet, is frozen and thickly covered with snow. Near the shore we see masses of rock which the pilgrims have flung on to the ice in the vain hope of breaking it. It seems to be an unfavourable year for pilgrimages.

"The eastern side of the pass leads steeply into a new and long valley, ending far to the north in a lofty pass which is an important route over the chains of the Transhimalaya. But we turn southward, leaving the savage granitic landscape to find ourselves once again amid imposing walls of conglomerate. Soon we are to reach a new monastery, the Tsumtulphu Gompa. For the moment, however, I am wholly taken up by my geological investigations. The strata of conglomerate, which have hitherto been horizontal, are here somewhat inclined, as if by pressure from the south. As we negotiate a curve in the valley, this impression is confirmed, and suddenly I come across a most interesting geological phenomenon. At a well-marked transitional line, the conglomerate strata have been covered by a number of convoluted strata sharply contrasting with the flat Transhimalayan sedimentary rocks and the granites. Compared with the Transhimalayan rocks, this superposed series must have undergone a recent and intensive convolution. These observations show that we have to do with the northernmost vestiges of the Himalayan chain proper, which has been superimposed upon the Transhimalaya from the south — backwards, that is to say.

"'Look out, the sadhus are coming!' This shout of warning from Paldin comes as a sudden interruption to my geological studies. Paldin and I secrete ourselves in a small lateral valley, while my other companions wander ahead with apparent unconcern. They must make for Darchen, while Paldin and I lag behind. It is just as well that they should not know too much about my geological activities, which are peculiarly important here.

"On the Pilgrims' Way are advancing four lean figures, wrapped in grey blankets. These four sadhus have fine-looking heads, and wear long, black beards, while their heads are thickly covered with black hair. One of them, in due time, will become our special friend, but for the moment I wish to steer clear of devotees."

As soon as they had passed, I continued my geological work, while Paldin pressed some new botanical specimens, for this branch, too, must not be neglected. Although I have nothing but some old pasteboard biscuit boxes in which to store my herbarium, the specimens have kept very well. Of course, could I have foreseen that most of them were to be lost in a difficult river-crossing amid the southern Himalayas, I should have spared myself a great deal of valuable time.

Night was close at hand when I finished my geological sketches and dark storm-clouds had gathered. We entered Tsumtulphu Gompa as pilgrims, to find it a place lacking interest. Comparative disorder prevailed, for the head-lama had gone to Lhasa, so the inmates were

104

a little out of hand. Still, I found it worth while to visit a number of caves excavated in the cliffs, the habitations of famous ascetics in former days, now vacated. The valley widened here, and we had a good view of the broad plain that lies on the southern side of the Transhimalaya. We are only about six miles from Darchen, whence we started upon the circuit of Kailas. The sanctified sheep await us there. On the way thither, next day, we passed huge heaps of inscribed " mani stones ", on which " Om mani padme oom " had been chiselled (Plate 131). When I moved to pick one up Kali cried : " No, no, Sahib, don't touch it ; the gods will be angry ".

" Still, Paldin sympathises with my collector's fever, and would like me to have one of these stones. A storm is threatening, and it grows darker. I look cautiously round, and then secrete a particularly well-carved mani stone beneath my caftan. There comes a loud clap of thunder, followed by a cloudburst, as if the Last Judgment was at hand. ' Put down the stone, Sahib, put down the stone ! ' Paldin is pale from anxiety. Certainly the elemental hubbub is enough to make the poor fellow anxious, and convince him that the gods are angered by my sacrilege. Still, the stone remains in my pouch, where I feel it will prove a mascot. A pitch-dark night has fallen. It is still raining heavily, with lightning-flashes and peals of thunder. Paldin is carrying some of my geological specimens. The space within my caftan is somewhat restricted, and the drenched sheepskin is as heavy as lead. After an arduous tramp, we reach Darchen, stumbling in one place over a lama who lies in the pouring rain, having fallen asleep exhausted after a long day of belly-crawling."

LAMA TURNED SHEPHERD

We found a Nepalese at Darchen, a sheep-buyer. As chance would have it, we had met him previously in Changru. I spent the night in his tent, Paldin having persuaded him not to betray my identity. I gave him a box of coloured vulcanite and a packet of meta fuel as a solatium. Unfortunately his tent was not weatherproof. The rain-water dripped steadily upon my sleeping-sack, but I was so tired that it only lulled me to sleep.

" Our sheep and goats are closely packed in a walled enclosure. A few extra-fine beasts are still needed, for sacrifice to the manes of Chandru's father. I expect to be able to get these ' very-particular ' rams and he-goats together to-day, so that we shall be able to start home to-morrow. Pending this, Paldin and I climb the southern foothills of Kailas to trace farther the superimposition of the strata detected the day before.

"By good luck I have made acquaintance with a Tibetan notable who has given me a certificate or testimonial of my admirable qualities, written in Tibetan. Such a document, duly sealed, may prove useful in a critical situation. I also have with me a vest-pocket alarm with which, should it become necessary, I may be able to work a miracle. Luckily, as yet, there has been no need. My Tibetan has also promised to give me a particularly toothsome yak-tail. By evening the flock was complete, and since in Darchen there are a great many sheep, variously marked, all our beasts have been painted with a green streak to distinguish them from the red-ochre mark which is no more than a sign of sanctity. At Darchen, all beasts are thus sanctified, so the ochre stamp does not suffice. I passed a second night in the tent of the Nepalese, with the rain still rattling on the roof and dripping through on me as I lay. I still had another important job to do with Paldin's aid. We had procured one of the sheep-packs, the twin sacks in which the Tibetans convey salt to India and bring back sugar, rice, and flour. Having labelled our geological specimens and put them away in little bags of cloth, we have prepared what looks a thoroughly ordinary sheep-load.

"My role as pilgrim is finished, and the lama has become a shepherd. 'Chaloo, chaloo!' I cried, driving our sheep. A he-goat is my special pack animal. Various other beasts are carrying blankets, and sacks filled with tsamba, which is our chief diet, with a little flour and tea. These stores have been purchased for the return journey, our original provisions having been exhausted.

"Our two Tibetan companions have done good business, their trade in bellows-nozzles having brought a satisfactory return. One of them intends to come back with us as far as Kuti, while the other (the old devotee, of course) proposes to make a considerable stay at Mangshang Lamasery."

The broad river that crosses the steppe southward of Darchen offered considerable difficulties to our caravan, but, having made a detour to the west, we found fordable branches (Plate 126). Still, it proved heavy going. The strange-looking yellow clouds burst in an unexpected hailstorm just as we were fording one of these tributaries. The water was icy cold, and the hailstones whipped our naked legs, which suffered from cold when we were wading and from this aerial bombardment when we were on "dry" land. A number of black, stork-like birds watched us stoically from sand-banks, seeming utterly

106

regardless of the bad weather. Each of us made the traverse taking care of a couple of sheep or goats at a time, seizing some of the biggest by the horns, forcing them into the water until they waded, half-swimming, across, and the others followed. Many of the smaller rams or he-goats were completely submerged and could only draw breath by jumping.

Thus, over broad, gravelly wastes, and across sand-dunes covered with a thin growth of green, my geological collection made its way back to the shores of Lake Raksas. This may well have been the first time that a geological collection was ever transported on sheep-back. Even the herds of wild kiangs regarded our caravan with interest, and did not gallop away until we were within a hundred yards of them. When they scattered thus, it was a wonderful sight. We heard the thunder of hoofs, and saw the sand fly. A chief stallion led, making sharp wheels from time to time, while the others played the game of follow-my-leader, and raised huge clouds of dust. We saw at least two hundred such creatures that day — a marvellous spectacle of unbridled freedom.

Towards evening we reached the shores of Lake Raksas, which this time was worthy of its name of " haunted lake ". A storm-wind lashed the water. The foam-crowned waves broke with a roar upon the sandy beach. I could not but be reminded of the stormy boat-journey of Sven Hedin, the first European to explore this lake. Beneath overhanging rocks we found a camping site well sheltered from the wind, I think the best camp of this journey. In front of us was the raging lake, and northward the partially obscured Transhimalayan chain, overtopped by Kǎilas, round which the storms were raging. To the S.E. we could see the slopes of Gurla Mandhata, with their shining glaciers. We caught the sheep and relieved them of their burdens. This was an easy task to-day, for the beasts were tired.

When they had been unloaded, we let them run whithersoever they pleased, and hungrily they gnawed at the scanty tussocks. We, meanwhile, were in search of fuel. Having gathered a sufficiency of gorse, and especially of roots, we made a huge fire. The Tibetans at Darchen had given us a big leg of mutton, which had been carried hither by one of our rams. This creature, with his two side-pouches and in the middle a sooty saucepan and a leg of mutton, made a comic appearance. These gifts were a substitute for the promised yak-tail, which had been unobtainable. It was locked up in the lesser lamasery at Darchen, and the lama who kept the key was making pilgrimage round Kailas. Well, the leg of mutton, seasoned with garlic gathered by the way, would make a savoury dish. In this sandy upland steppe wild garlic is often the only vegetation, and was now to be a savoury supplement to our menu.

Tsamba broth was simmering in the Tibetan's big saucepan. My small aluminium utensils would not suffice to cook for so large a party. Of course we were also baking some unleavened bread. I had by now learned how to make chupatties, and took pride in my skill. In somewhat more civilised regions than this, many an Indian had been astonished to see a sahib squatting in the kitchen of a dak-bungalow beside the cook and kneading dough for chupatties with the skill of an expert. We had to use sheep-dung and yak-dung, of which there was plenty lying about, to supplement the scanty supplies of wood. With the aid of the goatskin bellows the little balls of dung burned like straw. The chupatties were baked on a metal plate and then placed among the embers to keep hot.

" Everything goes off like a house afire. Chupatties, sliced garlic, and tsamba provide a feast. Meanwhile the darkness falls. The storm over the lake has subsided. The full moon rises, and across Raksas, towards Manasarowar, we can see the pointed hills where Giu-Gompa lies. The waves have a silver sheen in the moonlight. Gurla Mandhata peeps spectrally above the clouds. We must tether our sheep. The big billy-goats give us the greatest trouble ; it is necessary to catch them with an agile leap, and seize their horns. The smaller beasts are easier to manage. They are tethered head to head, close to the fire. This is necessary, for there are said to be many wolves about. So far we have not seen any.

" I lie in my sleeping-sack and contemplate the glowing camp-fire. Its light is reflected by the overhanging rocks. The two Bhotias and Paldin are already asleep. The two Tibetans squat beside the fire warming their hands. The old man turns his prayer-wheel, and, while he mutters his petitions, I fall asleep.

" Next morning we are off at peep of day. The sheep are not so easy to load as on the previous occasion, for it is almost as if they know we have a long day's march before us. One grips the beast's head between one's knees while the twin sacks are adjusted. Then, the instant they are released they rush off to nibble whatever they can find. The animals that do not eat during the march will go hungry in the evening, for seldom does one camp at a place where fodder is obtainable. They therefore have to make the most of their opportunities at every halt. During the march, the hungry beasts must be ruthlessly hunted along, though they are perpetually trying to snatch a bite or two as they pass. ' Sho, chaloo ! ' one shouts and the sheep scurry

108

on. But the two big he-goats, those that are to be sacrificed to the manes of Chandru's father, are not laden, being too sacred for such menial activities. For this very reason, they are the most difficult to catch when they have to be tethered at night, being practically wild."

LITTLE JUNGBWA

Late in the afternoon we got back to Jungbwa, the settlement of nomads' tents. Here I sat at the time of our first passing, in front of a tent, to watch three Tibetan puppies at play. In Darchen I was able to get a dog-chain. Now one of my men from Kuti returned after a visit to the nomads' camp where, for three silver rupees, he had secured me one of these fine specimens. She was a bitch, not yet three months old. The latest member of our expedition is generally admired, even though her belly is so full of tsamba that it almost touches the ground as she runs. I have called her " Jungbwa ", and am delighted with her. All the same, she proved a thorny problem. For Jungbwa, at first, simply would not use her legs. She preferred to be carried. When placed on her own paws, she lay down to rest comfortably on the first grass-patch she could find. If I persuaded her to move a pace or two she promptly sought out a tuffet of edelweiss, rolled over on it, and looked up at me piteously and roguishly, asking to be picked up. Still, among the kids she proved a little more lively, and thus the problem was solved. Jungbwa took her place, on the march, behind these youngsters, and no longer lazed on the edelweiss. At length she has begun to drive the flock, finding, to her delight, that even the largest billy-goats take to their heels when she barks at them.

" We are camping on the sward in a wide upland valley. There are still traces of a nomads' settlement — the ashes of burned-out fires and yak-dung. An icy wind is blowing down from the Himalayas, the peaks being hidden in thick clouds. It is obviously snowing up there. We have made a Tibetan fireplace with three big stones, between which, under the persuasion of the bellows, the yak-dung burns like tinder. On the three stones stands our big saucepan. Butter-tea and a few chupatties we have brought along form our supper. Jungbwa is lying close to the fire, of which she has no fear. Having snuggled down on my sleeping-sack, she is dead to the world.

" ' Chaloo, Jungbwa, you lazy little bitch ! ' She does not seem best pleased that we start in the cold, before daylight. We are crossing the interesting zone of exotic blocks, so I have let the caravan go ahead, and Jungbwa is following the flock. They will wait for me at the ford across the Singlabtsa, when I have found some more geological specimens for those of our animals that are not overloaded to carry. Accompanied by Paldin I make various little excursions, and sketch while Paldin is packing the labelled specimens in the vestiges of the ' Hindustani Times '. At length, towards noon, we reach the ford, but there is no trace of the caravan. We continue on our course up the long Mangshang Valley. Rich fossil-beds invite me to further divagations. I send Paldin ahead, to find the flock and our fellow-travellers at the top of Mangshang Valley, and he takes some of our stones with him. Then I get to work upon a rich store of belemnites, and resume my southward journey heavily laden. My companions have certainly made a very long march to-day. It is already dark, and there is no trace of them, nor of Paldin, nor of our camp. Being now rather tired, I stumble as I cross the stony steppe. They must have gone this way for there is no other, and I shall find them sometime. Among the rubble, scrub-willows are growing, so at any rate we shall be able to have a fire. Look, there it is, the camp-fire. I quicken my pace. A little below the head of the valley I find, not the camp, but only Paldin, lying on the ground beside a huge fire. No sleeping-sack for me yet. But, as night was falling, Paldin had caught sight of the camp farther on, so he had lighted a signal fire here and waited for me. ' There are a great many vicious dogs about, Sahib ', he says. He means wolves. I have not seen or heard any, but they probably are wolves, since there is an abundance of hares for them to eat. After a rest, we leave Paldin's fire and make for the camp. The sheep have been tethered in the usual fashion. Jungbwa has snuggled down on the sleeping-sack which my companions have unrolled. It is cold to-night, for the wind is still blowing down from the Himalayas — a wind more or less like the Swiss föhn, except that there is no warmth about it. The sheep are restless. One of the big rams is bleating pitifully, having twisted his halter round his throat until he is half strangled. Hardly has he been relieved from his discomfort, when the younger beasts begin to bleat, anxiously. Not until towards morning is peace restored. Probably they scent wolves, which prowl round the camp without venturing to attack. Much as these voracious beasts would prize some raw mutton, they are too much afraid of us bipeds.

" The glacier rivulet flows milky this morning as usual. The two Bhotias and the young Tibetan wade across to pull up some more willows for fuel. The old Tibetan left us yesterday, making for Mang-shang Gompa. Now we start, and soon we have to get the sheep across the torrent. We push the big he-goats into the icy water. For a wonder, the whole herd gets across safely, although great rocks are being rolled along by the current. Some of the smaller beasts are swept a good way downstream before they reach a footing on the farther bank. However, here we all are in safety, on dry land. But wait a minute, there is one stray. On the other shore stands a black puppy, which ventures now and again a little way into the stream, and then shrinks back in alarm. Jungbwa is only three months old, and the torrent is too strong. I wade back and pick her up to carry her across safely, while her wet paws drip.

" This same day I meet my fellow geologist. Bara Sahib has crossed Mangshang Pass. Beside the big Mangshang glacier stands a white tent, over which the Swiss flag is flying. The following day we re-climb the Mangshang on our way back into India, stand beside the cairn on the summit of the pass, and look back towards Kailas. A couple of prayer-flags flutter from a withered bough. ' Look, Jungbwa, that beautiful country with its sacred mountain is your native land, which you are about to leave for ever.' "

CHAPTER ELEVEN

ACROSS THE HIGH MOUNTAINS TO MILAM
(HEIM)

A HAPPY REUNION

ACCORDING to our understanding, Gansser was to be back on July 10th at latest, and since there was no other way hereabouts across the mountains he could not possibly miss my tent in Mangshang Valley.

Overnight it had been snowing again, and I did not leave the tent until the weather cleared. Then Kirken shouted : " Chota Sahib ". Yes, it was he, in his red caftan, with Paldin and the two men from Kuti (Plate 118). They had a fourth companion, a Tibetan, wearing a quaint-looking felt hat. There were also 12 sheep and 17 goats. A shout of welcome! The sight of him, in good health, was a great relief, for I had been anxious. Then I saw that he had brought back yet another companion, a three-months-old puppy, named Jungbwa, after its birthplace. A pure-bred Tibetan, one of those dogs that are dreaded for their fierceness, black, with brown-and-white spotted paws, light brown streaks under the eyes, in build like a Newfoundland, and young enough to be friendly. " Come into the tent for a good breakfast, and then tell me all about it. How did you get on with the Tibetans ? " —" Splendidly. I made the whole round of Kailas, was received by the head-lama with pomp and circumstance as a learned Bara Sadhu." — " Is it true that a head-lama never drinks, never smokes, never eats meat, and never says anything but ' Om mani padme oom ? ' And have you acquired merit by your pilgrimage, like an Indian ? "

No less remarkable have been the scientific results of the expedition — geological and botanical collections, sketches, the diary, photographs.

TOGETHER WE GO BACK OVER THE MANGSHANG

Although Gansser had come back from Kailas by forced marches, he would not rest for a day or two, but insisted on our making for the north-eastern plateau. But when we reached a height of 17,700 feet it was plain that there was to be no view, not only because of the sleet, but also because these Tibetan mountains are rounded and covered with debris. Of the yak herds that had been there yesterday there was nothing to be seen but their footprints (Fig. 12).

At dawn we started again with our flock of pack-bearers, straight across the glacier (Plates 133 and 134), above which an ice-encrusted twenty-thousander now showed over the clouds. Then followed a frightfully steep climb. Gansser walked ahead with Paldin, breaking a trail. The drovers shouted and whistled behind, but the sheep and goats could do no more than crawl. Only little Jungbwa intelligently kept in the broken trail.

At eleven we reached the top of the pass to make our way down on the other side through soft snow and wet rubble, the puppy being carried in Gansser's rucksack. This time we camped on the green floor of the valley opposite Wilsha, amid edelweiss and marmot holes.

Next day opened mistily, but soon the sun broke through the clouds, and we enjoyed the sight of a magnificent double rainbow. A huge caravan, including horses, met us, its destination being Darchen at the foot of Mount Kailas, but not by way of the difficult Mangshang. They were making for an easier pass, Lampiya Dhura, farther to the north-west.

When we reached Kuti, far ahead of the shepherds and their flocks, we found the villagers holding council in the village square, under the presidency of the patwari (head policeman of the district), who had come over from Garbyang. This official was a short, fat Bhotia dressed in white. He spoke in an arrogant voice which is most unusual among the Indians — probably an assumed characteristic. As the council went on, we frequently heard the word " Kailas ". When the session was over, he asked us where we had been, saying that the villagers could not tell him precisely, and he had had the impudence to impound some of our letters, in which he certainly exceeded his authority. After a good deal of palaver, we made out that he had received orders to arrest us and bring us back to Almora if we should try to cross the Tibetan frontier. The situation was awkward. Still, without any taradiddle I could send the deputy commissioner a written assurance that we had no intention of visiting Tibet — since there seemed no need to mention that Gansser had already been there.

Now the patwari's attention was engaged by the festival of the dead being held in honour of Chandru's father, who had been mayor of the village. To the accompaniment of drum-taps, the sheep from Kailas were painted with red and blue stripes, decked in white raiment which had belonged to the deceased, and stuffed with meal and arrack. Then, as in Gunji, the keening of the women began.

Meanwhile the Sherpas had brought down our tent from the mountain, where it had been exposed for three weeks to the rains and the snows. The weather continued so bad that it would be useless to attempt the climb of Shangtang.

During an interval in the ceremonies, we heard the patwari still talking at great length, and such words as " sahib " and " Switzerland " were frequently audible. Then he threatened to take strong measures, and keep us under arrest for a fortnight until he got an answer from the government, though he has no proofs of any transgression on our part, being much too fat to climb to the top of the pass. Whatever happens, we must reduce our baggage, must send our geological collection to Almora, and sell one of our tents, since money is running low. Now the patwari presented himself as a buyer, in which capacity he was somewhat more civil.

GOODBYE TO KUTI

Although we have had a good time at Kuti, we shall be glad to get away from it, even if the immediate future opens with a rather uneasy prospect. Gansser is more confident.

Our present plan is to cross, if we can, the lofty passes of the central chains, the Lebong and the Ralam, making for the valley of the Gori Ganga, in order to take up fresh headquarters at the loftiest village there, Milam.

Since, owing to the festival, it was difficult to hire porters, we started, to begin with, with no more than five men. Nine others will follow us three days hence, when the festival of the dead will be over. We have agreed to pay 17 annas per day, the men to carry a load of 60 lbs. each and to have a gratuity if we are satisfied with them at the end of their service. Of course they are to receive an advance.

The village folk showed they had taken a liking to us, for they all greeted us with farewell " salaams ", and many of them, both old and young, accompanied us as far as the torrent, with three drummers leading the way. This affectionate farewell was a cheering contrast to what happened the day before, when we believed ourselves once more in danger of arrest.

Wild roses were blooming abundantly by the wayside, and hundreds of butterflies fluttered around us. Now and again there came gleams of sunshine, but the peaks were invisible.

That evening we sought the protection of the overhanging rock at Joling Kong, where we had cached a tent. We paid another visit to the neighbouring moraine lake (Plate 138) where we saw a pair of large grey-black-yellow-and-white ducks, which were much concerned about their ducklings. Next day we were to visit previously unexplored country.

CROSSING THE LEBONG PASS

The morning mist cleared away quickly. To the south-westward, in front of us, still in the shade of savage rocky peaks, the northern Lebong glacier ended at an altitude of 14,750 feet. Above it shone a splendid pyramidal peak darkly bordered with rock. So closely did this resemble Kailas in shape that our Kuti men called it Kailas Baba (Baby Kailas). We estimated its height at about 20,000 feet (Plate 137).

Vain had been our hope to reach the top of the pass in time to get a good view of the frontier chain with the Shangtang, for the morning dispersal of the mists was brief. When we reached the top, after an hour and a half of slow and heavy progress through the snow, and our aneroid showed a height of 17,384 feet, we encountered a raging monsoon wind laden with wreaths of fog, while the avalanches thundered down the slopes of Kailas Baba. However, we have now made out the geological profile as far as the pass. Here, likewise, white Silurian quartzite has been superimposed upon black clays which, weathered between the quartzite walls, form the pass. A rare and wonderfully preserved ammonite bore witness to the fact that the black schistous clay dated from the Permian epoch.

The descent was a scramble down a couple of thousand feet or more of rough, rocky declivity. Without a guide we should never have found our way in the mist, for only in a few places was it indicated. Jungbwa got along very well, sliding down the steep snow-slopes on all fours. Only on the worst part of the scramble did Gansser find it necessary to tuck her under one arm. Not until seven o'clock, when we had got down to an altitude of 14,760 feet, did we find a camp. This was on a flowery mead, among rocks and murmuring springs, outside the right lateral moraine of Kailas Baba Glacier, as we have christened it. The ice-precipice descends almost perpendicularly to the glacier, which flows from the east between Kailas Baba and its loftier neighbour to the south (Plates 139 and 141).

Since the porters had not turned up yet with the tents, and we were wet through and chilled to the bone, my indefatigable comrade went a league or two farther down the valley in search of juniper-wood

115

for fuel. Meanwhile, night had fallen. Where were the two porters, for whom we hallooed in vain ? It was a wonder that they turned up safe at last, after nine o'clock, for even in broad daylight it had been no joke to descend this rocky couloir. I need hardly say that the pass is impracticable for caravans.

Next day we spent the morning upon supplementary geological observations. Gansser clambered by a new route back to the top of the pass, but had poor luck with the weather, while I was at work on lower levels. There, amusing themselves among the flowers and the grass, were numerous specimens of a bird more or less of the blackbird type, but of an exquisite dark-blue, the wings and tail being brownish-black.

In the afternoon we went on down the valley. It was only a few miles' march to our camp at Bidang. While the porters marched a little farther along the pass, we climbed over the moraine-strewn ridge to the end of the glacier, where we made a remarkable discovery — a little lake at an altitude of 14,260 feet, from which, under considerable pressure, the outflowing water emerges in a dome-shaped stream having a flow of something like 1000 gallons per second.

Bidang is not permanently inhabited, being no more than a summer resort for trade by barter. Upon a grassy terrace above the gorge of the roaring Dhauli Ganda (13,000 feet) were about sixty white tents of Tibetans, Bhotias, and degenerate-looking half-breeds with cattle and sheep, encamped among erratic blocks as large as houses. We could not get any milk, but were able to procure rice and onions, while our porters clubbed together and bought themselves a goat to slaughter and eat.

IN THE DHAULI AND LISSAR VALLEYS

From Bidang an excellent path led down the valley, running from 150 to 300 feet above the Dhauli. It rained unceasingly. On the other side of the gorge, beneath an overhanging rock, was a bearded vultures' nest, easily discoverable by the white splotches on the rocks beneath. The birds had nestlings. Much lower down, at 10,660 feet, we crossed the torrent by a bridge leading to the right, and then made our way up the Lissar Ganga (joined here by the much smaller Dhauli) to the little village of Tijang, where we secured a room with mats on the floor, above a goat-stable. We were so thoroughly drenched that we decided to halt until next day.

Near the village, at 10,820 feet, is a remarkable sacred tree — a birch with a spread of 80 feet and a double trunk 10 feet in diameter.

About three miles farther on is Sepu, 11,480 feet, the highest village in the main valley of the Lissar, standing on a terrace on the right side of the valley. Kali having gone ahead to herald our coming, a number of youngsters appeared to welcome us as we climbed the last part of the steep ascent from the bridge. They made profound obeisances, with their hands clasped together. No less friendly was our reception at the village, where the headman accommodated us in a hut, and would accept no payment but was glad to be given a written testimonial.

The fields are planted with buckwheat, barley, and potatoes, and, the crops being under way, the men for the moment seemed to have nothing particular to do. They were spinning lazily, and stood agape among the children. They are taller than the Kuti men, and wear long, hand-woven woollen robes, slit at the side as far up as the knee. As in all the Bhotia villages, the little boys wear trousers with a widely opened buttonless slit fore and aft to simplify attention to the calls of nature both for mother and child. The little girls, on the other hand, wear an old-fashioned petticoat which reaches almost to the ground, and makes them look rather stupid. Many of the children are fair-haired. The women and the larger girls were busily at work. In the paved square, rice and spelt, having been soaked for a couple of days in water, were being baked in a flat iron pan, to be subsequently pounded with long wooden pestles. In addition to silver ornaments and red necklaces, they had another peculiar piece of " jewellery " which showed up well on their black clothing. It consisted of strings of the long curved teeth of the musk-deer, which in former days was a favourite beast for the chase (Plate 143). The costly perfume known as musk used to be prepared from the musk-gland of the male musk-deer. Not until the creatures had become almost extinct owing to reckless hunting did better times come for them when chemists learned to make synthetic musk. But even to-day a musk-gland, which is of about the size of a walnut, is worth twenty rupees.

A DANCE AND TRANCE FESTIVAL

Now, when we have to wait for the porters from Kuti, the weather has cleared, and we are " unemployed " in the village, where there is nothing much to see. The snow-peaks are free from clouds, but are hidden by the nearer hills.

Although, when we first arrived, the men among the villagers appeared to have nothing to do, things have now altered and there has been a busy time. From afar we could see that several hundred sheep were coming. They were driven by six Tibetans, who have piled before the huts a vast number of twin sacks filled with salt, which, later on, the men of Sepu will convey to Almora. I estimate the total quantity at not less than three tons. Many of the poor beasts that have carried it are lame, having very sore hoofs. Manifestly they are suffering from some kind of foot-rot. In Kuti, too, we saw a number that were thus affected. There ought to be considerable scope here for veterinary practice, seeing that so many sheep and goats perish on the long and arduous marches. Their corpses form the chief provender of the vultures.

At noon the village-drummers announced that the Sepu men were about to start for the Tibetan trading centre of Gyanyima about half-way between here and Kailas. This trek takes place only once a year, and is preluded by a festival. Two small and one big drum were sounded with a peculiar rhythm interrupted by short intervals. Then began the festival, which was as crazy and savage as anything that could be seen among the cannibals of the South Seas. The whole population, consisting of about 50 men and 30 women and children, forgathered upon a small potato-patch surrounded by a wall (Plate 142). Two young birch-stems, still bearing their crowns of foliage, adorned with white and coloured rags and with garlands of a strange-looking green flower, were stuck on one of the walls and smeared with butter and rice ; then rice was scattered among the crowd, and a yellowish water was squirted about. One of the men who had been crouching with the others, jumped up, climbed one of the birch-trees, and then fell into a trance, in which he had convulsive movements like those of an epileptic. Two other men carried him about until he was able to stand. Then his coat and shirt were stripped off, and, bared to the waist, he began to dance in time to the drums, more and more wildly, until his condition became one of frenzy, while he foamed at the mouth and sweat dropped from his forehead. Like a maniac he dashed against the birch-trees, and then attacked the headman. Having bitten this man's ears, he poured milk over himself. Meanwhile platters of brass laden with rice and wheat grains had been brought, and the contents were scattered. Next came exorcist rites. The dancer fixed his teeth in the neck of one of the crouching women and lifted her as a terrier lifts a rat. Then he attacked a girl of about fifteen, whirled her round, bit her in the throat, blew in her ears, and " massaged " her back with a forked iron rod. He flung ice and ashes violently in her face. Then, still convulsed, the dancer turned his attention to the frightened and screaming children, and last of all to myself, powdering me with rice

118

117. Paldin, my trusty companion in Tibet. (G)

118. Geologist and Lama. Gansser as a Tibetan Pilgrim. (H)

119. Raksas Valley, the "Haunted Lake". Altitude 14 924 feet. July 2, 1936. (G)

120. Young scamps at the foot of Transhimalaya.
July 5, 1936. (G)

121. Tibetans belonging to the thievish Boen-Po tribe. July 5, 1936. (G)

123. She offered me tea flavoured with rancilla "

122. Luckily she did not notice my camera. July 22 1936. (G)

124. Islands in the Haunted Lake. July 2, 1936.   (G)

125. The snow-peaks of Transhimalaya are disclosed across
the Raksas Valley. July 2, 1936.   (G)

126. Returning across the High Steppe. July 6, 1936.   (G)

128. The most sublime Throne of the Gods, Kailas, 19 910 feet. July 3, 1936.   (G)

129. A Haunted Landscape. Kailas from the west. July 3, 1936. (G)

130. The highest Gompa (at an altitude of over 16 400 feet), north of Kailas.
July 4, 1936.   (G)

131. "Om mani padme hum", the uncanny mani-
stone. Half actual size. Tibetan writing, carved
on sandstone.   (G)

132. The first collection of geological specimens to be carried on sheep back from

133. Climbing over the Mangshang Glacier. July 10, 1936. (H)

134. Back across the glacier to the Mangshang Frontier Pass. 17 056 feet.
July 10, 1936. (G)

135. The finest rams in our Tibetan company. July 9, 1936.   (H)

136. Inquisitive visitors after Gansser's return. July 9, 1936.   (H)

137. "Kailas baba" seen beside Lebong Pass (to the right) in the morning light. July 15, 1936. (H)

138. Beside the tranquil lake beyond Joling Kong. 14 430 feet. July 15, 1936. (G)

139. Unnamed mountain (19 680 feet) south-east of Lebong Pass. On the left is "Kailas baba". July 16, 1936. (G)

140. Moraine lake beyond Joling Kong. 14 430 feet, at the foot of what

141. Fluted icy precipice south of Lebong Pass. July 16, 1936.   (H)

142. The trance dancer at Sepu. July 20, 1936. (G)

143. Headman's wife at Sepu, wearing a necklace of musk-deer teeth. (G)

144. Bhotia girl pounding rice at Sepu. (G)

and ashes, giving me a bout with the forked iron staff, shaking a black yak-tail over my head, gesticulating all the time and muttering words which, we were given to understand, signified that the women ought to wash more.

While, to begin with, we stood a little apart, venturing with some diffidence to take photographs, we were now drawn into the inner circle of the dance. The semi-nude trance-dancer handed me a red ribbon and strewed grains of rice upon my ski-ing cap, prophesying that we should have good luck upon the dreaded Ralam Pass. As far as we could understand, his instructions were that we were to tie the red ribbon somewhere at the top of the pass, and make an oblation by strewing rice grains.

Meanwhile the headman's wife was engaged in sticking some moist rice on our foreheads and those of the others. But this was by no means the end of the festival. Another spectator fell into a trance, jumped on to the back of the semi-nude man, and, in that posture, continued his twitching movements, until at length the semi-nude man clambered up one of the birch-stems. Having slid down again, he began a madly gyrating dance, and, when it was over, flung himself on the ground. Rice was strewed on him, whereupon he came to himself as a normal human being. With a general round dance to the accompaniment of the drums, which were beaten with a slow and peculiar rhythm while the drummers gradually disappeared into the alleys, this strange festival of the Bhotias came to an end.

WE CROSS THE TRICKSY RALAM PASS

Our first business on reaching Sepu was to find a guide across the ill-famed Ralam Pass, or rather a porter who knew the way. The village headman had already pointed us out a good man. But what had become of them all after the festival ? Some of them had departed with the Tibetans' sheep, while the others were still having a " high old time ". In plain words, they were very drunk. Though they are thoroughly sober people most of the year, this was a special case. The new coolies from Kuti had arrived, but refused to cross the Ralam. So we were in a fix. Had not the excellent headman vigorously espoused our cause, we should have had nothing to do but retrace our steps.

With some difficulty we got an advance guard of porters to start at nine o'clock, and followed an hour later with a man who had un-questionably " dined " liberally, but who was supposed to know the way. We left hoping that the remaining nine Sepu porters promised us by the headman would really get under way and follow us by noon at latest.

We marched for an hour in blazing sunshine upon a narrow path leading along the rose-clad slope to the mouth of a tributary flowing from the west. On the map this stream is called Nipchungkang. We have never seen an alpine flora so rich as was this upon the north-eastern slope — blue geraniums and white anemones growing almost 3 feet high.

We waited for hours, and at length the porters arrived.

The waters of the Nipchungkang, the river up which we now deviated to the left, are greenish yellow, from the green quartzite, whereas those of the Lissar are greyish, obviously from the black clays in the catchment area. The lower part of this lateral valley has been excavated in the shape of a capital V, is partially blocked by ancient extremely hard moraine, steep masses of fallen rubble, the vestiges of avalanches, and is bordered by serrated limestone rocks in which are caves supposed to be the habitations of spirits. Here, according to our guide from Sepu, it was expedient for us to scatter some rice as an oblation, and to tie a red ribbon to the branch of a green shrub. This guide is one of the two who, the day before, had been the trance-dancer, but seems now to be fully recovered.

The wedge-shaped end of the big Nipchungkang glacier is at an altitude of 12,630 feet. Soon, from a considerably greater height, we were looking down upon this from the top of its ancient left lateral moraine (Plate 145). We continued up the valley along a grassy ledge between the moraine and the cliffs. Amid a good deal of fallen rubble, there was a wealth of flowers growing in the grass — everlastings, geraniums, and potentillas. At an altitude of 13,450 feet the pale-violet lousewort (*Pedicularis macrantha*) grew to a height of as much as two feet, and in one place were standing like soldiers the spikes of a species of *Saussurea*. Two kinds of forget-me-not were abundant, a light-blue one and a dark-blue. There was also a gentian. Soon we came to an admirable camp. Among the declivities and rocks to the side of it grew an abundance of juniper for fuel. As usual little Kyu, a Tibetan by birth who has been adopted by a local family, had kept pace with us, though more heavily laden than the others. The Sepu coolies with the tents were not yet in sight. Since, when night was falling, four of them were still lacking, Gansser went back in search of them, to find two of them lying among the stones suffering from the effects of yesterday's debauch, while a third was still lower down the valley in a shepherdess's hut amusing himself with the occupant.

120

The fourth, with a cracked crown and badly bruised, was lying in the ravine where he had tumbled. " These things will happen after a night out."

By the following morning they had slept off their drink, but the fine weather was over. The mist-wreaths were thickening round us. It always takes a long time to get away, for the coolies must boil their tea and bake themselves chupatties. Each of the sixteen had to add some fuel to his load. We began by climbing a little farther up the valley along the lateral moraine, to cross the detritus-covered glacier where a tributary glacier came in from the right, and where we found the last practicable camping-ground before the pass, at 15,400 feet. Here we pitched our tent, though it was only noon, since the climb before us was too steep to begin at this hour.

In the afternoon we were cheered by a sun-bath, which all of us enjoyed except Jungbwa, who sought a shady spot upon the snow.

Kyu, at work while climbing, has been spinning yarn from the hair of the goats slaughtered at Bidang, to make a fine rope 50 feet long. The hides have been converted into a pair of bellows.

While Kali was boiling rice in an improvised stone fireplace, we had time to write up our diaries and press our botanical specimens. Among plants new to us was a blue larkspur, as strongly scented as a society lady ; there were also dwarf gentians and the white stars of cerastium ; whereas everlasting and potentillas were no longer found.

Before dawn four camp-fires were already blazing amid the rocks. On this occasion it was not necessary to shake up the coolies, since they were aware of what sort of a day lay before them, and knew the risks of being belated. They made tea and ate some tsamba, and then we were off.

The climb began with a scramble over rocky ridges of greywacke and conglomerate, between which, on the eastern exposure, at 16,700 feet, there were still flowering plants : red knotweed, rhubarb, saxifrage (*Saxifraga flagellaris*), and everlasting, as everywhere.

To avoid stone-falls, which were a risk if we kept close to the cliff, we now took to the snow on the open glacier. Gansser distributed dark spectacles among the coolies, and took the lead, roped to Paldin, exploring continually for hidden crevasses with his ice-axe. The monsoon snows lying on the ice were in places nearly 3 feet thick, softened here and there where the sun had blazed on them. The coolies had hard work, but held out wonderfully (Plate 147). On the left, from time to time, we caught sight of a peak with an overhang and a steep fluted ice-coating. The past part of the ascent was a snow-slope that seemed almost ready to thunder down as an avalanche, and ended in a cornice. As our leader cut footholds, the rest of the party could follow panting. It was noon when we reached the top of the pass, and the aneroid showed 18,040 feet. Defying the evil spirits, Gansser shouted the call he had learned in Tibet : " Laa chaloo — sosososo ! " Then a stick we had brought with us was stuck upright in the snow, and to the top were tied the red and white rags given to us at the festival. This ceremony was to invoke the favour of the gods.

The monsoon lashed us with fog-wreaths and sleet as the coolies went slowly by, crossing the snow-slope, while Gansser and I waited hoping that the weather would clear sufficiently to give us a view.

Then came a call from below, and Gansser hurried on. An avalanche had started where one of the porters was standing. He had flung himself down and clung for dear life with fingers and toes, waiting motionless until, stretching hands, we rescued him.

" You go ahead ", said Gansser to me. " Cross the slope as quickly as you can, for it is dangerous. I will bring up the rear."

But I could not make the porters move quickly. It was distressing to see them as their feet sank deep in the snow, protected only by heelless slippers, for none of them wear socks. These seem to be an unknown luxury both in the Himalayas and in Tibet. Then the sun began to blaze. The surface of the snow became dripping wet. Below, at the foot of the declivity, dirty heaps of avalanche debris lay on the surface of the great glacier, which flowed westward and then took a turn northward. (The official four-miles-to-the-inch map — 1 : 253,440 — sheet 62 B, is extremely inaccurate in this region of Ralam Pass.) From close at hand there came, now and again, ominous crackling noises. The only way down was along the path of a recent avalanche. Hardly had we reached the end of this, when rock-falls began, and a new avalanche thundered. The porters flung down their packs, and hastened to one side, except the trance-dancer, who stood erect, and spat imploringly towards the avalanche. And behold, the wet mass of snow carrying rocks with it paused a few paces from his feet. Only one blanket was lost in this avalanche, for with ice-axes we were able to disinter a wooden case and a pair of boots (Plate 148).

By 1.30 we were in comparative safety descending along the border of the snow-covered glacier, called in the map Thercher Glacier. One of the coolies fell into a small crevasse, from which he was extricated without difficulty. All around us crackling noises were still to be heard. Mud, snow, water, and stones, dislodged by the melting process, continued to thunder down the slopes, forming regular " rivers " upon the ice-cap. Some came down a white glacier which, facing us, descended in a mighty cascade from an unnamed peak to the north, marked as having an altitude of 21,360 feet. Then the peaks were hidden once more in clouds, and rain began. The recent snows were not so thick. We walked over the ice to the next big crevasse, which had to be avoided by a detour to the right where a lateral glacier flowed down to join the main one. Between the two was the black rocky peak of Nunapak, surrounded by ice. The descent was difficult. Our feet continually broke through the wet detritus and loose snow to the icy surface. I was astonished that the porters, who wore nothing but ragged slippers, managed to get along without a serious accident.

Notwithstanding the rain and the lateness of the hour, we had to take a brief rest and a snack before continuing our course northward down the valley over what was now a fairly level ice-sheet. We no longer had to tramp through thick snow, and could make better progress over ice and moraine — for here to an increasing extent the ice was covered by detritus. But there seemed no end to the glacier. Night was falling when we reached its confluence with the huge Kala-Baland Glacier. There, close to the leftward rocky spur, we were faced by a precipice, to the right of which was a labyrinth of dirty séracs and crevasses from which, in the failing light, we could find no outlet. There was nothing else to do than, under torrents of rain, to put up our tents here amid the rubble and ice. All had to find accommodation as best they could — except for one man who was missing, and had not even a blanket with him. Vainly did we make flash-signals with our electric torches, and halloo through the darkness.

Next morning the rain had ceased, but the encampment was a drenched muddle (Plate 149). The stray made himself known early in the morning, hailing us from one of the ice-pinnacles. We were afraid that the fellow would be frozen, but he was not in such bad shape after his recent debauch followed by a strenuous climb and a lonely, unsheltered night. Gansser, who had gone ahead to explore, now called " djaiga " (all right). After some difficulties with a fissure, he had found an exit towards the left side of the glacier. Then, below the crevasse, we had to cross to the other cliff. At length, on the right side, lower down, we found some juniper bushes, so that we could dry ourselves at a roaring fire and brew a hot drink. The valley behind the old moraine was a paradise of flowers. In addition to the familiar potentillas, we found five species of lousewort (*Pedicularis*), one of which grew to a height of 18 inches and had carmine-red flowers. Even more

123

beautiful, among the stones, was a big poppy (*Meconopsis aculeata*), the flower, 4 inches across, having sky-blue or pink petals.

Since the skies were clearing a little, we went back to the big crevasse in order to photograph the remarkable convolutions of the ice, picked out with dirt (Plate 146). The surface looked very like that of a convoluted marble, the folds — as are those of marble — being produced by pressure, caused in this case by the confluence of the branch with the main glacier.

The joint ice-stream, flowing south-westward, is named on the map Shankalpa. It ends at an altitude of about 12,300 feet, a turbid torrent emerging from amid the debris at its foot. Once more was evident the contrast between the slothful ice and the mighty strength of the roaring waters, which had cut deeply through the heaps of detritus brought down by the tributaries. Here was a fresh proof of the intensifying erosion of the most recent epoch. The tributaries, too, had cut themselves such deep channels that we had to spend a lot of time finding a practicable way across one of them whose bed was 1000 feet down.

Mist and rain returned, but the air grew more sultry as we descended. At length we reached our goal. But what a disappointment. Ralam, writ large on the map, and declared to be at an altitude of 11,800 feet, was a poor, dirty-looking little place, most of the huts being in ruins. Five ragged men and a few women were the whole population. It was surrounded by green, terraced pastures, but there were no corn-fields. Ah, there was a man decently dressed, an Indian. He had recently arrived, and would like to go on with us next day to Milam. He had asked our boy whether we had been to Kailas. The prevailing mood of the village was inhospitable. Still, for a good, round sum we were able to rent the best of the huts for the night and secure a modicum of food for the porters.

THE GORI-GANGA VALLEY

" We have another pass to climb. The gorge which the Shankalpa River has cut for itself below Ralam has such precipitous walls and is so deep that there is no practicable path there. In a terrific downpour we climb across the flowery meads, interspersed here and there with fern-beds. On the boggier spots there flourishes a golden-yellow louse-wort with campanulate flowers nearly 3 inches long, vertically disposed (*Pedicularis tubiflora*); also a large edelweiss; and now for the first time we find bluebells, dwarf specimens, *Wahlenbergia gracilis*. But the most beautiful of all, here, is the carmine lousewort, *Pedicularis rhinanthoides*, with winged flowers more than an inch across. There are geraniums,

124

potentillas, and everlastings, as everywhere. As we climb, we get into the mist. Panting and weary, wet and cold, we continue the ascent, which seems unending. Not until noon do we reach the saddle, at 15,100 feet, the place being known locally as Dutuk Dhura. There must be a wonderful view in fine weather, for it is just opposite Nanda Kot. No use waiting, however. We shall get warm again as we go down the great longitudinal valley of Gori Ganga, which lies at our feet. There are two villages. At a little over 13,000 feet, on the upper limits of the birches and rhododendrons, are two primitive shepherds' huts, where we rest on a rock, surrounded by the warm stink of dung and slaughter-house, and pestered by flies, while we ask the shepherds our way. They point to the left, towards the village of Sumdu. Only when we get there (10,470 feet) does it become plain to us that the bridges marked on the map are non-existent, but that there are other bridges which will enable us to go on down the valley on the eastern side. First, however, we must climb 320 feet to the N.W. to reach a green terrace on which lies the village of Tola. The school teacher is friendly, and places his schoolhouse at our disposal, a dimly-lit place with a mud floor and two apertures for windows, through which the youngsters inquisitively scrutinise the strange and dripping guests.

" From Tola a path leads on down the monotonous valley over terraces and moraines. The slopes have been deforested. Only a little brushwood has been left : two species of juniper and two species of cotoneaster, one growing to the respectable height of over 6 feet. The finest plant along the route is a thistle, more than 3 feet high, its flowers like carmine candles. The river, which lies on our left, is yellow and turbid, and the mountains are still hidden.

" After crossing a lateral brook, we come to the large village of Burphu, amid neglected buckwheat, barley, and potato-patches. The large, corrugated iron roof of the dak-bungalow is visible from a long way off. The sheep and goats are away on pack-work, or in the mountain pastures ; and, as every traveller in the Himalayas and Tibet knows, pigs are rare in this part of the world, though they abound everywhere throughout China."

IN QUARTERS FOR THE THIRD TIME

Milam was conspicuous from a distance, being the largest and highest village in Gori Ganga, built on a terrace at an altitude of a little over 11,000 feet. For all that it had 2000 houses, it was a desolate place. From Burphu, our path led down into the gorge, across a bridge, and through a breach in the lateral moraine of what was once the big Milam Glacier — a moraine which has crowded the Gori against the schistous rocks. Within this moraine rampart lies the fluvio-glacial terrace on which the village is built, about 150 feet above the river that runs down from the Milam Glacier.

Although the inhabitants seemed friendly enough, when we entered the place at noon it was with little enthusiasm, seeking information. We never expected to find an inn here, but there was not even a dak-bungalow. Still, near the post-office at the upper end of the village having called to secure letters and money, we rested awhile in a dark hut until we succeeded in finding a better lighted and cleaner little house, which we were able to rent for eight rupees a month (Plate 152).

After mid-day dinner we sought out the patwari, who was also the mayor of the village, which is abandoned during the winter. He was a young Indian, Dhan Singh Nedi by name, wearing yellow gloves, knickerbockers, and a jockey-cap, which made him look like a Neapolitan cicerone. In broken English, he gave us a cordial welcome, but nevertheless the patwari peeped through, showing that he felt his responsibilities to the British Government. Kali, who in some of our previous difficulties had shown diplomatic adroitness, had already ferreted out that the official had instructions to arrest us if we wanted to go to Tibet or had been there. Happily the patwari seemed to know nothing about Gansser's pilgrimage to Kailas or of our previous arrest.

" Housekeeping in Milam is a simple matter. The patwari is empowered to fix prices, and all the necessaries of life, such as rice, flour, tsamba, and sugar can be obtained from him on ' monthly terms '. Every other day a runner arrives with the mail, which takes a week from Almora, so that we shall get air-mail letters posted in Europe ten or twelve days ago."

We gave our hard-working porters a day's holiday with pay, a week's wages for the return journey, a gratuity and cigarettes in addition to the stipulated fee, so that they seemed very well pleased. They did not intend to return by the Ralam but to take a considerably longer though easier route by way of the Dhauli Valley and over the Shiala Pass. The only one of the Sepu men we are keeping is Kyu.

" Every morning the village is visited by bearded vultures, one of them having black plumage, manifestly a rare variety. They seem especially interested in the sheep-droppings. Carrion crows and an indigenous redstart are among the regular guests. The patwari drops in daily for a chin-wag, this being rather an interruption to our work, but he has a good deal of interest to tell us and is eager to be helpful.

126

Now that he knows us better, he expresses open sympathy for our investigations. Occasionally he sends us a delicacy — a dish of potatoes, or a bowl of milk, which is very expensive here. He has also shown us over the village, where there is not much to see beyond an ancient gable adorned with woodcarvings. The produce of the women's handicrafts one can only see by penetrating the dark interiors. There, on the damp floor, they weave cloths or carpets. No factory-acts of any kind seem to be operative at these altitudes, but the people could greatly improve their own working conditions if they had any initiative and felt seriously inclined to do so.

" The end of July is close at hand, but the weather remains as bad as ever except for very brief intervals — and our news from Europe does not bring much better reports. However, when the sun cleared once at noon we were able to set our watches for the first time after three months. We simply dropped a plumb-line, marked the north on the ground, and made it twelve o'clock when the shadow coincided with this line. We found that our timepieces were almost half an hour out."

AUGUST FIRST

Amid the monotonous days of rainfall and " desk-work " came a wonderful surprise. The school teacher was obviously well enough informed to know that August 1st is our national fête day and that Switzerland is the oldest self-governing republic in Europe. This gentleman, Dhan Singh Pangatey, sent us a laconic message : " Please come to the schoolhouse at twelve o'clock. Everything is ready."

As requested, at the appointed time we made our way through the village to the square in the south-east on which the schoolhouse, considerable for these regions, stands. Garlands of flowers and strips of red bunting hung over the doorway, with inscriptions of welcome in English and Hindustani ; also a freshly painted shield showing a red cross on a white ground — the worthy teacher having made a little mistake here. On the stone-paved floor, barefooted in a raging draught, were about seventy youngsters, who ought to have been enjoying their weekly holiday. All rose as we entered. Facing them, on the dais, were two iron stools on either side of the teacher, who hung round our necks garlands of thyme and potato blossom. The walls were adorned with little flags copied from old-fashioned school books. The highest class, the fourth, consisting of children aged ten to eleven, sang to the teacher's accompaniment on a harmonium much out of tune. Then it was the turn of the younger pupils, who discoursed a long prearranged programme, giving dramatic recitations in Hindustani and not in their mother-tongue which is Bahari. One, even, did his level best in English.

Now came various athletic sports in the square. The most amusing were races on all-fours. We responded by showing the kids how well we could walk on our hands, of which one of them gave an excellent imitation. Having borrowed a couple of walking-sticks, we also gave a " cock-fighting " performance.

When we took our leave, the headmaster handed us the following epistle :

" Dr. A. Huem Esqr, & Mr. Gansser Profr.
  Respected Sirs ;
       we the people of Milam Village are very pleasure on your welcome to the Johar. You are very wise men & sample for us. So we very greatful for your kindness.
       We pray to God for your long life
       Your very greatfull

Dhan Sing Pangatey, Hd. master milam
Lal Singh teacher
Khushhal Singh teacher

Milam, 1st august 1936."

We were profoundly touched.

CHAPTER TWELVE

AFOOT ONCE MORE

WE were detained a good many days at Milam, not only on account of the bad weather and our " desk-work ", but because we were still in doubt as to how the rest of our programme was to be fulfilled. We wished to explore the Kiogar region on the Tibetan frontier in the far north of the Almora district. Geologically this is one of the most puzzling parts of the Himalayas, and here, at the end of the nineteenth century, A. von Krafft made some important discoveries, including that of the exotic fossiliferous blocks of dubious origin.[1] Krafft's explanation was that these exotic blocks must have been scattered in the Tertiary Epoch by formidable volcanic eruptions in Tibet. At that date very little was known about the great superimposed strata of the Alps, and we hoped that with the knowledge subsequently acquired fresh light could be thrown on the problem.

The patwari informed us that he had no authority to allow us to visit Kiogar, or even to cross the frontier into the district of Garhwal. As politely as possible, but no less energetically, we made a strong protest, insisting that the Government had issued a passport allowing us to visit every part of the province of Kumaon, without any restriction whatever. Surely he had been able to convince himself that, far from being political suspects, our aims were purely scientific. It would spoil his excellent record were he to treat us as dubious characters and put a spoke in our wheel. What we wanted, we explained, was to set off as quickly as possible, before untoward news could come from Almora. But now there were other hindrances. Beyond Milam the journey would have to be made Tibetan fashion, with pack-animals. The day before some men had been dispatched in the morning to round up the yak hybrids (dzos) which had been turned loose months before upon the pastures adjoining Milam Glacier. Naturally this took a little time, but by the evening of August 2nd the beasts had been

[1] Mem. Geol. Survey of India, Vol. XXXII, Calcutta, 1902.

secured and brought in. A strong mule turned up late that evening; and also, for four rupees, we bought a ram which could carry a provision of rice, and later, in case of need, could be slaughtered for food.

Kali has been buying necessaries : 10 seers [a seer is 2 lbs.] of rice for 4 rupees ; 12 seers of tsamba for 3 rupees ; 3 seers of sugar for 1 rupee ; scalded butter and honey for 2 rupees, but both of these delicacies are of poor quality and dirty. We also have remnants of the stores brought from Switzerland. Gadje, a yak driver we have engaged in Milam, and also Kyu and our two Sherpas must see to their own food. They know that they will need enough for ten days at least.

August 3rd was the great day on which we resumed our tramp. We must be a queer-looking lot : five men, two whites, two Mongoloid Nepalese, and a Tibetan ; with our little menagerie. The two strong black-and-white dzos and the mule are to carry one cwt. each ; the ram, 20 lbs. of rice ; Kyu the ordinary load of a porter in the mountains ; and the Sherpas, a heavy rucksack each. It was a pleasant surprise to find that the ram would follow Kali on a lead, though at first he curveted madly. Little Jungbwa is to take her own course, but will generally stick to Kali and the ram.

We marched on a badly made bridle-path running along the western side of the savage Gori Valley across old moraines flanked by striking pillars of earth which sometimes topped the river by as much as 650 feet (Plate 153), and then over more moraine slopes, while there were alternations of rain and shine.

Our first halt was made at Samsong, where a lateral glacial valley enters from the east. Then we crossed a bridge to the eastern side of the valley. At 13,300 feet we passed an empty shuttered hut. At 14,000 feet, a little above the path and not quite reaching the main stream, was the end of a lateral glacier, the ice of which projected over the main moraine. Soon after noon we arrived at the green, moss-covered camping ground of Dung, 13,700 feet, where we halted for the rest of the day and for the night, since higher up there would have been no pasturage for our pack-animals. Here and there there was disclosed in front of us a mighty striated spur of rock, so that we could make out a good deal of geological structure before thick cloud came down for the night.

ACROSS THE UTTA DHURA AND THE KIANGUR PASS

From Dung the path led across a bridge over the River Gori, which divided here, and turned to the left, high above the end of a second glacier. Then we mounted along the edge of the ice to a camping ground named Bamlas, where there was no feed. One who reads these names on the map might imagine them to be settlements, but the remote region we were now entering was completely uninhabited. We crossed the glacier to the last available camp, called Jim, before beginning the steep zig-zag climb in rain and mist. Our drover has had difficulties with the dzo, a big and strong but imperfectly tamed beast, who has twice angrily shaken off his load — happily not over a precipice. We passed numerous skeletons of sheep and goats which had perished from the hardships of the journey. Of course this was all the better for the carrion-kites and bearded vultures, which abounded.

At noon we reached the Utta Dhura. On map 62 B this much used though desolate pass is named Anta Dhura or Kyunam-La, the height being marked as 17,590 feet. It cuts through dark schistous clays of the upper Trias, which are accordion-pleated.

As quickly as possible we descended the northern side of the pass across snow and wet detritus, in which, again and again, our beasts were almost bogged, until, at Lauka, we came to somewhat drier ground. There, after wading through a raging glacier torrent, we happened upon a queer structure which looked like a cross between a tent and a negro hut, its rounded walls being built out of bags of tsamba. The Tibetan who was encamped here could get neither forward nor backward with his goods until help came, half his flock of 800 sheep and goats having perished after fifty days' heavy rain and lack of fodder. In addition to a dwarf gentian, the scanty vegetation here consisted only of *Thylacospermum* as hard as stone, and a few mosses, there being no fodder-plants, so we went farther on down the valley as far as Topidunga, where there was good pasturage at 14,750 feet; then southward across the River Girthy, the first tributary of the Ganges, for we had crossed into that watershed by the Utta Dhura.

Next day, despite devastating rains, we made good progress north-ward, over the Kiangur or Kungr Pass. At first we had to descend more than 300 feet into the Girthy Gorge, up which we then clambered for more than a quarter of a mile eastward through the narrowing ravine in the Trias limestone, to reach a spot where it was possible to jump across the torrent and find a practicable climb to the north. With astounding sure-footedness our pack-beasts managed to cross even the most ticklish places (Plate 154). Here, likewise, the gap in the steep limestone hills is due to the presence of black clays, which are easily weathered so that negotiable necks and passes have arisen. Up to 17,220 feet at the top of Kiangur Pass and beyond it, we were in the same excavated depression of so-called Spiti shale in which, here and there, we found fine complete ammonites, and fragments of much larger specimens.

Regarded as scenery, Kiangur Pass is dull, and on the sunny side is free from snow. On the northern declivity, however, there is a steeply sloping ice-cap which it would not be proper to speak of as a glacier. More and more in the northern regions of the mountain chains we are now crossing we are given a less rugged impression than that we have hitherto received on the present side of the Tibetan frontier. The landscape, of course, is only the outward and visible sign of the geological structure. This, with its northward, axially tending folds of limestone, its environing black clays, and its flysch, reminds us of the cretaceous formations on the northern slopes of the Alps. There are novelties, too, in the flora : at 16,400 feet, on the shady side, we have found a dwarf forget-me-not with a tap-root (*Eritrichium strictum*) and a dwarf edelweiss ; at 15,740 feet also dwarf gentians ; at 15,100 feet a strange-looking labiate, whose pink flowers are hidden beneath umbrella-shaped, satiny leaves (*Lamium rhomboideum*).

Not only on account of the rain and the damp, but also because of its picturesque situation and its green pasture, we halted early at " Encamping Ground Chidamu ", pitching our two tents at the outlet of a deep cleft in the hills (Plate 155). There were so many marmot-holes hereabouts that probably some of the burrows ran beneath the tents. From this on we should have a very agreeable journey, if only the bad weather would let up.

Instead of marching farther north next day, Gansser and I clambered up a savage lateral gorge which had been cut through symmetrical deposits of Trias chalk. In the upper layers of this were masses of shell-agglomerate, in which millions of shells lay stuck together upon what was once a seashore. The commonest were thick oysters and thick-shelled cardinias. Subject to correction, we were inclined to regard this uppermost calcareous stratum as homologous with the Rhaetic or Penarth beds of the Alps.

BESIDE THE RIVER KIOGAR

On August 7th the skies cleared. It was only a four-mile walk farther north to our next camp, an agreeable stroll along a little path leading amid flowery hillocks and lush pastures — whereas on the caravan route almost every blade of grass and leaf has been eaten.

Long before this we had pitched upon Laptal beside the River

Kiogar, which forms the boundary of the district of Garhwal, as likely to be an admirable camp. We reached the place before noon, to find it the most agreeable and romantic site of our journey (Plates 156 and 157). It is a green terrace about 14,100 feet above sea-level, at the outlet of the Kiogar Gorge. Here men and beasts alike could bask in agreeably warm air. We dried our clothes, bathed in the stream, and then oiled ourselves in the sunshine, to be prepared for fresh rainfalls. The red ground of the Swiss flag contrasted bravely with the yellowish-white tent, now happily dry once more ; with the green of the grass, the brown of the rocks, the blue of the sky. We gathered flowers to press them. Close at hand were blooming edelweiss, three species of blue gentian, and, on the marshy spots, a delicate white starry flower (*Genziana humilis*) ; while a little farther afield were masses of a red knotweed, with geraniums, and groups of violet-tinted thistles. Less congenial are the swarms of little mosquitoes, which we had not expected at so great a height. Our drover, Gadje, has had a misadventure. He had left the mule to graze at will, and in an unguarded moment the beast vanished. We have searched for it in vain.

The first fine day was followed by a clear, starry night and a lovely morning. My comrade had long cherished the wish to steal a march on me by seeking in Tibet the supposed source of the exotic blocks, for the discovery of this would solve an important problem in mountain structure. He set off, therefore, early in the morning, accompanied by Paldin and Kyu, himself also carrying a heavy rucksack, to explore, on his own, north-eastward over the Balcha Dhura.

I, too, wanted to turn the day to best account, so I set forth with Kirken up the ravine, in order to climb a peak from which I could get a good view of the Tibetan frontier chain, the Kiogars with their exotic blocks. The way along the gorge would have been easy enough had the river been low, but now that it is in flood it is seldom wadable. Since we had to cross at least a dozen times, the only thing to do was, regardless of a wetting, to plunge up to the waist into the ice-cold water at spots where the current was not so strong as to sweep us away. In jumping and climbing, young Kirken is not always my equal, but he is tougher than I am and has more staying-power.

In the central part of the calcareous formations, the gorge widened a little. Here, in the shelter of the cliffs, we came across a thicket of osiers, and also some willow-herb with carmine flowers (*Epilobium*). After that we had an arduous scramble along the eastern slopes, until the valley widened suddenly where the schists and the sandstone began. Making our way up the river-bed, we next climbed to the alpine meadows

133

on the southern side of the valley, where for the first time in this part of the world we found sheep pasturing, with shepherds watching them. Then we came to an abandoned pasture, where the marmots have made a settlement. At sight of us, these rodents scurried into their burrows. In many places they had cropped the vegetation bare. Now came a long and monotonous climb southward. Panting with the exertion, we quickened our steps, for a broad mass of clouds had gathered threateningly. At a height ranging from 16,400 to 17,000 feet there were many sessile gentians, the flowers being striped blue and white (*Gentiana frigida*, var. *nubigena*). It was noon, and the heavens were overcast when we reached, at 17,600 feet, the top of a ridge commanding a distant prospect. Facing us was the Tibetan frontier, a long sierra of snow-clad peaks. There were the Kiogars. Beyond question, as von Krafft showed, the white limestone summits of the Trias have been superposed as strangers upon the younger formation of the flysch. Vainly did I wait until evening, in the hope of better illumination. Again and again did the Kiogars don their cloud-caps. At length we had to scuttle for camp. Instead of going down the valley, where we should certainly have been benighted, we made a detour to the right over the calcareous crest, having to reclimb as much as 1000 feet, so that it was pitch-dark when, with difficulty, we found our way back to Laptal. Never in my life have I been so tired, being almost at my last gasp.

TO THE EXOTIC BLOCKS OF THE BALCHA DHURA

After spending another day upon geological work at Laptal, I wanted to make a new lengthy excursion. Alas, there had been heavy rain in the night, turning to snow, which had fallen on the adjoining hills almost as far down as the tent. The peak of Malla Sangcha, which we had intended to climb, looked like a ski-ing field. Our overnight packing proved fruitless, for it was raining once more. The temperature was 40°, and the important work I wanted to do on the frontier crests now seemed out of the question. I wondered how Gansser was faring across the border, with no tent.

Gadje got back tired, hungry, and disappointed after spending nearly two days upon a vain search for the lost mule, of which he could not find a trace. Anyhow I am glad that the good fellow has got back safely.

When, during our first night at Laptal, the stars shone brightly, although there was recent snow and it was very cold, we made a start before dawn, the drover coming with Kirken and me as supplementary porter. It takes the lot of us, now, to load the big dzo, two hanging on with all their might to the beast's horns. As soon as the load is fixed, agilely and simultaneously we spring out of reach of these formidable weapons. So wild had the creatures become from high feeding that as we began the ascent he again grew riotous, and tried to shake off the load. However, he soon settled down again, and accompanied the other beasts as decorously as if he had been familiar with the road.

The sun was now so warm that the snow was obviously receding to the rough heights, and Malla Sandcha, where we camped at a little over 15,000 feet, looked, with its geranium fields, like a garden. That evening we had quite a sensation. While I was sitting in the tent making notes and entries in the map, Kirken called me. On the opposite slopes were grazing a dozen chamois-like creatures, some of them with wide-spreading horns, equally unlike those of the steinbock and of the chamois. Our men called them " haren " in Hindustani and " nauer " in Tibetan. I supposed they might be bharal (*Ovis nahoor*). Later we saw them at a higher level, jumping from ledge to ledge on what looked like vertical precipices we should have thought absolutely inaccessible. Their hide was of an inconspicuous brownish-grey. The body was plumper than that of a chamois, and the feet thick as if swollen.

Next came the important day on which we proposed to study the exotic blocks of the Balcha Dhura crest, but the weather was again unfavourable. Climbing about 1000 feet per hour I made my way, accompanied by Kirken, over the detritus-covered flysch slopes to the north-east. Here the various zones of flowering plants could be plainly made out. The blue geraniums reached to 15,744 feet. Then, at an altitude ranging from 16,000 to 16,500 feet, amid bare moraines, we came upon huge, hard, flowerless masses of vegetation, one of these great plants attaining a diameter of nearly 8 feet (*Thylacospermum rubifragum*). Besides this, and flowering up to 16,700 feet, was an abundance of edelweiss, also two creeping labiates, one pink and one white, larkspur, knotweed, potentilla, houseleek, small, violet-coloured creeping papilionaceas (*Nepeta*), and violet asters. Up to 17,850 feet, on the shadier Tibetan side, where the snow lies deep and the plants are better protected from the monsoon, we found a yellow sunflower with a woody stem (*Potentilla fruticosa*), a pink-and-yellow composite, and a yellow one with a hanging head and fleshy leaves (*Crepis*).

From the top of Balcha Dhura at 17,700 feet, we caught glimpses, through rifts in the clouds, of the mountains of the central zone : a wonderfully steep gigantic peak, presumably Kamet, 25,420 feet,

L

bearing W. 14° N. ; while S. 36° W. we could plainly recognise the double-headed Nanda Devi, rising to a height of 25,584 feet. Northward and north-eastward was spread the beautifully coloured and mysterious land of Tibet, visible as far as the distant Transhimalayas, whose peaks were also veiled in cloud. Nearer, only about 15 miles away, was a corrugated calcareous crest, shining white, but free from snow. There was little snow even on Balcha Dhura itself, in spite of the recent falls — except for the old snow-patches in shady places. The snow-line here would seem to be at about 18,400 feet.

Now I had to make the most of my opportunities for geological study, so far as this was possible in the biting monsoon wind and under occasional storms of sleet. The long crest consisted almost entirely of basic, mainly greenish, eruptive rocks of the diabase type, as already described by von Krafft, but here and there interspersed with dark green shining and vitreous serpentine, showing numerous landslips.

Protected by the wind by keeping below the level of the crest, we climbed for more than a mile to the north-west, to reach the " Balcha Dhura Heights ", at a level of 18,110 feet, where we found embedded in the lava-like consolidations various blocks of red limestone and hornstone ; and 500 feet lower down, in a cleft on the south-western aspect, another red limestone block filled with finely preserved ammonites (especially *Cladiscites*, *Juvavites*, *Arcestes*), this being homologous with the famous Hallstätter limestone of the Eastern Alpine Trias. Here I hammered and chiselled busily, until it was getting late, and more than time to think about our return. Having climbed again, therefore, over the crest to the pass, and then made our way about half a mile farther to the south-east through an uncommonly steep furrow in the rubble, down which we had to slide rather than walk, we got back safely to camp.

ON KIOGAR NO. 2

Now we must make an attempt upon the mighty sierra of Kiogar which lies S.E. of Balcha Dhura, and of which we had a good view a few days ago. To get as near as possible with our pack-beasts, we had first to descend, and make our way along the Kiogar River for a mile and three-quarters to the south-east, until we could climb northward over the marshy meads of the broad, crumbling flysch region. Thus we reached a level camping-ground at 16,400 feet at the S.W. foot of Kiogar No. 3. The only drawback was that there was no water there, so it had to be fetched from far below.

136

On August 14th the alarm awoke us at 4 A.M. What luck, starlight and moonshine, no fog, not a cloud to be seen. At peep of day I set out with Kirken to make a first ascent. To begin with we crossed the mountain ridges towards Kiogar No. 3. Then we had to traverse the steep, detritus-covered slopes obliquely, to reach the gap between us and the next peak to the N.W. which, in my diary, I call the " Great Mythen " because, though about 12,500 feet higher, it so closely resembles the Great Mythen of Canton Schwyz (Plate 158). This was the worst part of the climb, for at almost every step we slipped nearly as much backward on the loose masses of white limestone. Still by seven o'clock our labours were over, as we reached the saddle at 17,870 feet. Quickly I took a photo, for Nanda, the distant goddess, was already assuming her cloud-cap.

Now came an easy climb over the white, fissured limestone rock to the summit of the glorious peak. The aneroid registered 18,700 feet. It was windless and agreeably warm in the bright sunshine, but we were too late to get a complete panorama. From west to south, the high peaks of the Central Himalayas were capped with vapour, while Tibet was hidden in black clouds, from which issued a thunderstorm more violent than I had ever seen before. Our descent, therefore, was extremely disagreeable. Nevertheless the weather had not broken in time to rob us of a magnificent result. I had seen the whole Kiogar region in one vast expanse from the north to the east. These mountains are not simply what von Krafft believed them, huge exotic blocks flung out by eruptions in Tibet. They consist of a widespread mountain mass superimposed from that region in addition to the stones hurled thence by eruptions — not unlike the rocky peaks of Central Switzerland (Mythen and Iberg) and those of the Préalpes of French-speaking Switzerland. I need hardly say that there are still a number of important though subsidiary problems that await solution, with the aid of more extensive and thorough investigations. Above all, we want to know whence the actual exotic blocks originally came — those blocks that are intercalated in the more superficial consolidated masses or in the subjacent flysch. Before this can be learned, geologists will have to make something more than casual and cursory visits to Tibet, and must be enabled to wander whithersoever they please in that gigantic tableland.

From our encampment I had still to take a number of photographs and continue my geological studies, in which I was hindered, not so much by really bad weather, as by treacherous cloud-caps which were incessantly settling down upon the Kiogar peaks. After we had explored the depression between Kiogar No. 3 and Kiogar No. 4, going far down into the Tibetan Sami Valley, I climbed for the third time to the best viewpoint, where I was at length able, from close at hand, to take an excellent photo of my favourite among the Kiogars, No. 2, the " Great Mythen " (Plate 158).

Now we were faced by a fresh difficulty. We had brought along food stores calculated to last us a full ten days, but we had now reached the thirteenth day of the expedition. The day before yesterday Kirken's and Kali's provisions were exhausted, and they had to draw upon my reserves. Now I, too, had nothing left but a very little rice and tsamba. Our good friend the ram had to be sacrificed to the needs of our importunate stomachs. I hoped that the vultures would be attracted by the slaughter, and that I should be able to get good photographs of them. A pair of ravens, indeed, turned up, eager for the feast, but they were too shy to come near enough for a photograph, while a bearded vulture did no more than take a casual glance at the offal as he soared past.

CHAPTER THIRTEEN

BY UNKNOWN TRACKS TO THE
SUTLEJ (GANSSER)

ACROSS THE BALCHA DHURA INTO TIBET

" ' Bahut, bahut kana tekit ', says Kirken, ' high feeding, high feeding ', as he struggles frantically to buckle the big dzo's girth. Paldin and I have to hold the beast's horns. All our animals have grown unruly as well as fat. Like Jeshurun in Deuteronomy, they wax fat and kick ; they are grown thick ; they are covered with fatness — for this camp at Laptal is a glorious pasture. The tent is encircled by succulent green meadows. I am still mourning the loss of my little geological hammer. It fell into the raging torrent when the pack-sheep carrying some of our stores was refractory and had to be pushed into the water. Still my preparations for a journey into Tibet have helped me to forget this mishap. In our idyllic camp I penned a second document declaring that I was about to undertake a separate expedition entirely on my own responsibility.

" We hope to make our way to the Sutlej by unknown and uncharted routes. The journey should solve the problem of the huge exotic blocks. Besides, the whole Tibetan region which now lures me across the northernmost chains of the Himalayas is practically unexplored. Kyu, the tough little Tibetan from Kuti, is to accompany me. He made a very good showing when we crossed the difficult Ralam Pass, but did not quite come up to my expectations on this journey. Paldin, of course, came along, and little Jungbwa, as my third travelling companion, was to return for a time to her native land. She was already old enough to play the part of watch-dog. Her inherited characteristics are becoming more obvious as she grows up, for she rages like a fiend when any stranger approaches our camp. We are taking enough food to last us ten days. Kyu is carrying a big gunny-sack, while Paldin and I have our rucksacks filled to bursting. On this expedition we have to dispense with the luxury of a tent. Food is the main essential, since we cannot count on being able to procure any as we go along. Naturally our diet has to be as simple as possible, thoroughly Tibetan.

"Bara Sahib, accompanied by Kirken, has already entered the gorge. They expect to be back in camp at nightfall. We exchange farewell shouts, and lose sight of one another for ten days. A herd of steinbocks gallops across the precipitous, desolate declivities of Balcha Dhura. They have young with them, these being sedulously kept in the middle of the herd. We look enviously at their agile progress, and at the ease with which they race up the steepest slopes, while we make slow headway under our burdens. It seems to me that Paldin and Kyu are also suffering a little from high feeding, but this does not show itself (as with the dzo) by exuberant activity. I have to wait a good while for them, until Paldin at length appears, and then Kyu much farther back. Still he catches up at last, with his big gunny-sack, a good deal of whose weight is borne by the forehead strap which passes round his ' ski-er's cap '. While waiting for them on the wind-swept pass I have time to admire a wonderful display of clouds, huge cumuli driving up from the south and devouring one peak after another. The tallest of these, the distant Nanda Devi, put up the longest fight until it, too, was in the end wholly wrapped in cloud. Westward was the Kamet group, 25,420 feet, still discernible, although a huge barrier of cloud was moving towards Tibet. It was a view never to be forgotten, of the sort by which I am continually being entranced upon the frontier passes.

"We descended into a lonely valley, and here, beside a brook, were able to sit down and have some food. Then came a climb to another pass, from which we are to descend on to the Tibetan plateau. The Balcha Dhura was 17,712 feet; this second pass was about 650 feet higher. Thence our ' road ' (an apology for a road) led down into the plateau, which is deeply grooved by numerous rivers, or rather what are called wadis in Arabia, being dry channels which occasionally convey water but are now empty.

"While waiting for my companions, I quickly climb a point of vantage to survey our route. The region is entirely unknown, and the maps thoroughly undependable. Before us lies the chain of the Trans-himalaya, most of the mountains being white with new-fallen snow. Towards Kailas, far away to the N.E., the sky is black, one of the usual thunderstorms threatening. I can still see the rocks of Kamet towering above the clouds. Cloud-wreaths are now creeping across Balcha Dhura. The fine weather is not likely to last long. An icy föhn-storm is raging round my outlook-point, the wind being so fierce that it is difficult to stand upright. This same wind accompanies us for the rest of the descent. We enter the small valley, down which a little water flows. Dark is approaching, so we must camp, for Lord knows whether we shall still find water lower down. Indeed water is scarce in this part of the world, and the wind never ceases. We discover a little yak-dung, the only available fuel. Pitilessly the wind tries to blow out our fire, so we have to erect a wind-screen of heaped ' cow-pats '. However, Kyu is a master at fire-building and soon we have a good hot oven built of stone."

HARD TIMES

We slept very little that night, the moon and stars shining down clear and cold from an unclouded sky, so that the radiation was intense. Moreover, the storm-wind continued to blow fiercely throughout the night, though it subsided a little when morning came. We made ready to start at the first glimmer of dawn. The sleeping-sacks were thickly coated with hoar frost, and even the rivulet was frozen over. We did not bother about breakfast, hoping to find both wood and water lower down.

Foxy-red marmots welcomed us with hoots like those of a motor horn. Hares were also to be seen occasionally, and even kiangs scrutinised our little column, being much less timid than those of Raksas Valley. Here too, they had a lot of young. The altitude was still above 15,750 feet, but it was growing sultry, and leaden cumulus clouds were gathering. We made our way slowly across the wide plateau, being frequently hindered by a toilsome descent into the wadis, many of which were fully 300 feet deep. The steep re-climbs to the plateau were almost too much for me, for I was suffering from violent diarrhoea and had no appetite whatever. Clouds grey as lead, limbs heavy as lead, throat throbbing painfully. Then I could go no farther. In a long valley we sought for water. Laboriously I crawled to our camp, got into my sleeping-sack, and tried to sleep, but my racing pulse kept me awake. My thoughts were gloomy, as I pondered over the loss of my little geological hammer. Then the ghost of Tibetan malaria haunted me. The gathering clouds were no blacker than my thoughts.

Now an icy rain began to fall. We were lying in the open, without a tent. The water made its way into my sleeping-sack, and I could scarcely move. Suddenly Paldin sprang to his feet and pointed down the narrow valley. Some 200 yards below us there were four men on horseback, driving a string of about twenty horses. It would never do for them to discover us. But Jungbwa had winded them or seen them, and, already a good watch-dog, began to bark furiously. I seized her without getting out of my sack, and pressed her muzzle to the ground. The minutes passed like hours until we knew whether the horsemen were coming up the valley or were merely crossing it. Should they discover us, it would be a disaster. We lay mousy quiet, watching the four horsemen who were driving their string up the opposite side of the valley. Jungbwa was sucking at my fingers, as she loves to do, but was still somewhat frightened after the scolding I gave when snatching her into the sleeping-sack. Gradually darkness closed round us, while it continued to rain. Everything was hopelessly drenched. I could not sleep, and knew that my temperature must be fairly high. Rain fell throughout the night.

Next morning I managed to crawl on with the others. Really the fever had abated, though I still felt frightfully weak. There was nothing to do but go ahead across the desolate plateau, up and down the sides of the steep gorges. Somewhere to the north of us must be the Sutlej, but it seemed damnably far away. That evening we camped beneath overhanging rocks, by the side of a broad river. There was a little gorse with which we were able to make a fire and dry our wet sleeping-sacks. The stars were shining again. We sat round the fire drinking tea, and then heard footsteps. Every one of us heard them, but we could make out nothing in the darkness, our eyes being dazzled by the fire. There must have been someone there. We crept into our sacks, each of us with his ice-axe handy, and a number of big stones.

WATER !

The skies were clear when we started at peep of day. The broad river beside which we have camped must be the Shib-Chu. As we waded across, the cold water reached to our waists. Now Jungbwa had to show her mettle. After whimpering a little, and making sure that none of us had remained on her side, she plunged into the water, valiantly breasted the waves, and reached the other bank about fifty yards downstream.

We left the main valley to cross some hills, probably those marked on the map as Chilamkurkur, though they are not correctly indicated. A broad, sandy steppe followed. The sun was burning hot. Occasionally the sand was caught up by the wind and bit our faces, making our eyes sore. Mouth and throat grew drier and drier, but there was no sign of water. We crossed several wadis, each time hoping vainly that there would be a stream at the bottom. The hares sported around us, doubling

142

derisively. Jungbwa watched them with indifference, her tongue hanging out of her mouth. She had long given up chasing them, and now scarcely vouchsafed them a glance.

Nor did we bipeds deign to feast our eyes on the wonderful cloud-castles which towered above the horizon. Heavily we tramped onward over sand or shingle. I led the way, with Paldin about twenty yards behind, and Kyu a hundred yards farther back still. The little column had a somewhat pitiful aspect. We had been marching all day since fording the Shib-Chu without a drop of water. Now we were going downhill. Kyu wanted to give it up and lie down, and even Paldin had begun to grumble. Nothing but their raging thirst and the hope of finding water kept my weary companions going. Our throats were on fire, and the fine sand was gritty between our teeth. Following down the bed of a dry rivulet, we entered a gorge. This was the only place where we could hope to find water. But it was inexorably dry. Another of our many bitter disappointments. "I am sure that there must be water in this valley", said I to my apathetic fellow travellers. Suddenly Kyu came to life, and he was running after a pair of birds that looked like rock-partridges. Having vanished among the gorse-bushes, he reappeared with a handful of eggs. A second raid was equally successful. Now he took off his most distinctive emblem, a cummerbund made out of a big woollen shawl, wrapped the eggs in it, and put it on again. I must give Kyu credit for the fact that when we camped late in the evening not one of the eggs was broken. With this treasure-trove round his belly, he walked considerably better, reducing the distance by which he lagged behind by one-half. Still, our thirst was undiminished. Although it was two days since I had eaten, all I was aware of at the moment was the dryness of my throat. Vainly did we dig at a damp spot in the river-bed. We got down three feet without finding water. As we went along the valley we struck several such damp places. At length, in a little hole between two big boulders, we discovered a dirty yellow puddle. Paldin and Kyu eagerly swallowed the lukewarm water, and were surprised that I would not quench my own thirst until I had boiled some. Darkness was at hand, and a suitable camp presented itself. Beneath an over-hanging rock we found a small walled chort full of inscribed clay-tablets such as are common in Tibetan monasteries. Close at hand was a deep cavern, a splendid retreat. Thunder was muttering over the mountains of Chilamkurkur. Above a fire made from dried gorse-stems we boiled a saucepan filled with the yellow water, and soon I was able to drink some tea. The sand crackled between my teeth, and the taste of the

143

beverage left a good deal to be desired. Jungbwa went to sleep under a projecting rock, her stomach well filled with tsamba and water. Kyu boiled his eggs for at least a quarter of an hour, and then thoroughly enjoyed them, although they were almost ready to hatch out. We were comfortably installed in our cave, as we listened to the thunder echoing down the ravine, rumbling but not crashing. The lightning flashes made a ghostly illumination on the walls of the cave as we fell asleep.

We were suddenly awakened by a loud roaring, the noise of raging waters that carried boulders along. The river-bed was filled three feet deep by a rushing torrent, and the great stones, rolling over and over, clashed against the rocky walls. The black waters continued to rise and reached the lower lip of our cave. We should have been drowned like rats in a trap had the freshet not subsided, for there was no possible escape up the perpendicular cliffs. However, the flood began to abate, leaving us uncommonly glad that we had not camped in the middle of the wadi. Beyond question our puddle had saved us from dying of thirst.

THE SUTLEJ AT LAST

Had we only dreamed of the freshet ? In the morning there was not a trace of water in the bottom of the wadi. Still, there were plain marks on the rocky wall to show where it had risen. This morning we all felt in better shape. My strange attack of fever was finished, and I never learned what it had really been. Anyhow it troubled me no more. Kyu's joyful shouts echoed up and down the gorge. The eggs seemed to have done him good. Having again taken off his cummerbund, he spread out the shawl, blew his nose in it trumpetingly, then refolded it and enveloped himself in it once more. Such were Kyu's little ways.

The gully ran northward, so it could hardly fail to lead us to the Sutlej. The farther we descended, the wilder did the valley become. It was a canyon, lined on either side by precipices ranging up to many hundred feet, although the channel at the bottom was never more than a few yards across. We often had to climb over big boulders. Unexpectedly we came upon green bushes as tall as ourselves with ragged prayer-streamers tied to the branches. Just below was a little wall. Not long before a sadhu must have dwelt here, a hermit, an ascetic, who has now vanished leaving only these traces. How did he reach this uninhabited spot ? For several days we have not seen a sign of human habitations. For hours we went on down the narrow gorge without reaching a big valley. Now there were plenty of nimble wild sheep clambering and jumping among the rocks. They could leap in a way which a chamois might have envied. Kyu began to grouse once more, complaining that his load was too heavy, although both Paldin and I carried just as much. " For God's sake don't go on strike here in the wilds ", said I (to myself of course, though in fancy the words were addressed to Kyu). I have noticed for a long time that he is as stubborn as a mule when he takes a fancy into his head. Now he would like to be at Gyanyima, the big Tibetan trading centre, but he has not a notion how many days' journey we are from that resort, which lies far away to the east. Our return march will almost certainly be made farther to the west, so Kyu cannot abscond. " Chaloo, you rascal ", I say angrily, meaning " Get on ", but using an expletive he can understand, and it works better than would any argument.

Suddenly we reached a big chocolate-coloured river. The Sutlej at last. Our " road " ended as a narrow gorge which opened into a broad, deeply cut ravine, down which this big river was flowing (Plate 162). No trace of a path along the river was discoverable, but this must be the Sutlej for it is of considerable size, almost as wide as the lower reaches of the Aare. Paldin lighted a small fire to boil some water for tea. While this was preparing, I stripped and plunged into the cold chocolate-tinted water feeling that a bathe in the sacred river was indispensable.

There was only one way of getting out of this gorge. We had to clamber up the precipitous schistous rocks to reach a vantage point from which we could get an extensive view. To find a satisfactory trackway across these twisting wadis is an extremely difficult matter. Kyu and Paldin would have liked to return by the same route, and I had to impress upon their minds that if we did so we should run the risk of being caught and drowned by another spate before I could induce them to scale the difficult cliffs. Even so, they were as depressed as fugitives after a great defeat, and would have gladly flung away their impedimenta. The fine though savage prospect was enlivened by the scattering of wild sheep. High above the Sutlej a bearded vulture was soaring, as if on the watch for fish. Gradually, to the northward, a few snow-peaks began to show above the top of the opposite cliff. As far as I could make out they were flattened, granite mountains. There was no sign of the conglomerates of the Kailas massif, although these peaks, too, must be part of the Transhimalaya. Above the schist, we found ourselves among white limestone, such as we had already seen twenty or thirty miles to the S.E. among the Chilamkurkurs.

For a long time, now, I had been alone. There was no sign of Kyu

145

and Paldin. Still, they had an idea of the direction I proposed to take. Alone ? No, I was not entirely alone, for the puppy followed me like a shadow, already as large as a small wolf-hound, with paws like a lion's. Together we sat on a limestone outcrop, studying the strange landscape. Far below I could now see Paldin, and a long way farther back was Kyu, toiling up beneath his gunny-sack. In my diary, under August 12th, I find the entry : " We are more than 2000 feet above the Sutlej. There is a magnificent view of the whole river-basin, with a medley of detritus-encumbered valleys leading down into the main stream. Towards Kailas the skies are obscured by blue-black storm clouds. A very peculiar agglomeration of them. Southward, over the Himalayas, are fierce masses of cumuli. Especially above Kamet, almost due south of us, is the aspect fearsome. The plateau to the west is crowned by a gigantic ' storm-fungus '. Beyond this, still farther to the west, are lofty ice-clad peaks. Perhaps they are part of the Leo Pargial group, where the Sutlej breaks through the northernmost chains of the Himalayas. The whole Transhimalaya region is blue-black. Some glaciers peep, ghostlike, from amid the dark cloud-masses."

Below us, westward, was a deep valley. That must be our objective for the day, for certainly we should find water there. The prospect of water and a rest invigorated my companions. But what a disappointment. Plenty of sand, plenty of gravel, but not a trace of water. A storm began to rage — a dry storm. We had to halt and cover our faces, which needed protection from the flying gravel. Continually it grew darker. The sand, which had been yellow, turned dark-grey. Then came a cloud-burst, the water falling in bucketfuls. A mad country, this.

Quickly we scaled the slope. Some way up, amid the screes, we found a cave. It was an ideal refuge in which, though wet to the skin, we installed ourselves with fair comfort. As a rule, this must be the home of steinbocks or wild sheep, for the floor of the cave is strewn with their visiting cards. That is by no means inconvenient, for we need fuel. Water could now be had below in the valley. We fetched what we wanted from a few dirty puddles, left by the rain-storm. The brew we prepared was very much like café-au-lait in appearance — but not in taste.

Next morning, of course, every trace of water had disappeared from the valley. Anyhow there was not enough yesterday for us to save a store. Somewhere to the west of us must be the Shib-Chu, flowing northward towards the Sutlej. My programme was to reach this tributary and follow it upward to the Kiogar region on the Indian frontier.

146

After crossing a valley devoid of water and almost devoid of vegetation, we regained the plateau. Yes, there to the west was a deep depression which must have been made by the Shib-Chu. Nearer and nearer we came to the top of the gorge. Then, a thousand feet below, we could see the river-bed, but, incomprehensible as it appeared, there was no trace of water. The river must be there. This was a puzzle. Now we gazed southward, to see the shining ribbon — but here, in its lower course, there was not a sign of the stream. We marched along the top of the cliff, remaining all the time about a thousand feet above the bottom of the gorge. Then we solved the mystery. At one point in the valley — where, no doubt, there must be an interesting geological change in the rock-formations — the Shib-Chu became engulfed in a deep cavern, and, so far as could be seen, no longer emerged. However, we all felt considerably better. Below us was a broad river, with a comforting strip of green vegetation on either bank.

Now we heard some shrill whistling calls, as a large herd of agile, light-grey quadrupeds of the gazelle kind flashed past us and over the cliff into the ravine. Kyu called them " goas ". Their Latin apellation is probably *Gazella picticaudata.*

THE DEAD CITY OF THE ROCKS

The valley widened, and we decided on a descent to the river. On the green bank were kiangs, almost as large as horses — a peaceful herd, which paid little or no heed to our coming. An anxious twittering roused me from my contemplation of this tranquil spectacle. Three young rock-partridges fluttered out from among the gorse-bushes, and of course Jungbwa was hot on their trail. Before I could intervene, she had wolfed one of them whole, bones, beak, feathers, and all. It gave a last despairing twitter as it vanished into her maw. " Wait, you young rascal, and I will teach you to respect our comrades of the wild ! " As we were climbing down the cliffs, we passed a number of caves, and then, close to the river, we found a ruinous chort. To the south was a broad, level surface, out of which rose a remarkable ruin, a structure which appeared to have been a fortress-temple dating from the twelfth or thirteenth century (Plate 161).

The view from this idyllic camp beside the river was one never to be forgotten. The walls of the gorge which, as already said, were about a thousand feet high, consisted of nagelfluh, roughly terraced. On these terraces were hundreds upon hundreds of caves, many of them manifestly excavated by human hands (Plate 163). Were any of

147

them now inhabited ? For days we had been wandering through wholly unpeopled regions, to find here a large city of the rocks. Yes, it was a city of the rocks, but a dead city, abandoned, and probably long since forgotten. Our first business after a strenuous march was to stay our stomachs, and then we set out upon explorations. We chose one of the large lower caves for our camp (Plate 169). In the middle was an ancient fireplace. The roof of the cavern was thickly encrusted with soot. At the back it opened out into a still larger cave. On the walls were niches in the rock. In one of these was a small but very artistically carved Buddha of serpentine. (We took this relic home to Europe.) While Kyu was redding up our " villa ", and gathering supplies of wood and water, Paldin and I made a voyage of discovery. Most of the caves closely resembled the one we had chosen as camp. First we examined the lowermost tiers, and then clambered up to the higher regions, which was by no means an easy job. In some places there may have been steps cut in the rock but now broken down ; and there also may have been ladders in the old days, though these have vanished without leaving a trace. The caves were connected by passages tunnelled in the walls. Then we came to some which were not begrimed with soot, and where the walls had been smoothed, more or less, with plaster. In the middle of one was a ruined altar. A great pile of manuscript lay on the floor, leaves from typical Tibetan books. There were painted tapestries, showing remarkable figures of the gods, the colours having been admirably preserved (Plates 164 and 165). The floor was strewn with clay figurines. This must unquestionably have been a temple. Thence a low-ceiled passage led to another cave, the entrance to which was partially bricked up. We contemplated it with astonishment. Here, likewise, the walls had been plastered, and the plaster was covered with magnificent frescoes (Plates 166 and 167). We explored yet other caves, which seemed to have been the dormitory cells of lamas. There could be no doubt that we were in the monastery of this cave-city. High up in the wall was an isolated cavern which had been painted a fiery red. We could not climb to the entrance. A huge mass of rock which once made it accessible had crumbled away, so we could only speculate vainly as to its interesting interior. Now we came upon three bearded-vultures' nests, unluckily abandoned. Still, we saw some of these fine birds of prey sweep past the cliffs once or twice.

After spending several hours upon these researches, we returned to our own chosen cave. On the way we were able to catch a rock-pigeon with our bare hands. It was fluttering aimlessly about, unable to escape, and, since our diet had been rather monotonous for some days, we were

naturally delighted with the prospect of roast pigeon. Just as we got
" home ", Kyu arrived with a bundle of dried gorse-stems. Proudly
he unwrapped his cummerbund to disclose a second pigeon. In the
fading twilight, Kyu and I devoured our respective prizes, which we
were content to toast over the embers on a wooden spit. Paldin had
no appetite, and was feeling ill. He crept into his sleeping-sack and I
felt his pulse. It was much too frequent, so I gave him some quinine
with a drink of tea. Jungbwa, too, was suspiciously quiet this evening.
She lay whining in a dark corner of the cave. No doubt the rock-
partridge she gulped down whole must be far from easy to digest.

As night fell, the weather looked bad over the Himalayas (Plate 168).
Black storm-clouds were gathering in the south. We heard the roll
of distant thunder, and a few heavy raindrops splashed down. Now
it had grown quite dark, and the weather was threatening. Kyu had
retired to the back of the cave. Paldin was groaning in another corner,
for he had a severe headache. Jungbwa was still wrestling with the
rock-partridge in her inside. I, too, found it hard to sleep, for our
wonderful finds to-day had made my head spin. The little serpentine
Buddha was sitting above me in a niche, very faintly illuminated in
the light of the dying fire. He grinned, as he swelled to superhuman
proportions. In all the caves were sitting little Buddhas, fashioned out
of serpentine, growing rapidly as I contemplated them. They emerged
from their caves and thronged at the entry to ours. The thunder of a
falling rock awakened me, and a great, black bird flew silently out of
our cave. The little Buddha of green serpentine, no larger than before,
was still sitting in his niche.

At peep of day Kyu appeared from the back of the cave, his arms
filled with masses of old, dark yak-hair. Paldin was all right again,
so I made him come out with me at once to explore a little way down
the ravine. Yesterday I had guessed that the geological formations
would be interesting, and, in fact, we found the remains of some
remarkable exotic blocks. Having crossed the Shib-Chu, we scrambled
among the steep rocks on the other side. Suddenly a miracle was
disclosed. There were grainfields, gently sloping, encircled by the
rocks of the gorge. Round these fields were planted staves, with
prayer-pennants. There was a little stone hut in the middle of the
fields, but no human being within sight. In excitement, we approached
the hut, to find the door fastened by a branch, but it was easy to open.
The interior was in perfect order, containing a number of agricultural
tools, a saucepan or two, and a big coverlet of dark sheepskin. This
must belong to a very exceptional Tibetan, who dwelt alone here, in

149

an otherwise uninhabited region, growing grain more than 14,000 feet above sea-level. Surely there was no cereal-farmer at such an altitude anywhere else in the world ? We looked hither and thither, but could not see a trace of him. From his stores, which were not hard to find, we were able to supplement our own scanty provisions. Helping ourselves in the absence of the owner, we filled our pockets with tsamba, ordinary flour, and a little salt ; while, stored in a " bladder " made from a beast's stomach, we found some remarkably clean and fresh butter. Had the man been there, I could have flung my arms round his neck. Failing this, we left a few silver coins, and Paldin wrote him a letter of thanks in Tibetan.

While we were away, Kyu had been baking chupatties with the remnants of our flour, and he was not a little astonished when we turned up with fresh supplies. Once more we clambered into the Dead City of the Rocks, to see if any of its curiosities had been overlooked. From the top I could perceive that on the southern terraces were traces of rectangular walls. Here, too, when the place was still inhabited, there had been cornfields. No doubt the city had been abandoned when the region became gradually depopulated owing to a reduction in the water supply, and when, because of the depopulation, there came a decline in opportunities for brigandage. Before starting, we had a fine feast on chupatties and fresh butter.

" CHALOO ! "

Jungbwa has made great progress. She can now swim across the Shib-Chu on her own, without prompting. Her huge paws thresh the water like the paddles of a steamer. She lands a good way downstream between two huge boulders, but would, if permitted, come quite close to us before shaking her drenched coat.

We marched southward past the ruins. The temple-fortress (which may have been a watch-tower) is a mere vestige, but there is enough left to show the typical Tibetan architecture. We left behind us this Dead City of the Rocks lying at peace beneath a huge mass of cumulus cloud (Plate 161).

Towards evening, for the first time during our journey to the Sutlej and back, we came across some domesticated yaks grazing. Some of them were fine beasts, light brown, or even white. These latter, with their luxuriant hair reaching to the ground, looked like fabulous monsters. Then we passed a black tent, inhabited by Tibetan nomads. Taking Jungbwa with me, I made a considerable circuit, while Paldin and Kyu

145. End of the Nipchungkang Glacier to the north-east of Ralam Pass.
July 21, 1936. (H)

146. Convolutions of the ice in the Shankalpa Glacier. July 24, 1936. (H)

147. Hard work for the porters climbing Ralam Pass, 18 040 feet.
July 23, 1936.   (H)

148. Only one blanket has been lost in the avalanche. In front is the
trance dancer of Sepu. July 11, 1936.   (H)

149. Higgledy-piggledy, when about to break camp after passing the night on the Shankalpa Glacier. July 24, 1936. (H)

150. The huge Milam Glacier covered with detritus. August 25, 1936.   (H)

151. Our sleeping-sacks on a flowery pasture. Kuti Valley. July 11, 1936. (H)

152. Comfortably housed at Milam, in our third quarters. Eiderdown sleeping-sacks with silk ticking. Snapshot. August 1, 1936.

154. Crossing the Girthy Gorge, but not by the caravan route. August 5, 1936. (G)

153. Through the desolate Gori Ravine beyond Milam. August 3, 1936. (H)

155. Camp life at Chidamu, 14 760 feet, during the rains. August 6, 1936.

156. Idyllic camp at lower end of the Kiogar Ravine. August 7, 1936.   (H)

157. Our merry companions: Paldin, Kali, and Kirken.　(H)

158. The "Mythens" of the Himalayas, Kiogar No. 1 and Kiogar No. 2, from the south. August 15, 1936. (H)

159. Sheep, the Tibetan's wealth. View across the Tibetan Plateau north-east of the Balcha Dhura. (G)

160. After many days' travel in the wilds—a Tibetan shepherd lad. (G)

161. Lonely Tibetan ruins from the early middle ages. August 13, 1936. (G)

162. The Sutlej at last. August 12, 1936. (G)

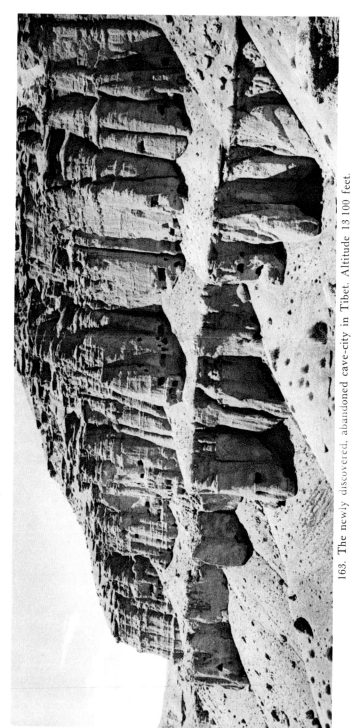

163. The newly discovered, abandoned cave-city in Tibet. Altitude 13 100 feet. August 13. 1936.   (G)

Tapestry in the temple cave

165. Buddha Gotama making the gesture of the teacher (Chakra).
(G)

164. A lamaist tutelary diety (Dharmapala), with his Shakti.
(G)

166. Frescoes with religious figures (Bodhi Sattvas, those fitted for enlightenment) in the abandoned cave-city. (G)

167. Coloured tapestry showing men on horseback, etc., in the temple cave. (G)

169. "Resettlement" of the abandoned cave-city.
August 13, 1936.   (G)

170. We return together through rain and mist over the
Kungri-Bingri Frontier Pass. August 18. 1936.   (G)

168. View of the Himalayas from our Tibetan
cave-dwelling. August 13, 1936.   (G)

172. We camp for the night beneath a rocky roof, "Baugodiar" on the river Gori. August 26, 1936. (H)

171. Indian and Tibetan: Kali with Jungbwa. (H)

173. Among desolate crevasses north of Traill Pass. August 27, 1936. (G)

174. West flank of Nanda Kot, 22 470 feet. August 27, 1936. (G)

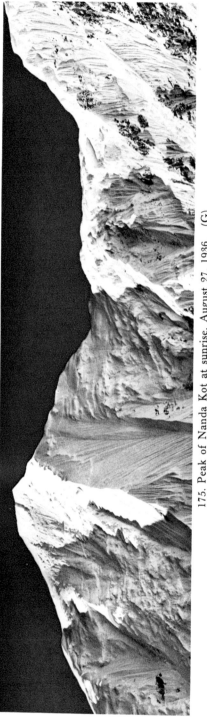

175. Peak of Nanda Kot at sunrise. August 27, 1936.   (G)

177. The two peaks of Nanda Devi.   (G)

176. Unnamed peak east of Traill Pass. August 27, 1936.   (G)

went to see if they could obtain anything eatable. They did not get much, for the Tibetans themselves were short of food, and these specimens were rather unfriendly — which is exceptional.

We continued our way southward up the river, the Kiogars, which mark the Indian frontier, growing continually plainer. Kyu has returned to his former occupation, for, on the march, he unceasingly spins the yak-hair which he procured in one of our rock-dwellings. His diligence was the outcome of a remark of mine : " If you can make a good rope out of the yak-hair, I will buy it from you for two rupees ". This seemed a most attractive prospect, so he promptly got to work. With wonderful skill he twisted it, carding the while with a splinter of wood. He made me a rope nearly fifty feet long, which I still treasure.

Another night spent under a cloudless sky, with the stars shining brightly. We can already feel the icy wind from the Himalayas, a föhn which chases the clouds over the frontier sierras towards Tibet. For supper, tea, chupatties, and butter; for breakfast next day, tea, chupatties, and butter. He is a man of gold, this unknown benefactor who grows cereals in so remote a spot and at such an altitude.

By now Balcha Dhura lay to the west of us. Our return into India must be made between the two highest Kiogar peaks. Towards evening we reached another big camp of nomads, with far too many dogs, which we found it difficult to fend off with our ice-axes. Close by the black tents stood a smaller white one. From it came a litany, accompanied by drum-taps — but the sound of the poojah was speedily overpowered by the barking of dogs enraged by the sight of strangers. Two unpleasant-looking mendicant lamas with bloated faces stared at us inquisitively, until we disappeared over a curve in the ground ; but still for a little while we could hear the unceasing prayer, the rattle of the drum, and the fierce barking of the dogs.

That evening we reached one of the rocky spurs of the Kiogars, and again admired the splendid-looking kiangs with their young, which, together with numerous reddish-brown marmots, enlivened the scene at an altitude of well over 16,000 feet. We followed up one of the sources of the Shib-Chu till the aneroid registered 16,750 feet, when we camped under cover of a big overhanging rock. Close by, absolutely alone, was a Tibetan youngster, many leagues from the tents of his tribe, on his way with a big flock of sheep to the high-mountain pastures. I shall never forget this sturdy little fellow, as he stood on one of the white limestone rocks, the stormy wind playing with his tousled black hair while he watched his huge flock of sheep (Plates 159 and 160).

On the horizon were gigantic piles of cloud, the edges golden in the setting sun, while, below, the violet-blue night clouds had lowered upon the snow-capped mountains.

The night in the open, with no tent to protect us from radiation, was icy cold, so that even in my thick sleeping-sack I could not get a wink of sleep. " Chaloo, you fellows ! " Kyu and Paldin would much have preferred to lie where they were until the warm sunshine awakened them. But the sun did not shine for us until much later, when we had reached 18,000 feet, and were still climbing Kiogar Pass. Kyu, with his gunny-sack, went on alone over the pass. Paldin and I wanted to try another, somewhat higher gap. " Jungbwa, you little devil, now you must show how you can climb ! " She could climb splendidly, following me at 18,350 feet as agilely as if she had been a chamois. Then we had to ascend the rocky ridge on the top of Kiogar No. 4. We pressed on, for the topmost peaks were already being shrouded in mist. Gurla Mandhata looked magnificent from here. When we were at over 19,000 feet, little Jungbwa stopped short, swallowed some snow, and lay down on the stones to go to sleep. This must surely have been a " world-record " for a four-months-old bitch to climb to 19,000 feet. She took small interest in our shadows which, encircled by several rainbows, were cast upon the fog. We were standing on the highest pinnacle of the Kiogars.

There was still time for a glance southward, but we could not espy Heim's white tent. Then in the valley beneath we made out our dzo, part of an expedition to Chirchun Pass. In a few hours we shall be there. Now the prospect was blotted out by mist, for it only remained clear towards Tibet. Once more I looked northward over this wonderful plateau. " Now then," I said to myself, " you must not dally. Time presses." Like the old Tibetan, I shouted : " Chaloo, sho, sho, chaloo ! " Then, in thick mist, I strode rapidly downward over a steep slope of detritus.

CHAPTER FOURTEEN

ORDERED BACK TO ALMORA (HEIM)

GANSSER'S RETURN

I SHOULD gladly have worked longer in the Kiogar district, but time was slipping rapidly away and our mutton was nearly finished. I was getting very anxious about my comrade, who was expected back at latest on the morrow.

In any case we had to break camp and move south-eastward. Thus we came into the upper part of Kiogar Valley where the sources of the river were, to find there a few shepherds with four tents, minding a thousand sheep for Hari Ram, the wealthiest man in Milam. They were friendly Bhotias who, amid their pastures, prepared tea and tsamba for us, supplying us also with a little ata (wheaten flour) and a sugarloaf. I could even buy fresh butter better than I have ever before eaten in Central Asia. I no longer mind that it is preserved in a goatskin bag with the hair inside, having by now got quite used to hairs in my butter. If my dear mother were still alive she would be astonished to find that her boy was no longer fastidious.

It would have been delightful to rest here for a good while in the sun, were it not for a second anxiety. The shepherds told me that the patwari of Milam had been seen on one of the glaciers, in search of us. It will be most inconvenient if Gansser does not get back before this official finds us.

Just as we were beginning to climb the slope leading to Chaldu Pass (Kiogar Pass), Kali and Kirken, who were some way behind me, shouted at the top of their voices : " Chota Sahib coming ! " With their eagle eyes they had seen Gansser and his companion on the top of Kiogar No. 4, where I had never expected him. However, I went on quietly with my climb. They must certainly have seen us, and have realised our intentions. Then, through the field-glasses, I saw that they were deviating to the right. In an hour we were together again, and I was delighted to know my companion safe back on British soil. But this time he looked pretty thoroughly fagged out.

We put up our tent on a small level space in the middle of the rolling flysch slopes, at 17,000 feet, beneath a snow-white overhanging cliff of Trias limestone. I had come down from this in the evening, and was writing up my diary in the tent when Gansser told me that

FIG. 14. AT A HEIGHT OF NEARLY 17,000 FEET WE ARE AGAIN ARRESTED. (G)

the patwari was coming. His arrival was dramatic as he rode on horseback over the slopes, his curved dagger stuck in his girdle, a soldier armed with a musket leading his mount, while a drover with our lost mule brought up the rear. I should have much liked to take a photograph, but did not dare, so I reproduce the scene in a sketch made from memory (Fig. 14).

Of course we exchanged courteous greetings, and he went on to express his regret at having to bring us disagreeable news and a letter from the Deputy Commissioner. He was instructed to arrest us and bring us back immediately to Almora. The letter, as was to be expected, confirmed this statement. The patwari of Garbyang had reported having received information of Gansser's visit to Kailas. However, the patwari brought us more agreeable letters, which have reached us from home at this remote spot. Then he went on, most good-naturedly, to tell us of his own experiences on this journey of exploration. When he was coming through the Girthy Gorge, he saw a mule much higher up, recognised the beast, and therefore believed that we must be stationed close to the glacier. He sought us there vainly, but was able to catch the runaway. Then he went on searching for us day after day, and at length gained tidings of our whereabouts. By then he was so tired that he could not continue the chase for a while. Besides, being in want of fodder for his horse and the mule, he would have to make another descent into Kiogar Valley. It was agreed, therefore, that Gansser and I, with our porters, should go back to Almora without waiting for him. This does not matter much, since we have already studied the local geology to good effect.

BACK TO MILAM

The weather was again hazy when we crossed Chaldu Pass, at 17,380 feet. As far as looks are concerned, this saddle is a desolate place, being constructed of flysch sandstone, across which, on the crest to the northward, the basic eruptive rocks have spread, to be crowned in their turn by the limestone peaks of the Kiogar. To the east and south-east there extends a deeply furrowed flysch landscape, which is monotonous and gloomy, but which we found to be of intense geological interest. Here, even from a distance, we could see, as upon the crest, lying like caps upon the cretaceous flysch the red and white exotic lime-stone blocks, often of enormous size, being indubitably the remnants of a once widely extended superposed mass which has been eroded except for the blocks above described — lying a storey deeper than those of the Kiogar peaks.

The dzos slipped agilely on all fours down the steep, soft schistous declivities. Then came a new climb to a second pass, about two miles south of the Chaldu and east of Chirchun (Chitichun), at 17,870 feet. Behind us was a green tarn ; in front, the broad Tibetan valley-bottom of Chirchun, partly filled by the large branched lake shown on map 62 B at 15,900 feet — figured as a lake, but really no more than a big gravel-bed.

155

While we were sketching at the top of the pass, there came up from beneath a train of beasts looking like a huge caterpillar. They were magnificent Tibetan goats with long hair and large, elegantly curved horns. Instead of going down straight into Chirchun Valley to camp, we made a geological excursion eastward to the top of Chirchun No. 1 (at 17,740 feet) where we made good use of our hammers on this deeper-lying group of exotic blocks. Von Krafft correctly ascertained them to be limestones of the Permian, lying here in and on the flysch of the Cretaceous. They are full of fragments of sea-lilies (crinoids), and also contain many of the brachyopod shells characteristic of the more recent Palaeozoic.

Meanwhile our porters had pitched the tent in a little valley at 16,400 feet immediately beneath a corniced Trias limestone cliff. It was spotted with white by droppings from the vultures which, from the cornice, keep watch for corpses. Obviously, then, we were now upon the great caravan route which is as important for Milam as Lipu Lek for Garbyang.

We set our alarum for four in the morning and packed in the dark, having three lofty passes to cross in one day, and not a place anywhere on which we could give our beasts a feed (Plate 170).

By eight we reached the top of the first pass, the Kungri-Bingri (17,040), one of the highest of the frontier passes leading back into India. It must command magnificent views in clear weather. Apart from views, the pass is a romantic spot. From the cairn with its staves decked with prayer-pennants, at which Kirken prayed devoutly, the path led down in zigzags across the terraced brownish limestone slope (belonging to the Trias) to a glacier covered with detritus, where a new ascent began. I have recorded the following incident in my diary : " There, amid the detritus on the ice, lay a big billy-goat, which must have been a fine beast. ' No ', said Kali, who was just behind me ' He is alive.' Kali lifted up the animal. It was suffering from foot-rot. After trying to follow us for a little way, it stopped short, bleating pitifully. In a few days the vultures will carry it to heaven." Such instances are of almost daily occurrence on the caravan routes. According to Christian ideas, we should put such poor creatures out of their misery. But the Hindus and the Buddhists have more "respect for life", and leave the beasts to an agonising "death from natural causes".

Two hours later we reached the top of the Jayanti Pass. It is about 160 feet higher than the Kungri-Bingri, but since it consists of slaty marl it is a gloomy place equally devoid of picturesque and geological interest. Then came a dirty and much-trodden path down and up again

156

to the Utta Dhura, which we had previously visited. Here we reached the top about one, amid fog and sleet, having been delayed by meeting an almost interminable caravan containing several thousand pack-sheep.

Another caravan was climbing up from below, forming as far back as Bamlas Glacier what looked from the height like a multiple string of pearls, the " pearls " being sheep and goats. Again and again we are surprised by the varying shape and size of their horns. If we had the frontlets only as relics of a vanished age, they would be classified into countless species.

By four we reached the glacial rivulet at Dung, the first of the Gori Ganda. We had been so thoroughly drenched that we were glad to accept an invitation to tea in a caravan tent. Then we had another hold-up at the next bridge, while thousands of beasts went by, when night was already falling. Seen through the fog the mighty pillars of earth loomed like ghosts. It was the night of the new moon, the stars were hidden, and it was so dark that without my pocket torch I should never have found my way along the rough track. At length towards nine o'clock we saw our destination, when the lights of Milam became visible. It was not until half an hour later that Gadje, with our pack-train, arrived safe and sound though he had had no lantern. I welcomed the drover as a man who had worked a miracle. The people of Milam could hardly believe that we had come from Chirchun in Tibet in one day. Our actual marching time was 15 hours, over three passes, climbing 4600 feet in all and descending 9200 feet.

ON MILAM GLACIER

On the way we had had time to talk over our prospects, and were very anxious about what would happen to our scientific documents. Still, there was a good side to the medal. The required documentary explanation why Gansser had gone to Kailas had already been sent off, the forbidden exploit having been admitted and justified. Besides, we had been wondering whether the British Government had any moral right to forbid a traveller to visit another independent country. We did not then know that the two governments have mutually agreed to prohibit crossings of the frontier.

The patwari would probably be back in another two days. Were we to forgo the exploration of Milam Glacier, which had from the first been on our programme? We could not continue our journey to Almora, for we had deposited our money with the patwari, and without his aid we could not recruit porters.

We decided, then, to make the most of our time and visit Milam Glacier, shown on the map to be the largest glacier in the Central Himalayas, surrounded by peaks ranging from 20,000 to 23,000 feet, and joined at right angles by lateral glaciers. But the first impression was disappointing. What was marked on the map as blue ice was a litter of detritus and dirt; and the first lateral glaciers, of which we wished to know whether they pushed their way above or beneath the main glacier, no longer reached it.

The glacier-end was about two miles to the N.W. of the village at 11,500 feet, and bore witness to a fact conflicting with the theory of valley-formation through glacial erosion which was fashionable thirty years ago. It was plain that here (as elsewhere) the ice has been super-imposed upon the main moraine, which the slothful glacier was not able to sweep out of its path.

A shepherds' track led to the old north-eastern moraine. The peaks were hidden. At eleven we halted beside Shangas Kund (Gadje called it Sangal Kuna), a little lake at 13,000 feet, behind the old moraine where we made a huge fire of juniper driftwood, to boil water for tea and a wash, of which we were much in need. A sandpiper was dis-porting himself on the shore. The elegant hoopoe (*Upupa epops*) with a reddish-brown crest, which is common in the plains, was also found at this level, and even at the higher altitude we reached later on in the day, 13,500 feet. This was the last place at which fodder could be obtained, about half-way up the glacier. It was plain here that the main glacier was stronger than the lateral glacier, the latter having been simply sheared off by the former, whereas in the Kali Valley and the Kuti Valley we found the opposite. We could see nothing more, for the peaks were still shrouded in cloud and the rain began again.

Our planned excursion into the regions above the snow-line had to be abandoned. Next morning our tent was encrusted with snow, and the rain was still so heavy that we made no attempt to get back to Milam. We lay in our sleeping-sacks or squatted round the fire when the rain let up for a little and Kali had succeeded in lighting a fire with the aid of a bellows. We cannot use meta fuel or petrol in the tent, for the moisture quickly condenses on the walls. There is nothing to do but eat. Most touching is the way in which Kali, despite the wet and discomfort, does his best to prepare us something tasty. He has brought along some of the new potatoes, meat, and spinach which the Milam plutocrat gave us. In addition, besides the daily ration of rice, we have some remnants of dried fruit to stew for dessert. We have become regular gourmets during these days of leisure, talking to one another of all the delicacies we shall enjoy when we get home — and we may have to return to Switzerland a good deal sooner than we wish. One of us speaks of aromatic wholemeal rye bread, with fresh butter and alpine honey, and plenty of raw fruit. The other rejoins by talking of chestnuts or strawberries and cream, so that the water does not merely drip on our heads but from our mouths.

Meanwhile we hear the avalanches thundering down the snow-slopes of the neighbouring twenty to twenty-three thousanders. But there is nothing of interest to look at, beyond a few ducks enjoying themselves as best they may on a yellow lake partly covered with dirty ice.

Since the weather did not improve on the third day, we braved the heavy rain and returned to Milam. During our absence the patwari had got back. He had money and our mail ready for us, and was on the look-out for porters, who were not easy to find. We had a day or two, therefore, for correspondence and packing.

DOWN THE VALLEY THROUGH RAIN AND MIST

For our return to Almora, we arranged that Gansser was to take a route of his own. He hoped to cross the ice-encrusted ridge between Nanda Devi and Nanda Kot, known as Traill Pass, and then to follow down the Pindari Glacier, while I pursued the well-beaten track by way of Mansiari.

August 25th was a lovely day. Had I instantly to bid farewell to the world of glaciers? No, for I had set my alarum to rouse me at four o'clock. While our men were still packing for the start, I made another quick climb to the glacier, in order to take another photo from the moraine beside the little lake and enjoy the view of the mountains (Plate 150).

I was back at Milam by half-past ten, but my comrade had already left. In eight or nine days, if all went well, we were to meet among the lower spurs. I still had a few difficulties to get over with the Milam coolies, who were not yet quite satisfied with the terms, so that I did not get away till noon. The schoolteacher and Dhan Singh Negi, the patwari, escorted me as far as the gap in the moraine. A fierce, föhn-like wind was blowing up the valley from the south-east, and the skies were again overcast. Of Nanda Devi, whose summit is, in fine weather, visible from the village of Bilju, there was now to be seen only the lesser peak, partially capped with mist. At Burphu we crossed a new bridge to the right side of the valley. There we met a man who brought me a chit from " Bara Sahib ". It ran as follows : " Have

159

got on splendidly at Martoli. The bearer was with Ruttledge. He wants no payment, only a testimonial. Greetings. G." Everything depends on the weather the day after to-morrow. If it is fine, Gansser will be able to succeed in his bold attempt on Traill Pass.

For hours we descended over old moraines, occasionally crossing lateral glacier rivulets, bordered by flowers, among which everlastings were the commonest, being of various species, many of them with long stalks. Also, at 10,500 feet, we found branched and many-headed valley edelweiss (*Leontopodium stracheyi*), as well as violet-coloured asters.

In the evening, according to programme, we reached Rilkot, a wretched little village consisting of only three or four huts, inhabited by cretins, all affected with goitre, where with some difficulty I secured accommodation in a damp and musty cellar.

Next day, in a Scotch mist, we went on down the Gori Valley, which had now narrowed to become a rocky gorge. It must be a lovely walk in fine weather. At a place called Nahan (uninhabited) the river has cut a canyon with vertical walls through a barrier of gneiss. A quarter of a mile below this were raging rapids, and then, in a couple of leagues, on the right side of the valley, we reached the end of our second day's journey, a place called Baugodiar, which means " the overhanging rock ". We were not the first arrivals, for in the soot-begrimed niches of the rocks there were already squatting some Indians who had sought shelter there from the rain (Plate 172).

Next morning the skies had cleared. I hope Gansser also has good weather on Nandi.

Above 8500 feet, in remote lateral valleys on the shady side, there are little clumps of fir-trees, but the slopes with a sunny exposure are treeless. Still, shrubs and bamboos of a sub-tropical character are beginning to appear. The screes leading down to the river are covered with a rank growth of stinging nettles (*Urtica parviflora*), whose stalks are more than an inch thick and nearly ten feet in height. There is also another stinging plant, less venomous than the nettle, with lobate leaves like those of the castor-oil plant (*Gerardinea*). Among the harmless flora are a yellow-flowering shrub (*Impatiens*), a forget-me-not which grows to a height of three feet, a white knotweed taller than myself, and a wild hemp. The rocks are thickly covered with yellow-flowering plants of various kinds, with ferns, and with mosses, and sometimes hung with a tangle of lianas. It is most amusing to watch the monkeys disporting themselves on these.

At noon we reached a place where a tributary to the Gori leapt down over the moss-grown rocks in a series of waterfalls. Farther on was a sandbank, which invited to a bathe. We had now got down to 6000 feet, and the heat was becoming tropical. Then there was another raging waterfall on the main stream, and I had to beat my way through the nettles to secure a movie of the cascade. There were plenty of butterflies ; not only the common little vanessa (*Vanessa urticae*), but also the large red admiral (*Vanessa atalanta*), white admirals (*Limenitis sibilla*), blue-black glistening swallow-tails (*Papilio*), " bears ", and (new to me) yellowish " coppers " (*Lycaena*). We were less enthusiastic about the way in which the mosquitoes and blood-sucking flies greeted our return to the lower levels.

At noon we reached Lilam, where the coolies, who had lagged far behind, wanted to spend the night. But as there was no accommodation except in a few ruinous straw-huts, I determined to push on with Kali, not bothering about a tent. It was said to be only four miles to Mansiari. However, in the Himalayas — as in many mountain regions — there seemed to be two different kinds of miles, long ones and short ones. This time they were exceptionally long.

As the valley widened, the path began to climb to the right. Fatigued by the sultry heat, and with frequent rests, we made but slow progress. From time to time we passed a hut surrounded by stubble-fields of rice. Night fell. We had been told about a bungalow close to a big cypress. At length, in the light of the half-moon, the black tree loomed in sight. We reached it at eight o'clock. Hold on a moment, though. There is no room for us, for the place is occupied by six Japanese with sixty-five coolies. This was a big expedition led by Yaichi Hotta from Tokyo, which was to climb Nanda Kot. Two native Sherpa guides belonged to the party, men who had taken part in the Mount Everest and other expeditions, one of them being Nursang, as sirdar (overseer). The other had been with the French expedition to Karakorum this year, and told us that the climb had been frustrated by bad weather and avalanches. The friendly Japanese placed at my disposal a tent they had pitched on the grass-plot, and brought me a cup of milk. Before they departed next morning up the Gori Valley towards Martoli, they insisted on taking various snapshots of the " hairy barbarian " who had inaugurated their new tent.

In the afternoon my coolies turned up. Hot and sweating, we climbed a couple of leagues from 5900 feet to 7050, where, the cynosure of inquisitive eyes, we were accommodated in the schoolhouse. Now at length I realised that the Mansiari about which I had heard so much was not a circumscribed village but an extended area of stubble rice-plots on the slopes of the valley, consisting of a number of scattered little settlements. At the schoolhouse we feasted on potatoes, sudji (semolina), French beans, and (wonderful to relate) cow's milk. For dessert, to be on the safe side, we dosed ourselves with quinine, being now back in the regions where anopheles flourish.

I had hoped to take a photograph of the white sierras of Panch Chulhi, which are now quite close to us on the east. We got a fairy-like glimpse of them in the moonshine, but the view was too transitory.

OVER FOREST-CLAD PASSES

The day on which we left Mansiari could be considered the most entrancing of our return journey to Almora, for we travelled an excellent path leading over two passes at a height of 9000 feet, at first through forests of oaks, rhododendrons, and horse-chestnuts, then through pine-woods where the stems of the trees were fully three feet thick and the needles more than two inches long. The pines were still with us up to a height of 7200 feet. Then came a long, very gentle ascent past waterfalls and across a grassy slope which must, in clear weather, command wonderful views over the richly wooded, still inviolate mountain landscape. But it rained all the time, more and more heavily, until we became so thoroughly drenched that there was no object in seeking shelter beneath overhanging rocks.

We had heard talk of a dak-bungalow at Girgaon. It was nothing more than a wretched stone hut at 6400 feet, with a corrugated iron roof in which there was no hole for a chimney, so we could not light a fire to dry ourselves a little.

Never can I recall another night such as the one we spent in this inhospitable place, with deluges of rain and peal after peal of thunder. Perhaps more rain fell during the night we spent in Assam, but the downpour did not continue without intermission.

We could not start until late next morning. Then we made our way down the Jakala Valley, the path having also been transformed into a watercourse. At 3600 feet, in a small lateral valley, we found that we were back at the level where bananas can grow. Since leaving Girgaon, where the gneiss was superposed, we have been traversing limestone and marble strata, mingled with more or less clay. The inhabitants of the villages we have passed are no longer Bhotias, but dark-skinned Indians with naked children. At the confluence of the Jakala with the Ram Ganga which flows thence to the south-east, we are to cross by a big iron bridge to the village of Tesam, where the houses are grouped upon two terraces made by the river in former days at an

162

altitude of 3280 and 3600 feet respectively. We are back in a tropical clime. When we bathe in the river, we find the water lukewarm (70° to 80°), while the vegetation is rank. In the fields there is a heavy crop of mand or finger-grass (*Eleusine coracana*), a sort of millet whose English name is derived from the fact that the ears resemble bent fingers. Insects are chirping everywhere. As in northern Siam, the pine-trees spread down from the hill-tops into the valley. Bananas can be bought, though only of the big plantain kind, which are hardly worth eating raw. But a fisherman was at work with a net to provide us with a meal, having been commissioned by Kali. Since we left Darchula to enter the high hill country, fish has been unobtainable. Thanks to a letter from the patwari of Milam we secured a friendly reception from the postmaster, who put us up. In fact all would be well with us were it not for the bad weather and the nightly torment of mosquitoes.

BRIDGES SWEPT AWAY

We had already learned from the postmaster that we were likely to have a heavy day. The big bridge across the Ram Ganga had been carried away. The river was fordable two miles above Tesam, where the waters are divided for a time into four arms, but in view of the freshet it was doubtful whether we should be able to get across now. Anyhow the government had engaged a dozen tall " specialists " from the neighbourhood to help in the transport of baggage across the ford until the bridge could be rebuilt. These men were ready for us there, but our coolies were long in coming. Without awaiting them, I swam across the first arm of the stream. Jungbwa (Plate 171) took to the water like a duck, and was soon across. But I was very anxious about our precious baggage — the books, the maps, and the apparatus. In this first part of the crossing, the water had been breast-high, while in the third and the fourth arms the current was deeper and swifter. I left this ticklish matter of transport to the experts. With a burden on one shoulder and a long staff in the other hand, they footed it carefully over the unsteady bottom, accommodating themselves to the current, against which it was impossible to make headway. Happily, after several hours' work, a number of the packages were safely across. Then the coolies, who could not swim, had to be helped over. One of them was submerged, sack and all, but the " specialists " fished him out again. Once more I trusted my powers as a swimmer, but was carried away by the current and dashed upon the rocks, being unable to regain my footing upon the rolling stones until a helpful hand was

163

stretched out to me. I trusted that everything was safely across, but we found later that one of our metal-lined cases was leaky, our collection of dried plants having got so wet that many of the valuable Tibetan specimens were destroyed.

At about noon, after a little rest and the payment of eight rupees to our helpers, we continued the journey. The zigzag climb in the oppressive heat seemed unending. To begin with there was a rise of 3300 feet to the first saddle at an altitude of nearly 6000 feet; then came a further climb along a steep declivity to Sama Dhura, at 6900 feet, about three miles to the north-west. Here we were once more in an oak forest, the trees being heavily encumbered with mosses, ferns, and lianas. Then, at Sama, considerably farther down on the other side of the pass, I was able to rent a room for the night at the usual charge of one rupee. Later, after nightfall, arrived the coolies, drenched to the skin.

Our difficulties were by no means over after leaving Sama, for almost all the bridges over the lateral affluents had been swept away. Otherwise this walk westward down the valley would have been quite easy. Close to the village of Karbogar, where a branch path led over an iron bridge into the Pindari Valley, I noticed a chit fastened to a fallen tree by the wayside. In mirror-writing, penned from right to left, which only those accustomed to it can read, was a message dated August 31st — the day before :

" Everything top-hole. Passing here at eleven in the morning, and going on to Kapkot, where I shall await you. Hard job crossing the Nandas, deep new-fallen snow. Except for sun-scorched lips, everything okay. Greetings, G."

What a relief ! I had not expected so encouraging a report. After a brief rest, we hastened on down the widening valley. Rice grew luxuriantly upon the terraces, yellowing and almost ready for the harvest. On a suspension bridge we crossed to the right bank of the Sarju, and from this, according to the map, it was another mile to Kapkot. But look, there was Gansser, with the Sherpas, coming to meet me. I could hardly recognise them in their white tropical shorts which had just been made for them in Kapkot.

Dewan Singh, who had accompanied my comrade on the journey from Martoli, was our host here, supplying us with potatoes, tomatoes, pumpkins, grapes, almonds, and honey. Kali had cooked some fresh fish for us to eat with our rice. At last we are in a land flowing with milk and honey.

TRAILL PASS AMID MONSOON SNOWS (GANSSER)

Next morning we were to start and I had still been unable to secure the coolies that were needed for the crossing of Traill Pass. All the men said it was too dangerous, and that big pay would not tempt them. Still, by hook or by crook I mean to try. A study of the depression between Nanda Kot and Nanda Devi will provide a most valuable supplement to our general profile of the Central Himalayas. If for that reason alone, I must manage to do it somehow. It may be our last expedition in the high mountains.

Lord knows what awaits us in Almora. Our instructions were to get back there as quickly as possible. Well, according to our calculations my proposed route over the Nandas should not take any longer than the way Heim will take down Gori Ganga, for though steeper and higher, the former is more direct. (The event showed that I reached Kapkot a day sooner than Heim.)

When, after several days of hopeless rain, the sky was cloudless on August 25th, the three of us set forth from Milam across the unsteady bridge, making for Martoli. I had decided to make the venture with no-one to help me but the two Sherpa coolies, Paldin and Kirken, each of us very heavily laden, since we had to take sufficient food with us to last a week. For the time being we marched in our tropical shorts, intending to don our wind-proof trousers when we reached the heights, wearing them over the shorts. This arrangement saved us a good deal of weight, and the shorts would be most comfortable when we had crossed the pass and got down to the lower levels again. The lightness of our attire did not prevent our sweating freely on the steep foot-paths to Martoli. To outward aspect, this village was as unattractive a place as Milam, but the street life was much more interesting. At least two women sat in front of almost every house, weaving or knitting brightly coloured carpets. The men went on spinning wool, even when engaged in the liveliest political arguments.

Although I had given up hope of finding a guide, a man who actually knew Traill Pass, I was lucky enough, at Martoli, to happen upon Dewan Singh who had been over it with Ruttledge, the leader of the last Everest Expedition. I thought he would be a great help. He proved rather a disappointment on the heights, but was a good man in forest and brushwood work. He declined to act as porter, so the other three of us had to go on carrying our heavy loads. There was one good point about his services, that he did not expect any wages, but only a

165

testimonial. He had to journey south, anyhow, so this was no great sacrifice on his part. I did not take it amiss when I found afterwards that the fellow, despite his ragged clothing, was the owner of several houses. He put us up in one of them when we reached Kapkot.

While Dewan Singh was getting his own equipment together and providing himself with food for several days, we started ahead up the savage Lwaln Valley, along a narrow footpath which soon lost itself in dense rhododendron thickets. Beyond the head of the valley two mighty cones beckoned, those of Nanda Devi, 25,584, and 24,272 feet. Gradually the higher western peak was eclipsed by the eastern one. Dewan Singh was not yet in sight. We intended to reach the foot of the glacier that day. It was rather an ambitious plan, but we carried it out at the cost of a good deal of sweating. We camped among alpine roses at 13,450 feet, just short of the glacier. Soon Dewan Singh turned up and sat down with us beside our blazing camp fire. We did not bother to pitch our little tent, but slept in the open.

" August 26th. Yesterday's sunset, of a rich and rare violet tint like a picture postcard, is followed this morning, between clouds, by a fiery red sunrise. Still we do not long enjoy this rich play of colour, for a monotonous grey soon succeeds. We cross the unnamed glacier which flows down from the Nanda Kot side — that is to say, we cross the endless moraine, seeing very little trace of ice. Like a river in flood, full to the brim, the glacier flows down the valley between the two lateral moraines. Thick clouds enfold the gap we wish to cross. To the west we can still see the 10,000 feet rampart of Nanda Devi. Quickly I make a geological sketch, the mist gathering as I do so.

" To the east I can dimly make out an ice-encrusted wall, terminating in a spade-shaped peak. It must be Nanda Kot. In good weather, this would be a splendid position, flanked as we are by the two Nandas. We decide to stay where we are and hope for better weather, but to-morrow we positively must get over the pass. I study the eastern face of Nanda Devi (Plate 178). As far as I can make out, there is very little metamorphic rock, and certainly no gneiss or granite as was formerly supposed. After this I sit in the little tent, which we have pitched for shelter, and write to the accompaniment of the too familiar melody of the raindrops which fall steadily, though not as yet very heavily. But to-morrow, what will the weather be like to-morrow ? Enough to reduce a man to despair, this weather, to make him pluck out his beard by the roots. Ice and snow avalanches thunder down from Nanda Devi. Nanda Kot is better behaved, almost sanctimonious.

" The baked rice given us by the patwari of Milam is delicious,

166

and the sweet mess of tsamba and brown sugar which he recommended me as a fortifier on this toilsome journey is excellent in tea. But this idling about plays havoc with our scanty rations. Now Nanda Kot is raging in his turn. He seems to wake up and growl when it snows on to his head and rains on to his belly.

" Night fell long since. I am lying in the tent and look at Nanda Kot which emerges from the clouds in the light of the half-moon. When I stretch forth my head and look in the opposite direction I see Nanda Devi like a ghost in the moonlight. Stars sparkle above it.

" August 27th. Stars sparkle above it, and the Milky Way shows in glory above the peak, as if it were smoking. The moon has set, and it is now the darkest hour before the dawn. Gradually a glimmer of light comes. The two Nandas shine with a silver light. Then Nanda Devi begins to redden. A glorious day is dawning (Plates 175 and 177). When we reach 15,400 feet, we come upon new-fallen snow. Hard frozen, it crackles beneath our feet as we trudge round the numerous crevasses. The large ones are partially filled with snow. We have to let ourselves down over an ice face, cautiously make our way over the bottom, and then scale the other face (Plate 173). Here, in most cases, there was a snow overhang through which we had to burrow. Having crossed the glacier, we began the ascent of the snow-slopes, high above which was an overhanging ice-crest, our main problem. We have plenty of time to study its flutings as we slowly and laboriously, cutting footholds, climb towards it. A great portion of the overhang breaks away, rushing towards us as an avalanche, but breaking up in the various runnels and racing safely past us. Nevertheless the danger increases, for avalanches of new-fallen snow are rushing down every-where, and both the Nandas are thundering. When we look down, we see that our climb has become almost vertical. A new fragment of the overhang breaks away. This time it sweeps down as one mass, but happily misses us, though we feel the wind of its passing. The overhang still looms threateningly above, and the glacier, with its great marginal gulf, is far, far below. The prospects are by no means rosy. Perhaps it is better not to look up. There may not be another avalanche before we get over. My companions steady their footing by thrusting their ice-axes home as they cautiously move from one to another along the footholds I have cut. I try to get round the overhang by moving a few paces to the left. Straight above me for 10 feet it is absolutely impassable. Very cautiously I use my ice-axe. The snow falls in heaps upon my sun-burned face. However cautiously, I must work furiously, for a minute's delay may lead to a general disaster. Yet there is no way back, now; the only chance of escape is to get over. Heavy masses of snow fall, jarring the rope, and almost wrenching me from my foothold. At length I can reach over the top with my ice-axe, thrust it deep into the snow and pull myself over. A moment

FIG. 15. ON THE DANGEROUS OVERHANG OF TRAILL PASS AT 18,400 FEET, AUGUST 27, 1936. (G)

or two, to take breath. Such strenuous exertion at 18,350 feet is very trying to the wind, but the rope is made fast. The others are pulled up safely, and when all are over the top we can relax a little from our ' do or die ' mood " (Fig. 15).

The other side is pretty steep too, but not for long. Soon we get down to the glacier which forms the source of the Pindari.

" Traill Pass proper is only at 17,700 feet — 650 feet lower than the altitude at which we crossed. It was owing to the recent heavy snowfalls and the amount of snow that lay on the rocks that we had to venture upon the steep ice of the declivity we actually scaled. Roped in pairs we go down the broad glacier. It has become intolerably hot. Often we sink in the snow up to our hips. Evening comes on. For a change, Kirken falls through the snow into a crevasse, but we are soon able to pull him out. By the last glimmer of daylight we reach a precipice where, at the edge of the glacier, we have to camp. There is a ledge barely three feet wide where we settle down. It surmounts a steep descent for the morrow. Our feet are icy cold and our boots freeze. For thirteen hours we have been tramping through deep, wet snow and they are absolutely soaked. Paldin and Kirken take shelter beneath an overhanging rock. Shovelling away some snow from the ledge, we pitch the little tent, and Dewan Singh and I crawl into it. The precipice below extends for about 1600 feet down to another glacier, and we are camped at about 17,700 feet. Dewan Singh disappears into my sleeping-sack. With meta fuel I boil a little snow-water to make tea. Both Paldin and Kirken are suffering from headache. A warm drink will do them good, but they are too tired to prepare it for themselves. This job done, I find that I really have not enough room in the tiny tent. Still, Dewan Singh has done his best, rolling himself into a ball as far in as he can get. I lie with my head in the open, contemplating the moonlit sky. Then I fall asleep, to awaken after a while in thick mist. Dewan Singh crackles as he stirs in his frozen sleeping-sack. Below our ledge a great block of stone thunders down the precipice.

" August 28th. Cautiously, our limbs stiff with cold, we clamber down the precipice. None of the stones is a secure foothold, and everything is covered with recent snow. Kirken, alarmed or tired out, is scarcely able to move. Dewan Singh relieves him of the tent.

" On the lower lateral glacier there are not many crevasses, and they can all be crossed on solid snow-bridges. On a bare patch of rubble, where there is no snow lying, at 15,750 feet, we find cactus-like saussureas, growing to a height of twelve inches, and covered with felted hairs. Soon we get below the recent snowfall, and at 14,750 feet have to make our way through thickets of alpine roses. The crossing of the lower part of the Pindari Glacier (Plate 179) is another difficulty, and takes up a good deal of time, for the going is very rough. Then we reach the lower end of the glacier, and immediately, at 12,000 feet, enter a thick mountain forest consisting of gnarled birches hung with long beard-moss, and in places we find almost impenetrable under-growth of rhododendrons as tall as ourselves. Still, there is a good path, so we make excellent progress in spite of this magnificent wilderness. At 10,800 feet we hear the first cicada chirping, and 600 feet lower down we come to fir-trees, with dense bamboo as undergrowth. We camp when we get down to about 10,000 feet, surrounded by a wilder-ness of mountain jungle, consisting of birches, maples, yews, and pines, with vast quantities of ferns, rhododendrons, and bamboos growing among them (Plate 181). Through the steep gorge the Pindari runs as a roaring torrent. Its milky, glacial water is making for the Ganges, for we have now found our way to the eastern head-waters of this sacred stream (Plate 180). To-day we have come down 8200 feet to reach our camp. The atmosphere is warm. We can no longer sleep in our thick sacks, rolling ourselves in blankets and using the sacks as mattresses. Large bats flutter round our camp.

" August 29th to September 1st. There is mist, with warm drizzle. The way leads down the valley through dense jungle. Mist wreaths creep down the wooded slopes, and at frequent intervals we pass water-falls. Heavy drops assail us from the giant trees. The thick carpet of fallen leaves, moist and marshy, emits a sweetish scent as we stir it up with our feet. It seems hardly credible that at 7500 feet an affectionate leech should get a good grip of my bare leg. A large bluish-green butterfly seems to smile at my astonishment. Though we are still over 6500 feet, green parrots are flying among the trees. In a little horse-chestnut grove a number of large, light-grey monkeys are sitting on a fallen tree trunk. The black-faced creatures stare at us inquisitively as we go by.

" In a small clearing lies Kapi, a little group of thatched cottages. I buy potatoes, fresh milk, and honey. A banquet follows, and our enjoyment is keener than I can describe.

" At Loharkhet, an old man comes up to me, bringing me milk and green walnuts. He asks me to give him a testimonial. We are getting back to civilisation !

" Two days later, on an extremely sultry day, we reach Kapkot. I camp under the porch of Dewan Singh's ' villa '. I want to be alone, and that is why I refuse to go in. Still, I do not manage to be alone on the porch. Next morning, making a careful examination of my sleeping-sack, I catch at least a dozen fleas. Overnight, the lightning flashes among the forest-clad hills. Darkness falls speedily. As I lie on my sack, I watch the summer-lightning of a wet night in the tropics. A few days ago it was almost impossible to take off our frozen boots, but now it is heat, not cold, which makes it hard to sleep. Storm-clouds are racing over the black hills. The great leaves of the banana-trees wave and rustle. Ice-axe and climbing-irons lie unheeded on the ground beside me. Close at hand is rice that awaits the sickle."

WE JOURNEY ON TOGETHER (HEIM)

Garlanded with flowers, we left Kapkot to march on down the valley. As we were passing the store of a well-to-do merchant, who had been told about us, he came out, expressed his profound regret that we had not been his guests, and would not allow us to depart before he had hung these bright garlands round our necks. The natives consider it most friendly of us to " demean " ourselves by lodging with simple private persons. Beside the Sarju a huge fire was blazing. A body was being cremated, and the remains were to be flung into the stream.

Again we had to waste a good deal of time making detours before we could get across lateral streams.

For the first time in four months we met some persons of our own race. We expected them to give us a cordial greeting. But these gentlemen in khaki shorts and topees passed by with their noses in the air pretending they did not see us. We had not been introduced, were unshaven and unkempt, and were therefore beneath the notice of British officials. Or had they perhaps heard about the two European miscreants who had been summoned back to Almora ?

This day we marched only fourteen miles to reach the little Indian town of Bageshwar, at 3200 feet, a place which in January every year attracts thousands of visitors from all parts of India to dance-festivals, but now seems no more than dead-alive with the shutters up in front of its shops and the pilgrim-resorts absolutely quiescent. On the left bank of the river, across the iron suspension bridge, we were housed like princes in the huge dak-bungalow. There were actually chairs, tables, beds, and window-panes. In the town was a cobbler who could make a fair job of patching up our worn boots. Luckily we were the only guests in the bungalow. Outside, on the lawn and in the boughs of the fig-trees, birds were disporting themselves ; impudent crows, starlings, and turtle-doves. For the first time in months we heard the cackle of fowls once more, since the hill-folk in the Himalayas do not keep any.

The porters are tired, and need a day's rest. The foreman has agreed that they will make up for lost time as soon as we start again. Well, to-day could be usefully spent in making geological observations in the neighbourhood, for this is another important zone of superposed gneiss formations.

Instead of sticking to the valley, we climbed to Dewaldhar, whither, last spring, old Rai Bahadur of Almora invited us to his " Fruit and Tea Garden Estate ". Not only was there a handsome bungalow with a red-painted corrugated iron roof — at present uninhabited — but also a well-equipped guest-house with fine books such as Sherring's *Western Tibet*. We were particularly delighted with the cement swimming-pool. It was too late in the season for the fruit to which we had been looking forward for months, and in this weather there was no chance of a view of the snow-peaks.

Next day we marched through rice-fields and fir woods to the dak-bungalow of Takla.

Then, hoping for an improvement in the weather, we climbed the forest ridge to Binsar, to see the panorama at dawn. A few peaks showed up in a romantic half-light, but on the whole visibility was poor. We had another twelve miles to cover over a fir-clad ridge, and reached Almora on the evening of September 6th.

CHAPTER FIFTEEN

BACK IN ALMORA — WHAT NEXT ?

A FEW months before, the friendly Brahman R. D. Bhatt, whose acquaintance we made in Almora, expressed the hope that we would stay with him on our way back. We called on him, and were soon comfortably housed in the upper storey of his place in Mall Road. Each of us has a study of his own giving on to the veranda. The rooms are comfortably furnished, though not perfectly water-tight, for few roofs which have been scorched throughout the Indian hot weather stand the test of the Indian rains. We have kept on Kali as cook.

Of course immediately on arrival we sent a special messenger to the Deputy Commissioner, to whom I had dispatched a letter from Milam acknowledging that one of us had visited Kailas.

Next day we were summoned before the young official, who charged us with having taken undue advantage of the country's hospitality. Of course we knew we had infringed a prohibition. I explained that, in view of the prevailing conditions, I myself had renounced the journey we had planned to make by way of Taklakot to Lake Manasarowar. But when, in Kuti, an unexpected chance presented itself to visit Kailas in the company of some sheep-drovers, I found it impossible to restrain my comrade from seizing the opportunity, and I did not deny my gratification that he had gone. It was very difficult for me to refrain from accompanying him, but I did so in view of possible political complications. Gansser, not wishing to imperil our expedition, had, before starting, left me a written declaration that he undertook the journey exclusively on his own responsibility.

After this conversation with the Deputy Commissioner, I sent a long telegram to the Indian Government. I explained that the only excuse was that Gansser, urged by scientific zeal, had gone entirely on his own responsibility, and at his own risk, without incurring any difficulties with the Tibetan authorities. His discoveries concerning the origin of the exotic blocks and the structure of Mount Kailas had been of the utmost scientific importance.

The palmy days of exploration in Central Asia are over. More and more the frontiers are being closed. After all, who can blame Nepal and Tibet for doing their utmost to exclude " western civilisation " — what is called Christianity?

Our position was not perfectly clear to us after our interview with the Commissioner. He said that it would be desirable for us to leave India soon, but before taking active measures he would await instructions from Delhi. It seemed to us a good sign when, that same day, our baggage, which had been impounded, was returned to us.

Now the days passed quickly. We had plenty of occupation, and nevertheless we felt that we were enjoying a holiday.

Four big cases were packed with mineralogical specimens and fossils, and sent off to Zurich. We had many visits from interesting Indians, from whom we had a great deal to learn. We visited a number of " old acquaintances ", by special invitation, and made some new friends. An American painter asked us to take coffee with him at his house, Snow View, where we once more enjoyed the pleasure of hearing some first-class music (Beethoven's last work) on the gramophone. But what the Indian scientist Boshi Sen had to show us at Kunden House surpassed all possible expectations. Who would have dreamed of finding at Almora a laboratory of plant physiology fully equipped with the most modern and expensive microscopes, electrometers, etc. ? Mr. Boshi Sen gave us a wonderful demonstration of the way in which he measured the electrical currents in isolated living cells. Using finely pointed needles as electrodes and a micrometer table which could be moved in three planes under the microscope, he was able, touching the cells with the point of the needle to determine their potential.

By friends of the world-famous Mahatma Gandhi we were told about the Congress movement and the exalted principle of " non-violence ". Has there ever, in the whole history of civilised man, been a more remarkable movement than this by which a people comprising three hundred millions is fighting for its independence without striking a blow or firing a shot ? How different is it in " Christian " Europe, where club-law is once more being extolled, and widely prevails. Tidings of the civil war in Spain had found their way to the Tibetan frontier. The cruelties described in the papers which have reached us at Almora exceed even the horrors of the World War. Will Europe, a prey to materialism, follow the Spanish example, or learn from the wisdom of the Indies ? One morning when the world of the glaciers lay spread before me in sublime grandeur and purity, far from short-sighted man, I wrote in my diary :

"That roseate splendour on the snow ?
A new day dawned while fled the glow !
As fled those hues, we fade and die.
Though corpses we, the sun strides by."

We have been a full week in Almora. The weather has been so bad that the time would have been wasted, even had we not been held up here. The general view is that this summer has been the worst within the memory of man, and it has unquestionably been the worst since meteorological observation became a regular thing. While the average annual rainfall in Almora is about 40 inches, during the last four months the rainfall has exceeded 48 inches. We are detained here in the middle of September, which is reckoned the finest month in this part of the world. It has rained heavily every day. All the more amazing is it to read the scare headlines of a newspaper inform-ing us that the Anglo-American Expedition has scaled Nanda Devi, 25,584 feet, the highest peak in the Central Himalayas. This was on August 29th when, not far away, we were suffering from torrential rain. Certainly it was a wonderful achievement.

After we had been nine days in Almora, since we were still without an answer from the Government, we began to form new plans and make preparations to carry them out.

CHAPTER SIXTEEN

AUTUMNAL EXPEDITION TO THE SOURCES OF THE GANGES

ON September 15th, as we sat on the veranda of our quarters in Almora, looking almost due north, the Badrinath group disclosed itself in the distance. There was a freshness in the air which, our host told us, was a presage of winter. We were preparing for a new expedition to the sources of the Ganges. It will take us two months. With Mr. Bhatt's kind help, we have hired an automobile which, for thirty-two rupees will convey us, our baggage, and the porters as far as the road extends — to Bajnath.

THE DRIVE NORTH

September 16th was the first day of one of the five Indian seasons. For us, likewise, it was a feast-day, since we were about to start afresh for the high mountains. The snow-peaks shone.

Unfortunately Paldin and Kirken have left us, wishing to return to their families, but Kali is still with us, also our young friend Jungbwa, and seven new porters. Two of them are having their first experience of a motor-ride, and, on the curves, hide their faces in terror.

By nine o'clock the valley was free from mist. The clearness, the limpidity of the atmosphere could not have been better. We drove up the west bank of the River Kosi, through an aromatic pine-forest peopled with woodpeckers and green parrots, past slopes terraced for cultivation (Plates 182 and 183). Instead of driving right on to the end of the road that first day, we halted at the dak-bungalow of Kausani, which stands at 6060 feet on a wooded crest among firs and cedars. Gandhi has described it as the most lovely spot in the world (Plate 184). Not only are the view of the distant mountains and that of the fertile valley close at hand incomparable, but the bungalow is one of the best furnished in the whole country.

We had ample time for a walk along the ridge up to a clearing where

176

between the trees we got a glimpse of some of the peaks in the evening light. With youthful enthusiasm, Gansser chose a site where he hoped some day to buy land and settle down with his family. As in our Swiss mountains on August 1st, when night fell bonfires blazed among the surrounding hills, red against a dark-blue background. We counted eighty of them.

Next morning, when there had been a heavy dewfall and mist-wreaths were streaming down the valley, there was nothing to complain of as regards beauty, but the light was poor from a photographer's standpoint. The most impressive object in the northern panorama was the western peak of Trisul, for the head of Nanda Devi was somewhat eclipsed by the eastern peak of Trisul. North-eastward we could make out the sierras of Panch Chulhi beneath a greenish sky — until the clouds gathered and hid the peaks.

CROSSING THE FRONTIER TO GARHWAL

We drove for a long league to Garur, where the road came to an end. For weeks, now, we shall travel on foot. In front of us, on either side of the River Gomati, there were spread over an area of several square miles the rice-fields of this broad valley, which is said to have the most fertile soil in the foothills. Half an hour later we reached Bajnath, beyond the iron bridge, and sent the porters ahead while we visited the ancient Hindu temple. The towers are four-square, with crenellated battlements, and crowned with lingams — some of which have been removed. Ghastly images stand in the atrium, which we were allowed to enter after we had taken off our boots and stockings ; among them an elephant-god with a human body beside a lingam to which prayers were being said (Plate 185). Of course the janitor of the temple expected a tip.

Gradually leaving the oppressive heat of the lowlands, having waded through a small stream, we reached cooler altitudes with pine woods growing amid rough granite rocks, and walked along green alleys, till we reached the water-parting over which, at a height of 6230 feet, crossing the frontier of Garhwal, we entered the Pindari Valley, finding quarters a little to the left of the path in the great dak-bungalow of Gwaldam. Across the lovely terraces framed by cedar-trees we saw, glowing orange-red amid the clouds, Nandakna and Trisul — but they speedily vanished.

A great many men were at work in the bungalow upon a sort of " spring-cleaning ", for the Deputy Commissioner is to arrive soon from

177

Almora. We therefore preferred to camp in the porch on the flag-stones.

Through the darkness came the calls of various night-birds, monotonous and phlegmatic. Each had its own musical phrase, which was clearly distinguishable. Here is one of them :

From the bungalow there was a steep descent to the River Pindari at 4260 feet. The water had lost the dirty yellow of the summer rains and turned green. In many places the path had been washed away, so that laborious detours were necessary. Lower down the river it is said that a whole village was destroyed by a freshet, with a loss of forty lives. The uninhabited gorge we now traversed is called Nanda Kesali, and we crossed by an iron bridge to the right bank. Then we reached a village named Dewali, situated on a terrace more than 300 feet above the stream. Here we bought rice and sugar to supplement our stores, since we are to cross a thinly populated and almost foodless region.

JUNGBWA'S DEATH

Since leaving Kausani, we have been anxious about our young Tibetan friend. She had twitchings and foamed at the mouth. We thought, at first, that this was only the result of her having eaten a huge grasshopper. But at Gwaldam came a terrible night when she had violent fits. Then, for a while, she followed us quietly on a lead, but here in Dewali the paroxysms became more frequent, and in one of them the poor beast fell over the bank and hurt herself, so that she could no longer walk. We wrapped her up in a sack and she was carried by one of the porters, while Gansser took the man's load of rice.

From Dewali, our path led along wooded slopes through little villages. The sun was still very hot, and the butterflies fluttered gaily as if it were spring instead of autumn. Especially common have been wonderfully beautiful swallowtails (*Papilio*), one of them having green front wings and blue back wings, another being of a beautiful blue, and a third blue-black.

After going over a pass, and descending a little, we mounted through a forest to a second pass at a height of 7700 feet. Instead of putting up there in one of the poverty-stricken huts of Lohadjang, although it was beginning to rain, we continued our way through the oak forest

178

in search of a good camp among the pine-needles in a fir wood. Not until night had fallen did the coolies arrive, although a new man whom we had engaged in Dewali to carry the food bought there was still missing. We offered our hungry men some of our own rice and packet-soups, but they would accept nothing save tea.

By now Jungbwa was so wretchedly ill, having no appetite, but twitching and whining without pause, that we decided to put her out of her misery by braining her with a hammer — having no firearms. Our eyes were streaming with tears as, with the ice-axes, we dug a grave at the foot of a big pine-tree, and covered it with heavy stone-plates. Such was the end of a beautiful dream.

Every dog-fancier knows that about one-third of all dogs perish of distemper ; and young animals imported from Tibet into warmer climates are said to be especially susceptible. Obviously Jungbwa must have taken the infection in Almora.

FESTIVAL FOLLOWS FESTIVAL

The morning after this camp in the open, the porter from Dewali turned up, having fallen behind because he was overladen. However, to-day we have reduced our store of provisions by about 14 lbs., everyone having fed to repletion while, in this sequestered wood, we listened to the braying of trumpets and the clangour of bells. A great number of men in white woollen robes were marching along the path, each carrying a huge umbrella, to whose birch-bark top shining little bells were attached. " They are the chattri-men ", explained Kali. " On this day, once every 12 years, they make pilgrimage to the foot of Trisul, where the gods live." The " trumpets " they were blowing were perforated triton shells, like those used by the South Sea islanders. We also encountered groups of women as we continued our march, many of them pretty ones of a distinctly Aryan type. Most of them wore dark-brown dresses but white or brightly coloured headgear. They had nose-rings, a red collar, and had red marks painted upon their foreheads.

The chattri procession went by at a run, with a red-green-and-yellow striped banner in front. This was followed by a model of a quadrangular temple with purple silk hangings, and over it an ornamental silver canopy, the whole being carried by four men on a couple of long bamboos. The men with the birch-bark umbrellas brought up the rear. We took a photograph when the runners paused to take breath (Plate 188).

At about noon, in the upper part of this remote valley, we reached a little mill at the entrance to a pleasant village named Wan, 7870 feet. It was surrounded by huge and beautiful cypresses (*Cupressus torulosa*), some of which had stems eight feet thick. The buckwheat fields were still pink with blossom. The huts were of stone, plastered with white-washed clay, some of them being roofed with quarzite slabs of stone and others being thatched. In front of each hut the ground was paved with quarzite flags. The inhabitants were most friendly, the women and children being quite at their ease and not in the least shy. The men were tall, wore shepherds' clothing of an old Hellenic chlamys type, and many had quite a Greek cast of countenance. Some of them were spinning or weaving, without hurry. Others squatted at ease on the flagstones while a big hubble-bubble went the round (Plates 186 and 187). While Kali was making tea for us and baking chupatties, the villagers assembled to greet the procession, and then there began a festival like that we had seen among the Bhotias of Gunji. Here, too, a lamb decked out for slaughter was sacrificed, and a dancer fell into a condition of trance.

We, however, had to push on notwithstanding the rain. The porters were in the mood for a " stay-there " strike, but we managed to persuade them of the error of their ways, and climbed steeply to a pass at 9850 feet, where we reached a forest of rhododendrons and oaks hung with ferns yellowed by the chill of autumn.

Beyond the pass we came to a clearing in which four tents had been pitched. Encamped here, accompanied by many porters, were some Indian topographers from Dehra Dun — commissioned by the Government for a survey which was to improve the obsolete map No. 53 N. These men were most hospitable, inviting us to tea, with Swiss condensed milk, so that it may seem ungracious to criticise them ; but we could not resist the impression that as surveyors they were hardly less obsolete than the map which was to be bettered, although it would be hard to find domains better fitted for modern photogrammetry than are the higher parts of the Himalayas. These topographers had much to say about the badness of the weather, having found that work was seldom possible except for an hour or so immediately after dawn. Precisely because weather-conditions are so difficult, they should have been using up-to-date methods, but, owing to false economy and conservatism these seem not to have been adopted as yet in British India.

Not until after a considerable hunt, and when night had fallen, did we reach the village of Kanaul, whose scattered cottages were on the slopes among magnificent cypresses. The inhabitants lighted torches to guide us, but it was hard to find accommodation, for we had struck another annual festival and the " hotels " were crammed. While we were hunting for rooms, we could see far down the valley the procession approaching by torchlight, and ere long the paved square amid the huts, the stairs, and even the roofs were thronged with holiday-makers.

I had already retired to sleep in an out-of-the-way cottage when my nostrils were assailed by the fumes of incense, and I heard a choric chant of male voices, repeated by the women an octave higher :

After midnight, hearing the beat of drums, I rose to see a picturesque sight, of which, had the light been better, I should gladly have taken a " shot ". Round a bonfire and encircled by torchbearers, some men were dancing convulsively in a circle, entranced or ecstatic, declaiming verses, gesticulating and leaping, one of them with a Tibetan dagger between his teeth, another chewing lighted rags, while grains of rice were being scattered as an oblation. To scare away evil spirits, the spectators crowded on the roofs and staircases were blowing long, straight copper horns, while others frantically waved white cloths.

OVER GRASSY SLOPES AND THROUGH PRIMEVAL FORESTS

Our coolies were dispersed in various cottages, and once more we had to shake them out of their slumbers, so that we did not get away until nine. We told them that we must reach Ramri that night, and that if they did not make it we should have to cut their wages. Unfortunately the weather was still wretched, so that we could not take photos of the beautiful country through which we were passing. One of the most striking features was the repeated alternation of tilled areas and cypress forests. We passed huge walnut trees on which the starlings had gathered. The nuts were very large, but the shells were so hard and the kernels so woody that when we attempted to crack one it was the stone which broke instead of the nut.

Descending by zigzags into Nandakini Gorge, at a height of 5300 feet we entered a forest of tall slender pines such as we had not seen before. They had short, bluish needles, and cones as much as a foot long (*Pinus excelsa*). We had hoped it might be possible to climb the valley to the gap between Trisul and Nandakna, and from this to make the ascent of the latter peak, but the gorge proved impracticable for men carrying loads.

Instead, we engaged upon a steep climb up the sunny slope of the valley, after crossing a rickety wooden bridge — not through a forest this time, but over rocky and grass-covered slopes. At noon we reached a crest where there were a few huts. Some friendly shepherd lads brought us " dud " (milk), which was delicious (Plates 189 and 190). A storm came on, so we took shelter in a goat-stable until the rain ceased. Then we went on downhill, no longer a steep descent but one which seemed never-ending, until at length we reached the village of Ramri. It lay at an altitude of 8200 feet upon the debris of an ancient landslip. The inhabitants pointed out a bungalow on the opposite slope, towards which we ought to have diverged, but we were too tired to retrace our steps and make a fresh climb. After all, what could we wish better than the accommodation provided by the village headman, who, with a crowd of willing helpers, cleaned a place for us in one of the cottages. They actually brought a couple of chairs which they covered with red rugs ; and we were able to buy potatoes, flour, even onions and milk.

The passes we have now to cross grow higher and wilder. This time, after a heavy dewfall, we climbed in zigzags through a dripping oak-forest, to a height of 10,160 feet and then down again through a marvellous virgin forest. Never have I seen such a variety of trees as on this shady side of the Bihari Valley. Amid tall, pointed pines, from which hung festoons of wild vines and clematis, were fine specimens of sycamore (*Acer*), horse-chestnut (*Hippocastanum indica*), walnut (*Juglans regia*), oak, yew (*Taxus baccata*), and ilex, the interspaces being filled with tropically luxuriant bamboo-groves (as in Fig. 181). We are passing through an exceptionally wet and cloudy region of the foothills.

At 6230 feet, by a primitive bridge, we crossed the Birehi, whose source-waters come from the glaciers of Nandakna. This stream has cut its channel through an ancient landslip. Above the forest-line, the slope had an autumnal tint of light brown.

On the steeper, sunny side of the gorge we again climbed a grassy slope to an eminence where we got a splendid view down the valley. Penned in by rocky slopes overgrown with green was a slender lake, sparkling bluish-green in the sunlight (Plate 191). Since this lake is not marked on the map made in the year 1882, and with the field-glasses we could easily make out the places from which a landslide had fallen, we supposed it to be of recent formation, and hoped to visit it on the return journey.

182

178. The eastern face, more than 9 840 feet, of the eastward peak of
Nanda Devi, 24 272 feet. August 27, 1936. (G)

179. The famous Pindari Glacier, from the south. August 28, 1936. (G)

180. Downward through the mountain jungle of the Pindari Valley. (G)

181. At 8200 feet through pine-forests and bamboo-groves. (H)

182. Back in ordinary hill country with terraced wheatfields. September 16, 1936. (H)

183. Without water-buffaloes the ricefields of Asia are
hardly conceivable. (G)

184. Trisul, towering to 23 288 feet above the cedars of Kausani. (G)

185. Sculptures at the entrance to an ancient Hindu Temple. Baijnath. (H)

186. Madonna types? In a hut at Wan, Garhwal. September 20, 1936.   (H)

187. Masculine types, same date and place. The hubble-bubble
goes the round. (G)

189 and 190. Shepherd boys near Ramri, Garhwal. The older lad is of Greek type. (H)

188. Procession of "Chattri" through cypress-forest. Wan. September 20, 1936. (G)

191. Birehi Valley with the Gona landslide lake, seen from the east.
September 22, 1936. (H)

192. In spirals the bearded vulture volplanes out of the Dhauli Valley. View from the
north side of Kuari Pass looking E. N. E. towards Dunagiri, 23 348 feet.
Morning, against the light. (H)

193. View northward from Kuari Pass. Kamet, 25 420 feet;
Mana Peak and Hathi Parbat. September 23, 1936. (G)

194. "Chua" (Amarantus frumentaceus), the motley wheat-like plant
of the Garhwal Hills. October 15, 1936. (G)

195. Joshimath, a hill village on the pilgrims' way.   (H)

196. Joshimath: in Garhwal or Ticino?   (G)

197. Wooden architecture in Joshimath, Garhwal. (H)

198. Old Hindu Temples and a new one in Joshimath. (H)

200. Entrance to Badrinath Temple. Looking north.　(H)

199. Ancient pilgrim with halberd and whisk on the
way to Badrinath.　(H)

202. Temple and bathing-place, Badrinath. (H)

201. Nilkanta (21 650 feet), above Badrinath. (H)

203. Massive granite walls overhanging our camp behind the
moraine of Bhagat Kharak.   (H)

204. An ice-avalanche falls on to the Bhagat Kharak Glacier,
which is laden with detritus. October 1, 1936.   (G)

205. Nilkanta (21 650 feet), from the north. October 1, 1936.   (H)

206. Ice-wall on the north-western side of Kunaling. October 4, 1936. (H)

Facing us to the N.W., at the entrance to a " cirque ", is a village. Pana is its name, says Gansser, who, with Kali, has been to inspect. But it is a poor place, with a few wretched hovels, inhabited by stand-offish cretins, who refuse to sell anything. We have therefore, camped in the open, supperless. — The coolies did not arrive with food and the tent until several hours after dark, or rather when the half-moon was still shining.

THE FAMOUS KUARI PASS

After an uncomfortable night, punctuated by heavy showers — the water finding its way into our sleeping-sacks in spite of our umbrellas — there came a radiantly clear morning. We started at peep of day, fasting, in the hope of reaching the top of the lofty pass before it became encumbered with other wayfarers. This is the highest and last pass on the road to Badrinath, the one from which, a few years ago, our countryman Marcel Kurz took wonderful distant views of the Badrinath Group and of the Kamet.[1]

We gained nothing by this early start. After crossing a preliminary pass at 9840 feet, we descended 1300 feet into a wooded gorge, diverged to the right up a steep lateral valley, and ascended by zigzags through the forest to a ridge of gneiss. We thought, at first, we had reached the pass, but found we had still to climb eastward behind the ridge to a height of more than 12,150 feet. The mountains had long since been veiled in mist. Still we had been able to make out very plainly the limits of the various kinds of forest growth. The trees prefer the northern slopes, on which conifers extend as high as 11,480 feet, while birches and rhododendrons grow up to 11,970 feet. This is far from being as high as the upper limits of the conifers at the same latitude of 30° in the more continental climate of Eastern Tibet, where the pines and junipers are found up to 14,760 feet and here and there even to close upon 16,000 feet, which is higher than the top of Mont Blanc.[2]

Gansser hurried ahead to take photographs, of which the one shown in Plate 193 turned out very well. I awaited him at the upper limit of the forest, where we warmed ourselves beside a huge fire. But what on earth had become of the coolies ? It was hours before they arrived, when night was falling, and we were fearfully hungry, having had nothing to eat all day. The climb had been rather too much for them, so we promised to give them two half-days' rest.

[1] *Le Problème himalayen*, 1934, p. 44 ; also *Die Erschliessung des Himalaya*, in " Die Alpen ", ninth year of issue, 1933, p. 41.

[2] Cf. Arnold Heim, Minya Gongkar, *Forschungsreise ins Hochgebirge von Chinesisch-Tibet*, Berne, 1933, p. 160.

Gansser and I rose again at dawn, and climbed the nearest gneiss eminence, but on this occasion the mists rose out of the valley before sunrise, so that we could only catch a glimpse of Dunagiri, 23,156 feet, as a silhouette to the E.N.E., with the sun rising behind it. The end of September is at hand, and the weather is still very bad. The devil take it.

N.E. of Kuari Pass the Dhauli flows N.W. through a deeply cut valley towards the Alaknanda. Between us and the Dhauli lies a huge mass of landslip, almost continuously covered with conifers. Above are mainly short-needled pines (*Abies*), and lower down chiefly tall firs (*Picea morinda*) with long needles, stems as much as five feet thick, growing to a height of 160 feet; while among them are sycamores, horse-chestnuts, and actually hazelnuts. Lower down still, the land is inhabited, being terraced for buckwheat, millet (*Panicum italicum*), and a peculiar wheat-like plant characteristic of the Garhwal hill-country, which is cultivated up to a height of 8200 feet. It is known locally as Chua, the scientific botanical name being *Amarantus frumentaceus* (Plate 194). When the huge ears are ripe they are brilliantly coloured, the tints ranging from yellow through orange and red to deep violet. In taste the little rounded grains resemble millet. With the addition of sugar and milk, Kali was able to prepare us a dish which tasted like grapenuts.

We spent the night beneath an overhanging fallen rock, and in the morning sent the coolies ahead while we climbed a rocky view point to sketch the landscape. It was wonderful to watch black-faced monkeys playing recklessly in precipitous spots on which a skilled human rock-climber would scarcely venture. They seemed identical with the long-tailed monkeys (*Cercopithecus*) we had previously seen in the plains. Wonderful was it, too, to watch the scavenger vultures and bearded vultures being carried without a wing-beat on the warm currents of air that rose from the valley, to shoot past our coign of vantage on the rocks and then soar in spirals high above our heads (Plate 192). Carrion crows and kestrels enjoyed the same lazy method of attaining the heights. In the neighbouring forests we met other old acquaintances, nut-crackers of more than one species.

After this little excursion, we went down the left side of the Dhauli Valley along an excellent path as far as Joshimath, a big village high above the gorge where the Dhauli joins the Alaknanda, the holiest of the source-streams of the Ganges.

We thought we had got out of reach of political complications, but a well-dressed Indian, after dogging our footsteps for awhile, demanded our papers. He was the patwari, and, as he explained with many

184

apologies, had received instructions not to let us go any farther without passports. In Joshimath we learned that (though we had been told the contrary) in Garhwal, too, there is an " Inner Line " which can only be crossed by those provided with a special permit. We wired to Pauri promising that we would make no attempt to cross the Tibetan frontier, and while awaiting the answer we began to consider other plans should permission be refused. However, that same evening arrived a permit from the Deputy Commissioner of Garhwal, who kindly agreed to our visiting Badrinath, merely demanding that we should leave a rupee at the telegraph office as fee. This was a great relief.

We had time to inspect the village on the Pilgrims' Way, with its stone or wooden houses which in many respects reminded us of those to be seen in Tyrol or Valais (Plates 195 and 196). There were splendid wood-carvings of various kinds, painted reddish-brown ; verandas with fluted pillars surmounted by images of elephants, picturesque doors and window-frames (Plate 197). The proprietor of the largest and finest house, which used to be the winter residence of the high priest of Badrinath, invited us in, entertained us with tea and sweetmeats, and fetched some tomatoes from his garden for us to take with us. There was plenty of food obtainable in Joshimath, but at high prices.

ON THE PILGRIMS' WAY UP THE ALAKNANDA GORGE

The sacred river has cut a deep channel through the hard gneiss and quarzite mountains, and once more the convexity of the walls, growing steeper as they near the water, shows that the current must have grown steadily stronger. Up the gorge leads the ancient and well-kept Pilgrims' Way, along which, every year, some fifty to a hundred thousand pious Hindus climb to the springs and temple of Badrinath, vast numbers of them dying " meritorious " deaths en route. From Joshimath, 6200 feet, which all must pass and where everyone must halt, there is a zigzag descent for 1300 feet to Vishnu Prayag (Fig. 16).

An iron suspension bridge crossing the Dhauli immediately above its mouth gives access to Alaknanda Gorge. After ascending the left side of the roaring torrent for a mile and a half, one crosses to the right side and then back again. As we went up the gorge it began to rain once more, and rained more and more heavily till at noon, wet through, we reached Pandukeshwar. This was a halting-place on the Pilgrims' Way, now abandoned. Hotels, of a sort, remained beside the stone-paved street. Each consisted of a dirty room on the ground floor and an upper storey supported on pillars containing dark and empty rooms with boarded floors. In one of these we at any rate found a water-tight roof.

When the rain ceased towards evening, we visited the temple. Its roof, a blunt, four-sided pyramid with a gilded point, rose prettily above the walls of rock. But the interior was horrible. In one of the dark, damp, and filthy stone-paved rooms was seated upon a red-and-gold chair a huge idol. The place stank of blood, no doubt that of

FIG. 16. ALAKNANDA GORGE, LOOKING DOWN THE VALLEY FROM JOSHIMATH; V, VISHNU PRAYAG; P, PILGRIMS' WAY TO BADRINATH ALONG THE ALAK-NANDA. (H)

beasts sacrificed here. A cultured Hindu once told us that we must regard these idols not as in themselves divine, but merely as objects which instigate to religious meditation — this being precisely what the Roman Catholics claim for the images of the saints.

Next morning new-fallen snow was lying upon the mountains down to a level of 10,500 feet, and deeper than any we have hitherto seen in the Himalayas. If this goes on, our plans for a last high mountain climb will be frustrated. However, the sky cleared. Many caravans

186

with sheep and goats met us as we climbed the valley. They had come from Tibet over the Mana Pass; and also men from the mountains bringing with them their cattle and all their possessions, on their way back to winter quarters. Although spring is the chief season for pilgrimage, there were many pilgrims of both sexes on the Way, all Hindus with painted caste-marks on nose and forehead. Among these we shall never forget an aged man who looked so venerable that at first we did not venture to photograph him. His silvery white hair fluttered in the wind. The top of his pilgrim's staff was fitted with a halberd head crowned by a trident. In the right hand he held a brass bowl, and in the left a big white whisk as a symbol of the fight against the spirits of evil (Plate 199). We were reminded how other tribesmen in very remote parts of the world, the Lobi negroes of West Africa, for instance, always carry a whisk to wave away demons — and flies.

A few miles above Pandukeshwar, at 6560 feet, we reached the end of the moraine of the Ice Age, climbing thenceforward over rocks and glacial detritus. Beside a roaring waterfall in the Alaknanda was a group of houses where Indian sweetmeats were for sale. We could not resist the temptation of sampling some of them, a sort of dark " bulls' eyes " made of butter, flour, and honey. A few miles farther on began a really steep climb to a moraine dam at a little over 10,000 feet. Beyond this the valley widened out, and from the top of the dam, little more than half a mile farther, Badrinath, our goal, was plainly visible.

IN HOLY BADRINATH

Our first impression of this famous pilgrims' resort was disappointing. To the left, close to the bridge across the Alaknanda was a group of half-ruined huts, called Bamani; and to the right, somewhat farther on, New Badrinath, consisting of sheds with corrugated iron roofs, rebuilt in recent days after partial destruction by an avalanche. On the left, a little short of the bazaar and beyond the temple, were legends " Flagged Area for Females " and " Flagged Area for Males ", which we did not understand until we looked within to see rows of little trenches and it occurred to us what would be the use of these " flagged areas " when Badrinath, a place without privies, was crowded with pilgrims.

Though there is a finely situated dak-bungalow on the moraine opposite the village, the place was occupied and otherwise unattractive so we sought and found accommodation in the street next the bazaar. The house-owner put at our disposal a clean room with a hard mud floor and a window commanding a view of the river. All necessary food could be bought, at rather high prices, in the bazaar ; even condensed milk, which in general has been unobtainable in the Himalayas — though it is on sale in other out-of-the-way parts of the world. We, struck up acquaintance with an Indian trader who could speak English and proved very helpful. He invited us to tea in his booth, where we squatted on the floor beside his dog amid cases and crates, and gleaned all sorts of information. While conversing volubly, he continued to drive his trade. With monkey-like agility he would hop over the trays and kerosene tins filled with viands into the street, foul with cow-dung and sputum, not hesitating to tread barefooted in one of his tubs of flour or sugar. As the reader will have gathered more than once in the course of this narrative, the traveller in remote parts of the East must not be squeamish about such little matters. Here one could buy ounce-skins if one wanted, and pick up plenty of fleas for nothing.

Immediately after reaching Badrinath we sent a letter of introduction we had been given to His Holiness the High Priest, and he was now awaiting us in the " episcopal palace " opposite the temple (Plate 200). When we entered the big reception room we found the élite of the clergy already assembled, eager to see the white strangers. Camp-stools covered with coloured mats were brought, and we seated ourselves. Above us hung a gigantic gold-framed picture of the (recently deceased) British King-Emperor with his wife, the pair contrasting grotesquely with two oriental brass figures of grinning lions which stood beneath.

After we had waited a little while, the Rawal, " His Holiness ", entered. We bowed in Asiatic fashion, with joined hands raised above our heads. The Rawal responded in the same way, after decorating each of us with a garland of aromatic flowers, a kind of daisy-chain of small yellow composites. We introduced ourselves as " pilgrims of science " who had come to study and admire the mountains where the gods dwell ; and we were, we explained, pilgrims who ate no meat, drank no liquor, and did not smoke. This statement aroused general approval. We had hardly expected the Rawal to be much interested in our work, and were stumped by linguistic difficulties when he put us geological questions. We were able to make him understand that the huge block of granite beneath his house must have been carried hither long ago by a glacier. But when he inquired whether there were stones which grew as did animals and plants, even with the aid of an interpreter it was by no means easy to make the matter clear to a layman.

We were about to take leave when the Rawal expressed a wish to conduct us in person, attended by his train, down the stone steps to the sacred spring. We could tread these when we had taken off our shoes, but were not allowed to enter the cement basin in which the pilgrims bathed. Still, we were able to examine the outflow of the spring, which issues by several channels, and discovered it to be a ferruginous, calcareous water containing very little sulphur, and having a temperature of 130°. The volume of the flow was about one gallon per second. Great masses of sinter have formed wherever the thermal water trickles down over the rocks. Here was our chance, and we instantly pointed them out to our cicerone as stones which grew. The high priest was quick to grasp the point. Steps behind the spring led down to the foaming torrent, where the most pious among the pilgrims have a cold douche after the hot one (Plate 202). No-one hindering, later on, we too, higher up the Alaknanda, plunged into the milky glacial water. In parting His Holiness expressed a hope that God Almighty would shower blessings on us and our work.

The high priest was not at all the sort of man we had expected. He was a young, vigorous, dark-skinned Indian from Madras, with a big nose of the Hebraic type and flashing eyes — clean-shaven. When he appeared to welcome us he was wearing a ski-er's cap and a long blue cloak of European cut. Had we met him in the southern part of our own continent, we should have taken him for a Sicilian taxi-driver, or something of that sort. We were told that the Rawal was not a celibate priest, but had a wife and child. He does not stay at Badrinath in the winter.

Accompanied by the friendly manager we were able to enter the temple, barefoot of course. With its onion-shaped cupolas and parti-coloured façade, it was a strange mixture of Arabian, Indian, and Chinese styles. The corrugated iron roof gave a European touch (Plates 200 and 202). Owing to subsidence the walls are badly cracked and in a terribly neglected state, although large sums of money are brought to the temple every year by pilgrims. Of course we did the proper thing by leaving a small offering in the plate.

We were not allowed to go beyond the court. The manager lent us some old field-glasses belonging to His Holiness, and through these we could look into the gilded interior, to make out a gilded image, wearing a crown and lighted by torches.

But there was another temple visible from Badrinath, and this did not disappoint us — a natural temple. It was the shining pyramid of Nilkanta, never yet climbed, which towers above Badrinath to a height of 21,650 feet and reflects the first red glow of dawn into the valley (Plate 201).

ON THE BHAGAT-KHARAK GLACIER

Lacking the Sherpas, our first care at Badrinath was to find a man familiar with work in the high mountains, and one able to guide us into the little-known valley of the Bhagat-Kharak Glacier. With the aid of our merchant friend, we have discovered what we wanted, though at a wage of 1½ rupees, which is somewhat higher than that usually paid in this part of the world. On the last day of September, therefore, we set out. It was a glorious morning, and distinctly cold, the temperature being just below 40°. For a couple of miles we marched across flat areas of detritus, where buckwheat was being harvested, and where there were also barley fields and potato patches, to the primitive little village of Mana, the highest in the valley, at an altitude of 10,500 feet. This was where our new man, Bopal Singh, lived. We had to wait a long time while he was preparing his food for a week or more, consisting of tsamba, here called satu — barley grain which had to be roasted and ground while we waited. Large quantities of meat were hung out to dry in the village, but he did not take any of this.

Over an imposing natural bridge we crossed to the western side of the main valley. Huge masses of fallen rock had wedged themselves into the ravine, and the torrent ran raging beneath them to a waterfall just below. On the walls of the gorge, amid the flashes of foam, lived the beautiful alpine wall-creepers, long-billed birds whose flight resembles that of a butterfly.

As in the case of the Kali, the name of the main stream has been wrongly applied to a tributary. We have been climbing up the Alaknanda, and this appellation is borne henceforward by a comparatively small stream, while the Sarsuti, which here joins it from the north, brings down about three times as much water as the little Alaknanda flowing in from the west.

But it was up this lesser stream that we continued to climb over alpine pastures upon the ancient lateral moraine, keeping steadily westward, and always on the northern side of the torrent. The flowers were over. Only here and there could one still see a little thyme, forget-me-not, or gentian, but there remained sufficient feed for a few horses, ordinary cattle, or dzos. We also met women carrying on their backs baskets filled with dung collected for use as fuel.

Otherwise there was little sign of life in the mountains. The pilgrims, for whom it has grown too cold, have returned from the sacred heights, but traces of them have been left here and there in abandoned huts.

The bold cliffs consist of white granite or of a peculiar kind of pegmatite, injected into the gneiss and filled with black, shining prisms and needles of tourmalin (borium silicate). (See Plate 203.)

At 12,300 feet we were at the level of the two big glaciers, whose lower ends still almost touched. One of them is the holy Satopanth, flowing from the S.W., whose icy gate is, according to the Hindus, the true source of the Ganges; and the other, coming from the west is the Bhagat-Kharak, which is nearly 12 miles long. Almost completely

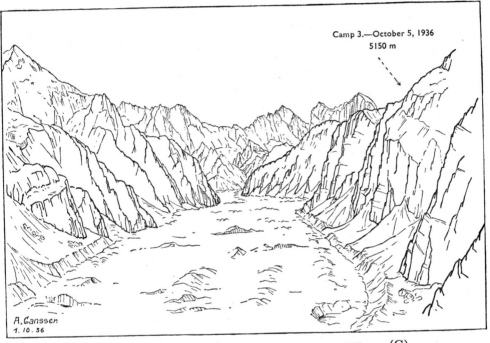

Camp 3.—October 5, 1936
5150 m

A.Ganssen
1.10.36

FIG. 17. BHAGAT-KHARAK GLACIER FROM THE EAST. (G)

covered with detritus, they are not of an impressive appearance, being slothful ice-rivers unable to free themselves of the rubble which falls on them. Another peculiarity of these two glaciers is that between their high-gabled lateral moraines and the rocky walls of the gorge are little valleys where pastures flourish around tarns or where tarns have been — this showing that the glacier has had no lateral expansive energy. By the same token, there is no sign of glacial excoriation on the walls of the valley. One gets the impression that the ice flows in a furrow between moraines, like a sluggish river that builds up its bed higher instead of excavating it.

We pitched our tent on one of the charming little meads, between the moraine ridge and the cliffs on the northern side of the Bhagat-Kharak Glacier, at a height of 12,450 feet, beside a spring that welled up out of the white granitic sand. The coolies, who turned up later, dossed at the foot of the rocky wall, down which from time to time stones hurtled.

A black snow-cloud above the Satopanth boded ill for a while, but then dispersed, and the full moon shone so brightly than Gansser and I, instead of going to sleep, climbed to a vantage-point on the top of the moraine crest, from which we could see Nilkanta displaying the glories of its icy coat. Here, by moonlight, with a time-exposure of 15 minutes, we took a photo of this sublime peak, with the source of the Ganges in the foreground.[1]

October 1st began well, with a cloudless sky. The long-desired clear autumnal weather seemed to have begun. What a relief! Sending on the porters, Gansser and I climbed some way up the cliffs to take a daylight view of Nilkanta, and had to wait until ten o'clock because we were in the wrong light at first (Plate 205). Then we followed our men up the northern lateral moraine. As we did so there came a thunderous crash, for an ice-avalanche was falling from a lateral glacier to the left. The spume rolled like mist right across the main glacier and extended to its northern wall (Plate 204).

On the last good camp beside the glacier, at 14,430 feet, there stood a tent. It belonged to the Government surveyors, who had left one of their men here while they worked higher up. We pitched our own tent beside theirs. Then we had to make up our minds what direction to take next day. Should we go on along the main glacier, without attempting a climb as yet?

Over the crests opposite there showed a dazzling peak with a coat of fluted ice and overhangs which made it resemble a nun wearing a white wimple. On this shady side the new snow, which will neither melt nor evaporate before winter sets in, reaches down to the main valley; but on the sunny side the snow does not yet lie. There we can still see the remains of juniper (*Juniperus recurva*) growing at a height of 15,400 feet. When Gansser had enquired about a climb on which the coolies can follow us, we decided on that for the morrow. To-night our men have found another rocky shelter, and the huge masses of stone look like the wings of a theatre as they reflect the red light of the camp-fire.

---

[1] The result with F/6·3 or F/9 stop was such that the night view is scarcely distinguishable from the daylight one, except that in the former the relative movement of the stars makes them show as tiny streaks.

Cloudlets appeared for a little while to-day on the mountain-tops — streamers which were not quite sure whether they belonged to the monsoon or to the new regime, but really this day, October 1st, was the first on which we had perfectly clear weather since, after climbing Sabu, we began our four months' struggle against the S.W. monsoon.

AMID DAZZLING PEAKS

During the night the temperature fell considerably. There were 5° of frost and the water left in our saucepan was a solid block of ice. The snow-covered peaks flashed in the dawn. We climbed rapidly over the granite rocks to 16,900 feet, where we found a snow-free pitch for the tent (Plate 211). But Gansser and I had no time to lose, so we continued our climb in search of the best viewpoint. We found this on a moraine crest at 17,400 feet, a spot commanding a good outlook in all directions. Very fine was the Badrinath Group seen from the N., extending from Nilkanta in the S.E. to the " Schwarzhorn " in the N.W. Stupendous, facing us, were the " Nun " and, close by, the still higher " Monk ", bearing S. 30° E., marked on the latest map as Kunaling with an altitude of 21,226 feet (Plate 207). From its dazzlingly white armour, ice-avalanches were breaking away, to thunder down on to the lateral glaciers far below (Plate 206). More splendid than all, to the S.S.W., was a rounded, ice-capped giant which, having no satisfactory map to guide us, we christened " Mont Blanc ". This is the highest of the Badrinath Group, and on the most recent map it is given an altitude of 23,420 feet (Plate 208). To the right of it, W.S.W., stood the " Schreckhorns ", and behind them a still loftier tooth, no doubt the second twenty-three-thousander (peaks shown in Panorama II b). In this group, which in their boldness reminded us of Karakoram, we were particularly struck by the ice-flutings to which we have given the name of " Sägerills " (Plate 209).[1] They were not the ordinary branching convolutions, but more like the dog-tooth ornament seen in a Gothic cathedral. It was obvious at the first glance that they were not moulded in the ordinary fashion out of either ice or snow ; for snow could not lie on these almost perpendicular precipices. They could only consist of hoar-frost ice, deposited in situ on the rocks by precipitation from the clouds. I had previously described hoar-frost — though not in this form of " Sägerills " — in the Minya Gongkar Expedition ;[2] and

[1] Cf. *Die Schweiz. Himalaya-Expedition*, 1936, in " Die Alpen ", 1937, No. 3, Table 259.
[2] A. Heim, *The Glaciation and Solifluction of Minya Gongkar*, " Geographical Journal ", London, May 1936, p. 447.

the Baur Expedition found it very hard to deal with on Kinchinjunga, where the lofty crests of rock were completely encrusted with it.[1] As far as is yet known, in these mountains of Central Asia it is only found in altitudes exceeding 20,000 feet.

A fourth mountain chain, containing a number of peaks above 20,000 feet, was visible to the W. and N.W. ; while far to the right, above the catchment area of the Bhagat-Kharak Glacier was an un-named peak with a cap of black schist crowning the light-coloured granite. We called this fellow the " Schwarzhorn " (Panorama II *b*, to the right).

The following night, as we lay on the stones, we found our eider-down sleeping-sacks none too warm, for there were 18° of frost — by no means a low temperature in October at 16,500 feet. We speedily got warm when the sun rose, and we could not have felt better. We parted company once more. My comrade, with Bopal Singh, had designs upon a pass to the N., from which he hoped to get an un-encumbered view of Kamet. I took with me our tallest and strongest porter, Noval Singh, having provided him with a pair of mountain boots, and made for the W. Leaving Kali in charge of the tent, we sent the other men to fetch food from the valley, or to gather juniper-wood.

To get a view of the panorama from a still higher level, I trudged along a snow-slope and then clambered on all fours up a rough granite ridge where, at 18,000 feet, I found a ledge on which I could just manage to install the tripod. So dazzling was now the light, so dark the sky, so clear the atmosphere, that I left the red stop out of action, and used only the ultra-violet filter, getting ample illumination with an exposure of $\frac{1}{30}$ sec. and F/25 stop. As regards the snow-line, the result was interesting. This year it was a little over 17,400 feet, which was distinctly lower than we had found it 20 to 30 miles farther N.E. on the Tibetan frontier. Since we are in practically the same latitude, there must have been unusually heavy snows of late.

In the afternoon, when Noval Singh had diverged across a local glacier, I met Gansser, returning from a bold first ascent. Quite alone, cutting footholds for four hours in snow-covered ice, he made his way up the N.W. range of an unnamed peak of about 20,000 feet (Plate 210) ; and from the top, in a biting wind, took a circular picture with the movie camera. Another twenty-thousander to the W., which we had also thought of trying, seemed to him almost unscalable ; he also decided that the Arwa Valley to the N. which has often been visited, was uninteresting ; and even Kamet (25,320 feet) seen here from the

[1] P. Baur, *Um den Kantsch*, Munich, 1933.

S.W. and scaled in 1931 by the British Expedition under Smythe, did not seem particularly inviting.

We made a comparatively easy day of it on October 4th, confining ourselves to geological excursions close at hand. We went eastward to a little greenish moraine lake, and hammered out specimens from the tourmalin rocks until our packs, though lightened by our dinner, were heavier than when we started. Still, we had no occasion to weight ourselves with botanical specimens, since all the vegetation had been frozen. For the first and last time we watched the glory of the mountains in the evening sunlight beneath a cloudless sky, which had never been clearer. Then, in the E., as the sun went down, the shadow of the earth's shoulder rose blackish-blue across the red-and-green heavens. That evening we were struck by a phenomenon we had never before seen — a greenish tint along the uppermost border of the violet earth-shadow. Was it produced by the moon, which was to rise in that quarter two hours later ?

One might have supposed that ice-falls would take place mainly during the diurnal thaw. In actual fact we heard their thunder chiefly during the first hours of the night, the masses being perhaps detached by a rending expansion as congelation occurred.

ON THE SOURCE-GLACIER OF THE GANGES

Though we should gladly have spent longer on the heights, our most glorious days were over. If only by shortage of food, and because our coolies were unwilling to stay later at this inclement altitude, we had to descend. Nevertheless, we determined to explore the sacred Satopanth Glacier. Then a difficulty arose. After a few hours' march the men went on strike and, though we spent several hours trying to persuade them, they departed, leaving the baggage where it was. We had to follow them and plead with them before they would return to work. The real trouble was neither cold nor fever nor lack of food, but fear lest they should suffer the fate which had befallen some of their fellows at Badrinath, where four of the surveyors' porters had recently fallen sick, and two had died. Were not the sacred mountains haunted ?

At length, with the faithful Kali, Bopal, and old Bulli — without a tent — we crossed the detritus-covered Bhagat-Kharak Glacier to reach the spur of rock where the Satopanth Glacier joins it, and went up the Satopanth as far as a protecting rock where we crept into a fissure. Again the skies were threatening, and it began to snow.

Next morning, when we continued our way along the moraine, we scared large numbers of lemmings. Having climbed about 1000 feet up the grass-grown slopes on the sunny side, to get a more extensive view, we realised that, with our reduced numbers, we could not make much more headway. The pass, rising to a height of about 18,500 feet, leading from the Satopanth Glacier to the S.W. into another valley, which was once crossed by Eric Shipton, was now too thickly covered with fissured ice and rendered too dangerous by the avalanches which were thundering down the mighty southern wall of Badrinath. But the glacier which was spread out before us still offered some remarkable sights. There were three crater-like little lakes on the surface of the ice; also a greenish-blue ice-cave with black borders, in which fantastic reflections were secured; and lower down, behind the tall right moraine crest, was the sacred Lake of Satopanth, beside which we spent the night. At an altitude of 14,400 feet, it is triangular, about 1300 feet across, lying in front of a spur of rock, held up by the moraines of the main glacier and that of a lateral glacier which here comes in from the right. The mountains were beautifully reflected in the green waters. On the shore, about 20 feet below the flood-water mark, human bones and rags of clothing can be seen — relics of the dead who had been committed here to the sacred waters. On a big boulder at the acute end of the triangular lake are the remains of faded red-and-white prayer-flags; and under the shelter of this rock the pilgrims have built a protective wall helping to provide a night-shelter. We were informed that some of them spend weeks up here in summer, drinking the water, and filling bottles with it to take home. We, too, had to drink the water, but we boiled it before doing so. Cold though the lake was, my hardy comrade could not resist the lure of a swim (Plate 212), and discovered while doing so that the water was swarming with tiny, fiery-red plankton crustaceans. Ducks also come hither on a visit.

We lingered longer than we had intended beside the sacred lake. It was noon, and we had no more food with us, so we were compelled to make all possible speed down the valley. For about six miles we clambered over the rough moraine to reach the end of the glacier, where the Ganges rushes out with a roar from beneath the detritus-covered ice (Plate 213). Now we could mend our pace, since we were afraid of being benighted, across alpine pastures down the uppermost right bank of the infant Ganges. For the last time we encountered a few alpine flowers: a scattered edelweiss; a yellowish alpine rose, still scented; while surrounding it were grass-tufts, yellowed or reddened

196

by autumn, and brilliant red leaves (*Bergenia stracheyi*), covering large areas of the rock-strewn surface.

In this gorge, it was dark by six o'clock, and the way was difficult until the lights of Mana loomed in sight. Not until eight o'clock, later than my comrade, did I reach Badrinath, glad to have got there without an accident.

We stayed another day at Badrinath, to record a few observations and take some photos, and were delighted to make the acquaintance of a famous sadhu. His name is Ram Sarikh Singh. He has studied geology in Indian museums and from books, and he gave us a pressing invitation to visit his hut on the other side of the river. He was a merry and humorous old baldhead who had spent a good deal of time in a tent beside the glacier, and had as strong a love and veneration for " the true Badrinath " as he had a dislike for all that is modernised and degenerate about the cult.

BY DEVIOUS PATHS

In November, Badrinath is depopulated. No-one lives up there in winter, and already at the beginning of the second week in October most people had returned to lower regions. We started down the valley, in glorious weather, sad at leaving, not Badrinath, but the surrounding virgin mountains.

This time we covered the 21 miles' march to Joshimath in one day. Our mail awaited us there, letters from various parts of the world, and one from the Deputy Commissioner at Almora to tell us that the Government made no objection to our visit to Badrinath. We were glad to get news of our loved ones and to make plans for the journey home. But before this, we have decided to make acquaintance with the western side of the Nanda Devi massif, which has been frequently visited and described since Longstaff was there in the year 1905, but of which few photographs have been taken, to say nothing of the scarcity of geological observations.

After a night in Joshimath, much disturbed by fleas, and by dogs which made a raid on our provisions, we went up Dhauli Valley. We soon disposed of the six miles with which we were previously acquainted, to reach the landslip ravine. While, that evening, we were making sketches beside a rock, waiting for our coolies, I suddenly perceived a marvellously long-tailed monkey with a black face, and a general aspect which recalled that of a creature seen in a dream. The beast was watching me with interest.

197

We camped amid sheep-dung close to the bridge where the Rishi joins the Dhauli, beside caravans that had crossed the Niti Pass, which leads from Tibet to the head-waters of the Dhauli. Then, with a new local guide named Daram Singh, we went up the Rishi Valley, whose catchment area is in the Nanda Devi cirque. Soon there was no path worth mentioning. We had to force our way through thickets and entanglements of tall grass and luxuriant brushwood, interspersed with hemp, mint, stinging nettles, thistles, barberry, white-flowering giant knotweed, blackthorn, roses, brambles, and bamboos ; then we traversed a mixed forest of sycamores, birches, horse-chestnuts, fig-trees, and firs, amid boulders and precipices of granitic micaceous schist until, when night was approaching, we were literally " stickit ", and had to abandon the attempt to make our way farther up the gorge. We ought, indeed, to have expected as much, since several other assaults on Nanda Devi before ours had terminated in this fashion.

We could find nothing better to do than, with the aid of ropes and sticks, to cross the Rishi Valley, and scramble up the northern slope to the little village of Peng, which lies amid precipices on a tiny terrace at about 8000 feet. It was a pleasant little place, with cleanly paved areas in front of the huts, which were roofed with slabs of gneiss, and overgrown with pumpkin trailers. The good woman, on the flags beneath whose porch we have laid out our sleeping-sacks, and to whom we have given a few boxes of fusees, cannot do enough for us in return for the latter. She baked for us some freshly harvested chua, and brought us one sack after another to make our couch softer, startling us several times out of sleep.

In the morning, since there was nothing else to do, we sent the coolies downstream to await us at Lata, while Gansser and I climbed the giddy precipices to reach the crest above us. Thence, looking N.W., we saw the bold peak of Nanda Devi framed between the walls of the Rishi Gorge, and Gansser was able to fix the support for the camera amid the topmost bows of a cypress which overhung the precipice and take a couple of splendid photos while a bearded vulture soared inquisitively just over our heads. Obviously the magnificent bird had never seen such a crazy sight before (Plates 214 and 215).

Southward, Nandakna is freely visible, but the whole northward massif, including the Niti Pass, Kamet, and Parbat, is again wrapped in cloud. We scrambled down as straight as we could to the little village of Lata (7700 feet), where Kali was awaiting us with tea, rice, and potatoes. This is a place where we could easily make a long stay, for the soil is fertile and there are ample supplies. We note buckwheat,

198

barley, chua, kauni (Italian millet), another kind of millet, a small-grained rice, potatoes, pumpkins, beans, maize, and rape seed. A little tobacco is also planted, but only for local consumption.

The weather being again unsettled, I decided, with much regret, to renounce any further attempt upon the mountains. I have presented our latest guide, Bahram Singh, a charming young fellow, with a pair of heavy but little worn mountain boots, in which he takes immense pride. Gansser, going for a stroll by moonlight, took one of his old boots to the village temple, where he secretly placed it among the rams' horns as an offering to the Goddess Nanda. I wonder what the inhabitants will think when they find it there.

Since the coolies knew that we were going home, and should leave them at their homes on the way, they did not need to be called and urged to start, for they felt as a horse feels on the return journey to the stable. On the bridge, Bahram Singh's father was awaiting us with a load of good things: maize baked in oil and sugared, a huge brass plate full of balls of chua and honey, and a string of sun-dried meat and bacon. They are really most obliging fellows.

At Joshimath we had an agreeable surprise. Eric Shipton was there, with his two faithful Mongolian Sherpas, back from Dunagiri. Of course we knew his name as one of the first Himalayan climbers, for he took part in the various Mount Everest and Nanda Devi Expeditions; but it was news to us that he had been on Everest this year, and had narrowly escaped death there in an avalanche. It will always remain a delightful memory, this personal acquaintanceship with so outstanding and modest a Briton. It was he who, working with Tilman, gave such signal proof of how much can be achieved in the Himalayas with very slender means by persons who are content with local articles of diet and learn to live like the coolies.[1] Besides, we had a lot to learn from him, although we too had been content with a scanty equipment and very slender funds — perhaps no more than a tenth of that available for the big expeditions, but had got through very well indeed.

I was allured by Shipton's friendly invitation to accompany him upon a first attempt on Nandakna (20,660 feet), but we renounced the idea in view of the shortness of the time available and the uncertainty of the weather.[2] Like myself, Gansser was, for once in a way, against the climb. The night before we made up our minds, on September 16th, there was very heavy rain, and snow lay on the hills as low as 10,000 feet.

[1] Cf. Eric Shipton, *Nanda Devi*, London, 1936.
[2] We learned afterwards that Mr. Shipton was forced to abandon his attack upon Nandakna owing to the badness of the weather.

However, we had a very pleasant evening with Eric Shipton before departing, having all been invited to what for us was a princely supper served upon fine china in the bungalow of Mr. and Mrs. Ford Robertson of the Imperial Forest Service who were on a tour of inspection with a big column of porters and bearers. Mr. Ford Robertson, being a highly skilled botanist, was able to solve a good many problems which had puzzled us.

CHAPTER SEVENTEEN

THE HOMEWARD ROAD

TO LAKE GONA

ONCE more we followed the sacred river downwards, along the rough bank, high up on the Alaknanda Gorge. On the excellent Pilgrims' Way were various bushes in full autumnal beauty, among them a yellow composite shrub, and another shrub resembling daphne, this last having scented lilac flowers with long tubal corollas (*Hamiltonia suaveolus*). We also encountered some remarkably beautiful song-birds, the cocks being fiery-red and black, the hens canary-yellow. These are old acquaintances of mine from the western Chinese mountains (*Pericrocotus*).

The skies were again overcast, and it was thundering out of a huge mass of black clouds when we entered Pipalkoti where, a little way from the village, on a hill amid terraced fields and fine trees, a dak-bungalow awaited us. But it was a long time before the caretaker arrived with the key.

Having had to renounce Nandakna, we clung all the more to our wish to visit the lake we had seen some time ago when looking down from a distance into Birehi Valley. It is called Lake Gona. Having at length found a man who knew the way, we climbed over terraces planted with grain past village after village through a magnificent oak-forest, swarming with monkeys and jays, ascending from 4250 to 8000 feet. Then, for several hours, we marched along an extremely steep slope 2500 feet above the Birehi River. It was near nightfall when we reached a spur of rock from which we got a free view of a concavity to the left, whence an enormous landslip had recently descended. It was obvious that an amount which we estimated at somewhere near 100 million cubic metres had fallen several thousand feet into the river-bed, to make a dam nearly 700 feet high. Above this recent excavation a second and older one could be made out, the fall in that case having come from a considerably greater height (Fig. 18).

Far beneath us was the little village of Gona (indicated in the figure) to which we descended and found quarters for the night. Then it was a mile and a half to reach the other side of the landslip, the last mile being actually on the top of the fall. At length we reached the lovely, tranquil, green lake, with fiords on either side. The lake extended up the narrow valley for nearly two miles, and its mirror-surface contained lovely reflections of the snow-peaks. In many respects Lake Gona reminded us of the lake in Klontal near Glarus which, though much older, was likewise caused by a landslip — also of limestone.

We took a few hours' rest on the shore. The water was fairly warm, 56°. After a swim, we lay in the sun, and watched the trout

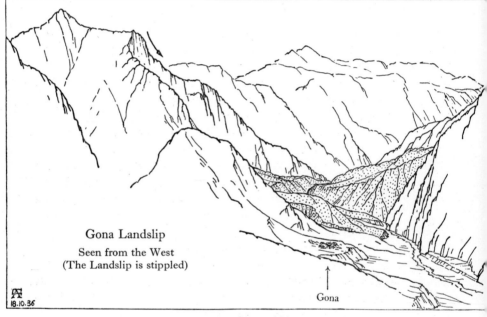

Gona Landslip

Seen from the West
(The Landslip is stippled)

Gona

FIG. 18.   (G)

leaping. It has been stocked by order of the Forest Service and there are strict regulations against fishing. Nandakna and Trisul, in the background, slowly clouded over (Plate 216).

We learned the history of the landslip in an official report by R. R. Pulford. It occurred in September 1893. The surveyors sent thither found that the debris had formed a dam rising to a height of nearly 1000 feet above the former level of the valley. Almost a year elapsed before the new lake was filled. Then, on August 26, 1894, the dam burst, and a devastating flood swept down the lower part of the valley. Since the imminence of the catastrophe had been signalised by the officials, only one life was lost, that of a sadhu who would not heed the warnings, and stood praying till the advancing waters swept him away. This first burst through the dam has gradually been cut lower and lower by the stream, so that the surface of the lake now stands at 5380 feet above sea-level, and the waters are about 400 feet at the deepest part. Considered in terms of geological time, the lake is, of course, an extremely transient phenomenon. In the course of a few thousand years, through further denudation of the channel and persistent silting-up it will completely disappear.

FROM VILLAGE TO VILLAGE

From Gona a path leads down the left bank of the River Birehi through little villages to the main valley of the Alaknanda, and then along this, rising and falling down to the modernised Chamoli, where a fine dak-bungalow stands well above the village on a terrace. It was hot and sultry. Throughout the night we were disturbed by the deafening chirps of a huge green grasshopper which sounded like the noise of a defective dynamo. Near by another beast was chirping on a higher note.

After three hours' exhausting march through a desolate, deforested valley, we reached the big Indian village of Nanda Prayag, where we had to take shelter from a violent hailstorm and then went on another three miles to the dak-bungalow of Sonola.

Next morning, new-fallen snow lay on the mountains down to a level of 7870 feet. At Karna Prayag, a few leagues farther on, and only 3950 feet above the sea, the Alaknanda debouches into the River Pindari, and the Pilgrims' Way divides. To get back to Ranikhet, we had to take the left route down the Pindari. In the evening we reached the little village of Simli, where we were put up in a private house close to a remarkable bamboo suspension bridge.

Now, when we have got out of sight of the snow-peaks, the atmosphere is once more extraordinarily clear. We always start with the coolies, fasting, at dawn, to halt after two or three hours for breakfast at some place where water is obtainable. For the last month and a half, food per day for the two of us has not cost more than one rupee.

From Simli we climbed up a deforested lateral valley on the right to a pass called Ad Badri, where we made a considerable halt, to inspect an ancient ruinous Hindu temple with four stone turrets, each of them square, and in a good state of preservation. Here, for years, has lived a nude sadhu, maintained entirely by alms. His only possessions are his long tousled locks and his loin-cloth. Kali told us the man's story. His father had been temple-guardian at Agra, and was stabbed by a drunken European, whom he refused to allow entrance to the temple and the taking of photographs. Since then the son, in mourning for the father, has remained at this temple, remote from the world (Plate 218).

The same day, in oppressive heat, we climbed through oak-forests over a pass of nearly 7000 feet to reach Debali. We secured friendly entertainment at a little farm, and were able to buy an abundance of wheat, huge corn-cobs, potatoes, and onions. We were scarcely housed when a tremendous thunderstorm began.

Next morning it was again so clear that we reascended the pass, and then climbed a hill of 7870 feet to get a view of the high mountains we had so lately visited. Splendid, but now far away to the north, the mighty front of the Badrinath massif showed up in the morning light (Plate 219) with the Gangotri Groupe to the left; while somewhat to the right were Kamet, Mana, and Parbat, partially eclipsed by a nearer and lower mountain. On the return journey we noticed that just below the view-point there was a big superposition of gneiss upon limestone and quartzite.

Now we continued our way down the valley amid flowering cherry trees, and then above Mehal Chauri over another saddle at nearly 5000 feet which marks the frontier between Garhwal and Almora. This day we made a strenuous walk of twenty mountain miles.

From the little village of Rewali, ascending the wide and fertile valley of Chaukutia, we reached a height of nearly 3000 feet, where the brown soil is tilled with the aid of zebus. It seemed to us that oranges would thrive in this region. But the people of the foothills here, as in Siam and China, care little about fruit trees, concentrating upon cereals. Thence for several hours we went down-valley to Dwarahat, a fairly large place inhabited by Indians of an Aryan type (Plate 217). It is situated upon a gneiss eminence and has modern buildings — church, mission, schoolhouses, hospital, and dak-bungalow. But there were also many ancient religious buildings; a round dozen of Hindu temples, many of them well preserved, hidden away among the trees, stood on the surrounding plateau at a height of from 4600 to 5000 feet.

Our journey farther southward was over granite and micaceous schist, to reach the bridge across the Gagas at 3280 feet. Here we disported and refreshed ourselves in a whirling green pool, while awaiting the coolies. After our bathe, we watched the fish, the lovely kingfishers,

204

and the water-redstarts. When we got under way again, it was two hours' steep climb through a pine-forest to the bazaar at Ranikhet. In a trice, Kali, who was once a chauffeur, managed to hire a lorry for a very small sum, so that the same evening, on October 26th, after a two hours' drive, we arrived at Almora. We were all tired but cheerful as, after our lengthy pedestrian journey, we finished the expedition comfortably in a motor.

CONCLUDING SURVEY

We had successfully carried out our main programme, but, owing to the badness of the weather, there was one thing we had had to forgo. We had not been able to get an extended view of the Central Himalayas from the best point, and take a photograph thence. It is generally admitted that the finest outlook can be secured from Jandi above Binsar, 7870 feet.

This time, having no occasion to do geological work on this well-trodden route, we hired horses and enjoyed the luxury of trotting or galloping along the fine road which led through the scented forest; and, on the peak, we slept under the stars in our sleeping-sacks. Over-night, indeed, the distant mountains were hidden in mist, and although the full moon soon rose it did not give sufficient light. By daybreak, however, the skies were perfectly clear, and the peaks in a circuit of 250 miles glowed in the hues of dawn. For hours we stayed there, Gansser, with his keen sight, being chiefly occupied with sketching (see Panorama I a), while I got a very successful photograph (Plate 220). The visibility northward steadily improved as the sun rose higher, until, late in the forenoon, even the distant Nepalese hills in the east were brightly lit. With the exception of the outermost summits in the semi-circle, they were all old acquaintances now — Badrinath, Nilkanta, Nandakna, Trisul, Nanda Devi, Nanda Kot, Panch Chulhi, and Nampa — to which, that day, we bade farewell, perhaps for ever.

CHAPTER EIGHTEEN

RETROSPECT AND PROSPECT

IN the end of November we reached Europe after being eight months away. One of us travelled by ship in eleven days, the other by airplane in two days. Soon this journey will be practicable in a single day. But one who wishes to pursue scientific study in the loftier Himalayas will probably, for all time, have to get along with Shanks's mare.

TOURISTIC RESULTS

Our achievements as " sportsmen " are not worth particular attention. From first to last, our aim was not (as has been that of most of those who have undertaken Himalayan Expeditions) to climb difficult mountains, but to carry on geological research in the Central Himalayas. Still, we had certainly hoped to make a few first ascents. If, in this respect, we did nothing remarkable, we are entitled to blame it upon two untoward circumstances : the fact that we were bereft of the most experienced alpinist of the party (Weckert) ; and to the exceptionally bad weather, which broke up long before the advent of the customary monsoon season.

These difficulties notwithstanding, August Gansser scaled two twenty-thousanders : Phung-Di on the Nepalese-Tibetan frontier (May 31st) ; and the unnamed ice-pyramid on the northern side of the Bhagat-Kharak Glacier in Garhwal (October 3rd). We also climbed several peaks ranging from 19,700 feet to 20,000 feet, on the Tibetan frontier. Between May 24th and August 29th, when the monsoon was raging most of the time, we crossed nineteen passes, each being well over 16,000 feet ; and, taking it all in all, during six months in which we travelled wholly on foot we covered more distance and climbed more mountains than most of the big Himalayan Expeditions in a similar time — the Everest Expeditions not excepted.

In the following compilation, the heights of the passes are given in accordance with corrected aneroid readings, which may be erroneous by as much as 300 feet, and are therefore given in round figures. G. = Gansser, H. = Heim.

Tinkar Lipu, 16,800 feet, Nepalese-Tibetan frontier, May 24th and 30th.   (H, G)

Lipu Lek, 16,500 feet, Kumaon-Tibetan frontier, June 7th and 9th.   (H)

Unknown pass in the Nampa Valley, Nepal, 17,700 feet, June 8th.   (G)

Unknown gap in the Nampa Valley, Nepal, 16,500 feet, June 12th.   (G)

Shiala, 16,550 feet, Kumaon, July 2nd.   (H)

Mangshang, 18,050 feet, Kumaon-Tibetan frontier, June 29th.   (G); July 8th.   (H) ; July 10th.   (H, G)

Amlang-La, 16,400 feet, Tibet, July 1st and 8th.   (G)

Dolma-La, 18,400 feet, Tibet, July 4th.   (G)

Lebong, 17,400 feet, Kumaon, July 15th.   (H, G)

Ralam, 18,050 feet, Kumaon, July 23rd.   (H, G)

Utta Dhura (Anta Dhura), 17,550 feet, Kumaon, August 4th and 18th.   (H, G)

Kiangur (Kungr), 16,800 feet, Kumaon, August 5th.   (H, G)

Balcha Dhura, 17,700 feet, Kumaon-Tibetan frontier, August 8th. (G) ; August 12th.   (H)

Ghatamemin, 17,700 feet, Kumaon-Tibetan frontier, August 15th. (H)

Chaldu (Kiogar), 17,400 feet, Kumaon-Tibetan frontier, August 17th. (H, G)

Chirchun-East, 17,875 feet, Tibet, August 17th.   (H, G)

Kungri Bingri, 18,050 feet, Kumaon-Tibetan frontier, August 18th. (H, G)

Jayanti, 18,400 feet, Kumaon, August 18th.   (H, G)

Traill (between Nanda Devi and Nanda Kot), about 18,550 feet. August 29th.   (G)

Whilst most of the peaks of the Alps have been scaled, and sensation-loving sportsmen whose main interest lies in outdoing others seek out crazier and crazier climbs (such as that of the North Wall of the Eiger) — in the huge domain of the Himalayas there is still a vast abundance of virgin peaks, although there have been so many expeditions and such a number of first ascents, like those of Nanda Devi, Nanda Kot, and Siniolchu in 1936. One who seeks enjoyment and spiritual refreshment in the mountains, and can keep his longings for sensation within reasonable bounds, will still find an abundance of splendid twenty-three-thousanders or twenty-four-thousanders to attack as pioneer, even though Nepal remains closed.

The most desirable peaks in those portions of the Central Himalayas we visited were Nampa (23,330 feet) and Badrinath (23,420 feet), both of which could, we think, be easily scaled in the early spring by experienced ski-runners ; also the Shangtang near Kuti (21,150 feet), which is the highest peak in the Tibetan frontier chain, and the highest of the Panch Chulhi group (which reaches about 22,650 feet). Among more modest groups, Gangotri in Garhwal is worth approaching, being still very little known, and yet, we think, easy to climb from the Mussoorie side.

The experience of the last decade has given abundant proof that the achievements of an expedition do not increase proportionally with the number of the participators ; and, indeed, that it is the other way about. Our experience in 1936 gave abundant confirmation of the view we already held, that for touristic purposes a party of three or four has the best chances of success. As the numbers swell, the requisite equipment increases " at compound interest ", while the obstacles to satisfactory provisioning of the porters are greatly intensified. A small party of two or three will often secure food and shelter in places where a larger party with a proportionally large number of porters could not possibly make a stay. Of course we intended to form a party of three, and the number of two participators to which we were restricted by bad luck is certainly too small for difficult climbs. When there are three, should one be struck down by accident or illness, the remaining two can at least go ahead. The Nanda Devi Expedition of Shipton and Tilman in the year 1936, needed, of course, very few porters for the two Europeans ; whereas the International Karakoram Expedition of the year 1934, led by Dyhrenfurth, had fourteen European participators. In our opinion, too, the Mount Everest Expeditions have been unduly ambitious and cumbersome. On all the large-scale expeditions there has been taken along a much larger quantity of tinned food than is either necessary or wholesome — as happened in the case of the British Kamet Expedition under Smythe in the year 1931. Naturally the requisite number of porters and the cost per head vary within wide limits. An expedition that was a record, both in respect of simplicity and of achievement, was that of Shipton and Tilman. The party of five consisted of themselves and three Sherpas, and the whole expedition cost no more than 6000 (Swiss) francs — although they had with them their equipment purchased for earlier expeditions. Contrasted with

208

this are the huge expeditions accompanied by from 400 to 600 porters, and costing from forty to sixty times as much money. Our own expedition, whose aims were science and not sport, came close to that of Shipton, but cost rather more. If we ever return to the Himalayas we shall, guided by the experience of 1936, live as simply as we did during the last two months, when we got along comfortably with 8 porters instead of 30.

It must not be forgotten that for the remote Karakoram more porters will be indispensable, since the region is uninhabited, and all the food needed by the mountaineers will have to be carried from afar.

I should like to take this opportunity of pointing out that our experience convinces us of the superior convenience and wholesomeness of vegetarian diet, consisting mainly of cereals such as unpolished rice, wheat, barley, maize, and millet ; and that it is needless as well as injurious to carry a variety of tinned foods — to say nothing of their enormous weight. Those will be most successful in the Himalayas who learn to travel as does the Tibetan, who gets along satisfactorily with no more than a sack of tsamba, and knows exactly for how many days' journey it will suffice.

As regards the question which is the best season, Himalayan mountaineers differ greatly in opinion.

The earliest authorities consist of those who have preferred the pre-monsoon period, the most important work being done in June. To this category belong the Everest Committee, Dyhrenfurth, and some of the Munichers. Most of the failures and disasters, like those on Mount Everest, on Kinchinjunga, on the Karakoram, and on Nanga Parbat, were caused by the coming of monsoon storms earlier than had been expected. In our view, it is only through exceptional good luck that a pre-monsoon expedition can succeed.

A second group, represented by P. Baur of Munich (Kanch) and Brown-Tilman (Nanda Devi), consists of those who advocate the monsoon season, making their main attack in August. Here, too, success is largely a matter of good luck, and even when the weather makes mountaineering practicable most of the expedition will be spent amid fog and mist, from which the highest peaks are free only on exceptional days and for brief periods.

A third, and small group, is composed of those who advocate the post-monsoon period. From our experiences on Minya Gongkar in Chinese Tibet and in the Himalayas we adhere very decisively to this third group, recommending October as the best month for travel at high altitudes.

I know that objectors will rightly contend that our experience does not entitle us to judge of prevailing snow conditions at altitudes over 23,000 feet, since there the chief snowfalls take place in summer. Still, we can answer by insisting that the proof of the pudding is in the eating. On October 29, 1931, after three months' futile wrestling with the monsoon, the Americans Burdsall and Moore [1] achieved the conquest of Minya Gongkar, which is only just under 25,000 feet. On November 18, 1935, Cooke and Schoberth [2] climbed Kabru, 24,000 feet, in the Kanch Group, the weather being fine.

Every experienced mountaineer will confirm the statement that 50° or 60° of frost are much easier to bear when the wind is moderate than 16° or 20° of frost with a raging wind. The lowest temperature we encountered in the Himalayas was in the beginning of October, 10° Fahrenheit, at an altitude of 16,500 feet. On a winter journey through Chinese Tibet, the thermometer seldom fell below zero Fahrenheit, and it often seemed considerably colder in the valleys than on the tops of the passes at 16,000 feet or more. As to temperature conditions at high altitudes (26,000 to 30,000 feet in October) we have information secured when instruments were sent up from Agra in unmanned balloons. Here is a table of average temperatures registered in the open atmosphere (in this table, heights are given in metres and temperatures on the Centigrade scale) : [3]

Altitude	April	May	June	July	August	September	October	November
5000	$-5 \cdot 5°$	$-1 \cdot 3°$	$1 \cdot 2°$	$5 \cdot 2°$	$4 \cdot 2°$	$1 \cdot 0°$	$-0 \cdot 9°$	$-6 \cdot 5°$
6000	$-12 \cdot 5°$	$-8 \cdot 0°$	$-4 \cdot 6°$	$0 \cdot 2°$	$-0 \cdot 9°$	$-3 \cdot 3°$	$-6 \cdot 8°$	$-12 \cdot 7°$
7000	$-19 \cdot 1°$	$-13 \cdot 8°$	$-9 \cdot 6°$	$-5 \cdot 4°$	$-6 \cdot 3°$	$-8 \cdot 7°$	$-12 \cdot 9°$	$-19 \cdot 9°$
8000	$-26 \cdot 1°$	$-19 \cdot 9°$	$-15 \cdot 6°$	$-11 \cdot 3°$	$-11 \cdot 8°$	$-14 \cdot 7°$	$-19 \cdot 1°$	$-25 \cdot 2°$
9000	$-33 \cdot 3°$	$-26 \cdot 3°$	$-21 \cdot 2°$	$-17 \cdot 3°$	$-18 \cdot 2°$	$-21 \cdot 6°$	$-26 \cdot 3°$	$-31 \cdot 1°$

The foregoing observations disclose the average decline of temperature with increasing altitude to be :

In August, a fall of 1° for a rise of 179 metres.
In September, a fall of 1° for a rise of 178 metres.
In October, a fall of 1° for a rise of 159 metres.
In November, a fall of 1° for a rise of 162 metres.

We infer that at the altitude of the summit of Mount Everest (8882 metres = 29,000 feet) in October the average temperature must be $-25 \cdot 5°$ C.

[1] R. L. Burdsall and A. B. Emmons, *Men against the Clouds ; the Conquest of Minya Konka*, London, 1935.
[2] Schweiz, " Illustrierte Zeitung ", No. 5, 1937.
[3] Kindly communicated by Dr. R. Billwiler, Zurich Meteorological Station.

After the exceptionally bad summer of 1930, in the border ranges of Eastern Tibet the clear autumn weather began on November 7th and lasted till January 12th, when a moderate snowfall came. During our own Himalayan journey the clear autumn weather began (though there were a few exceptional short relapses) on October 1st, and during the first days of November the weather was so splendid that the most remote peaks were visible, so that when they became invisible in the extreme distance this was not due to clouds but to desert dust. If we ever go again, we shall defer our attempt upon the heights until autumn, and do our work in the foothills during winter. We should like, in concluding this section, to reaffirm our convictions that even for the highest peaks in the world the post-monsoon season should be very earnestly considered by intending climbers.[1]

GEOGRAPHICAL RESULTS

Over and above the scattered observations that will have been noticed in the foregoing record regarding the region and its inhabitants, the heights of passes, peaks, glacier-ends, forest belts, etc., and apart from the purely geological work we undertook, we were not able to glean much information as to purely geographical questions. As regards Kumaon, in addition to the extremely antiquated map-sheet 53 N of the year 1882, we had at our disposal the 4-miles-to-an-inch maps of the Survey of India on a scale of 1 : 253,440. Although they are marked in the old way with rounded contour lines, their production has been a splendid achievement, and they sufficed us for the entry of our main geological discoveries.

In North-Western Nepal and Tibet we had to content ourselves with compass-bearings and sketches, which have been taken into account in preparing the map that accompanies the present volume (1 : 650,000).

To the knowledge of glaciation in former days and now, our geological researches contribute a number of accurate data. The four largest glaciers we visited were :

Name	Place	Distance in Kilometres to End of Ice-cap	Altitude in Metres ot End of Glacier
Nampa	N.-W. Nepal	10	3900
Shankalpa	Almora District	14	3800
Milam	Almora District	18	3500
Bhagat-Kharak	Garhwal	19	3750

[1] After the above words were penned, there appeared in the " Himalayan Journal " for 1937 a very interesting discussion by competent authorities concerning the best season for Himalayan mountaineering.

Thanks to its sheltered situation behind the lofty ridge on the north-eastern side of the Nanda-Devi Group and to the inflow of a number of lateral glaciers, the Milam Glacier extends down to a lower level than any other glacier we visited on our journey. Gansser, in his visit to the Nampa Glacier, made some extremely interesting observations concerning the reciprocal relationships of main glaciers and lateral glaciers with superposition of the ice (Figs. 9 and 10).

On one year's visit no more than approximate conclusions can be based as regards the snow-line. In the Transhimalaya on Kailas we estimate it to be about 18,000 feet ; on the Kumaon-Tibetan frontier (Balcha Dhura, Kungri-Bingri, and Mangshang Pass) at about 18,400 feet; and at Bhagat-Kharak, about 30 miles farther to the S.W., at somewhere near 17,500 feet.

Very important, too, were Gansser's observations concerning the depression that has been going on in the basin of the great Tibetan lakes Raksas and Manasarowar, which no longer feed the Sutlej. This depression is obviously bringing about a complete change in the direction of drainage in some of the valleys.

GEOLOGICAL RESULTS

Although we fell short of our hopes as far as touristic results were concerned, in the geological field we did more than we had expected, because we extended our stay by three months, and went on working until November was at hand. To complete our scientific studies we had to get together all the observations contained in six diaries, drawing about twenty special maps on the basis of our sketches and geological observations ; then there were profiles to make, a number of rock sections to study under the microscope, chemical analyses to be made of our mineralogical specimens, while the fossils and plants, where this was necessary, were identified by specialists ; and finally our data were checked by references to the extensive literature of Himalayan geology, and our conclusions were co-ordinated with pre-existing knowledge as concerns the structure of the Alps, the best-known and most highly complicated stratified areas of the crinkled surface of the globe.

Many readers of this book, however, will not be satisfied unless given some explanation of the results that were achieved, in so far as these can be made comprehensible to persons without a scientific knowledge of geology.

Our first discovery was that the so-called " main boundary fault " where the mountains pass into the Indian plains, must be regarded as a relief superposition, like that which is met with where the northern margin of our Alps abuts on the molasse that lies between the Alps and the Jura. In both these regions, to our way of thinking, the detritus formations which were washed down from the high mountains when they were in course of being thrust up, became involved in the horizontal push of the earth's crust and were heaped up to form an independent chain of foothills. This was then, in its turn, attacked by erosion, and, in places, scooped into longitudinal valleys after the manner of the contemporary " duns " (Dehra Dun). Only when these had been excavated came the thrust of the high-mountain formations upon the denuded foothills, to make what in the Himalayan region are called the Siwaliks. This supposition, which in the year 1906 I put forward as regards the Alps, has, after much opposition, been confirmed by the labours of a younger generation of geologists, and is now generally accepted ; nor have I any doubt that the same theory will be confirmed as regards the origin of the similar but much larger formations that lie to the south of the Himalayas. The main difference is that the formations and movements of this kind in the Himalayas belong to a much later geological period than the corresponding ones in the Alps. If we further bear in mind that in the Himalayas the mountain movement was directed towards the S.W. instead of towards the N.W., and if we realise that, *mutatis mutandis*, the Siwaliks are identical with the molasse, the essential harmony will be understood.

Very different from the Alps, geologically speaking, is the mountain region about sixty miles wide that lies to the immediate S.W. of the lofty central chains. It consists almost entirely of fossil-free ancient formations. No-one can tell whether the limestones are fossil-free because they were formed before any shelled molluscs existed, or whether it is for other reasons that they are not fossiliferous.

There is only one way in which we can determine the relative ages of such strata, namely by the study of metamorphosis. Under normal conditions the originally deepest and oldest sedimentary rocks have been most profoundly transformed by pressure and heat. When, therefore, in the outer zones of the Central Himalayas of Kumaon, as in the Darjeeling district, we find that the crest of the mountains are often composed of the most characteristic metamorphic rocks, such as granitic micaceous schists, and paragneiss, whereas the valleys have been excavated in the underlying, very little metamorphosed sedimentary rocks, and the two groups pass into one another, we are forced to assume that the stratification is inverted. Now such inversions only take place when a fold in the earth's crust has been bent on its side and super-

213

posed. Necessarily, therefore, we must likewise infer that the outer chains of the Himalayas consist of gigantic superposed folds which were thrust down from the N.E. over the Siwaliks. If you imagine that in the Central Alps the Swiss calcareous alpine zone had been removed and the primary Aar massif submerged, you would have a like situation. For in that case the almost fossil-free pennine convolutions (such as the St. Bernard top-layer) would be thrust over the eroded molasse. But, once more, the reader must never forget that the thrust from the Central Alps was directed from S.E. to N.W., whereas in the Central Himalayas it came from the Tibetan plateau, and therefore from the N.E. to the S.W.

Not only did we find inverted stratification, but also fairly acute superpositions of gneiss with granite upon sedimentary formations, as in the Kali Gorge and between Karna Prayag and Dwarahat. Farther northward, on the Alaknanda below Joshimath, the geologist J. B. Auden had previously observed such a superposition of gneiss. The granitic intrusions are older than the mountain formation, and passively participated in the movement.

Our views harmonise with recent discoveries made by such distinguished geologists as Pilgrim, Wadia, Auden, and West, when engaged upon the Geological Survey of India, for they found farther to the N.W. in the border zone of Simla superposed strata all directed from the N.E. to the S.W. We believe that we were able to recognise the roots of these superposed layers at the foot of the central chain, where gneiss and micaceous schists show themselves here and there unexpectedly in the depths.

We had long wondered whether and where in the Himalayas there might be found evidences of a counterthrust beyond the lofty chains consisting of crystalline rocks — something that would correspond to the south of the Alps (the Dinarics). Now behind the central chains we found, first of all, a schistous zone consisting of various superposed layers which overlapped one another like the tiles on a roof, and had all been thrust thither from Tibet. In this region as far as the Tibetan frontier chain there can be no doubt as to the primary succession of the marine stratifications, for these can easily be distinguished owing to the existence of rich fossil beds ranging from the Silurian to the Cretaceous. All the more striking is it, then, that so able a geologist as Griesbach,[1] who for two summers towards the end of the nineteenth century was engaged upon the study of this N.E. zone of Kumaon, and wrote the

[1] C. L. Griesbach, *Geology of the Central Himalayas*, " Memoirs of the Geological Survey of India ", Vol. XXIII, 1891.

208. Badrinath, ice-capped and inviolate (23 420 feet), seen from the north at an altitude of 18 000 feet. October 3, 1936.   (H)

210. Unnamed ice-pyramid, about 20 000 feet, between Bhagat Kharak and the
Arwa Valley. Gansser made the first ascent on October 3, 1936.   (H)

211. Our last camp in the heights, 16 900 feet, northward of the
Bhagat Kharak Glacier. October 4, 1936.   (H)

212. A chilly bathe in the sacred tarn of Satopanth, 14 440 feet.
October 8, 1936.   (H)

213. The lower end of the Satopanth Glacier, the source
of the sacred Ganges. October 8, 1936.   (H)

214. View of Nanda Devi taken from a cypress that crowns a rocky slope
leading into the Rishi Gorge. October 14. 1936. (H)

215. Nanda Devi, 25 584 feet. Topmost peak of the Central Himalayas. above
the Rishi Gorge. from the north-west. October 14. 1936. (H)

216. Two "New Indians" have had a refreshing swim in Lake Gona.
October 19, 1936.

217. Indian girls at the Christian mission of Dwarahat.
October 24, 1936.　(G)

218. The naked Sadhu of Ad Badri. October 23, 1936. (H)

219. Distant prospect of the Garhwal Himalayas from Diwali Khal. In the middle is Kedarnath, nearly 23 000 feet; to the right, in the north, the mighty Badrinath, 23 288 feet. Instantaneous. October 24. 1936.   (H)

220. Our last view of the Central Himalayas, from Jandi, above Binsar. To the left is the Trisul Massive, 23 288 feet; in the middle, Nanda Devi, 25 584 feet and 24 272 feet, 50 miles away; to the right, Nanda Kot, 22 469 feet. Instantaneous. October 29. 1936.   (H)

valuable work mentioned in the footnote — a book enriched with a map and very cleverly drawn profiles — should have overlooked most of the superpositions, so that his description stands in need of extensive stratigraphic corrections. The fine fossils we brought back with us and handed over to the Geological Institute of Zurich for study there and preservation — especially the ammonites of Tinkar Lipu, Kuti, and the Kiogar district — will form the basis of a new stratigraphic classification. Our friend Professor A. Jeannet has already discovered several new species, and is preparing a work on these fossils, which will be illustrated.

The whole structure of the mountain chains that lie to the S.W. of the Tibetan frontier, with their alternations of limestone and fossiliferous clays, with their convolutions and superpositions, strongly recalls the limestone Alps in the north of Switzerland. Being all of them marine formations, they show that down to the end of the Mesozoic epoch, there existed a sea — the ancient Asiatic Mediterranean, known by the name of Tethys — where subsequently the sea-floor was thrust upwards to form the present ice-clad mountains. One need not be a trained geologist to recognise that here in the course of the aeons gigantic changes must have taken place, seeing that to-day, at altitudes ranging from 16,000 to 20,000 feet, we find the fossils of animals that unquestionably once lived at the bottom of the sea. To the layman, who may think this hard to believe, I may also point out that we find there limestone full of corals and fragments of sea-lilies ; that in the upper parts of the Trias limestone there were beds formed by millions of sea-shells ; and that a first glance at sections of the hornstone of the cretaceous flysch showed, under the microscope, as was expected, the tiny silicious shells of radiolaria — that is to say of the microscopic organisms that lived free-swimming in the open sea, and whose close kin still live in the ocean to-day, their shells continuing to rain down into the depths of the ocean and form new strata.

Thus in days of old, when the world, geologically speaking, was still comparatively young, where the Central Himalayas now tower skyward, there was once a deep sea, deepest towards the close of the Mesozoic period ; whereas far to the south extended the Gondwana continent. The Kuen Lun and Tienshan, to the north, were forced upwards as mountains as early as the close of the Paleozoic.

But the profile of the Central Himalayas does not end in the fossiliferous strata that lie northward of the central chains. Far to the north of Milam, among the Kiogars, is found another superposed mountain system, that of the " exotic " rocks which do not properly belong to the Himalayas at all, as Diener already discovered at the end of the last century.[1] Von Krafft [2] who, as geologist of the Geological Survey of India in the year 1902, published his important *Notes on the Exotic Blocks of Malla Johar*, when trying to account for the strange appearance of exotic blocks of Permian, Trias, and Lias and the associated basic eruptive rocks, lying upon convoluted cretaceous flysch, could find no better explanation than that they must have been cast thither by colossal volcanic eruptions in Tibet during the Tertiary. It was thus, he held, that the exotic blocks were hurled into the marginal regions of the Himalayas. I think it probable that he would have found reasons for abandoning this fantastic view had not the British Government thought fit to forbid his proposed visit to Tibet. If he had had the chance of climbing no more than one of the Kiogar peaks, he could not have failed to learn that these were no mere exotic blocks, but a whole chain of exotic mountains. At that date our knowledge of the roof of the Alps was still slender, whereas now, after more than thirty years' further experience, there is much new knowledge available for geologists. In this Kiogar region, too, we found that the Kiogars were not mere caps on the peaks in the sense of E. Suess, but that their exotic rocks extend over many, many square miles. The analogy with the " exotic " superposed masses of the Swiss Alps to which C. Diener drew attention as early as 1898 — with such peaks as the Mythen and the Ibergs — is obvious. Gansser also succeeded in tracing the continuity of the exotic rocks far into Tibet, where he found them in the Raksas Valley as much as thirty miles beyond the frontier chains. Of course there remain many problems to solve in this connection, and they will only be solved when geologists, instead of making stolen and anxious raids across the frontier, can journey or stay wherever they please in Tibet.

Not only the Zaskar frontier chains, but also the exotic superposed masses, were pushed very far south-westward from the north-east. Great, therefore, was Gansser's delight on his return from the Transhimalaya, when he was able to tell me how, at the foot of Kailas, he had found and been able to get a good photograph of a superposed rock which had been thrust north-eastward. It was in the Transhimalaya, then, that the counter-thrust took place, as our fellow-countryman, Dr. Rudolf Wyss, has demonstrated farther to the north-west, in the Kuen Lun.[3]

[1] C. Diener, *Notes on the Geological Structure of the Chitichun Region,* " Memoirs of the Geological Survey of India ", Vol. XXVIII, 1898.
[2] " Memoirs of the Geological Survey of India ", Vol. XXXII, 1902.
[3] Rudolf Wyss in " Die Alpen ", August 1931, p. 291.

Now let us enquire as to the age of these formations, as to the geological period in which these huge contortions of the earth's crust took place. Since in the areas investigated no noteworthy discordance was discovered proceeding upward from the lower Paleozoic strata into the limestones, and in many places perfect parallelisms of the strata existed (so that the latest formations were caught simultaneously with the earliest ones by the horizontal thrust in the earth's crust), it follows that the main movement of the Central Himalayas must be younger than the Cretaceous, that is to say must be Tertiary or comparatively recent. But precisely how recent we could find, in the course of our investigations, no data helping us to decide, and we had to turn to the works of our colleagues de Terra of Philadelphia,[1] Wadia of Calcutta,[2] and Sahni of Lucknow[3] concerning the N.-W. Himalayas of Kashmir, since these are of fundamental importance to our understanding of the Himalayas in general.

In view of the stratification of the well-defined recent Tertiary and Quarternary deposits of that region, de Terra distinguishes various phases since the Permian, a particularly well-marked one in the middle Tertiary, and a final one in the Alluvium — the present time. But even to-day the upthrust of the Himalayas is continuing (this being a marked contrast with what is going on in the Alps, which are much older), and is made plain by the forms of erosion we encountered in the Central Himalayas. Again and again we detected convexities in the walls of the gorges (Figs. 4, 6, and 16), showing that the extent of erosion has been increasing as time went on. The same thing is manifest from the way in which the streams and the rivers have made fresh cuts into the deposits they previously laid down. Now this increase in the force of erosion must manifestly be due to a still progressing increase in the height of the mountains, whereby the amount of the rainfall and snow-fall is increased, and also the steepness in the fall of the currents. But while the Himalayas are rising, the Indian alluvial plain is sinking by fits and starts, to the accompaniment of catastrophic earthquakes (Bihar). Years ago I was able to show that a similar compensative counter-movement was taking place to balance the upthrust of the Chinese and East Tibetan mountains, and that this partly accounted for the

[1] H. de Terra, *Himalayan and Alpine Orogenesis*, 'Proceedings of the Sixteenth International Geological Congress ", Washington, 1933.

[2] D. N. Wadia, *The Syntaxes of the N.-W. Himalaya*, Recent Geological Survey of India, 1931 ; and *The Tertiary Geosyncline*, etc., " Quarterly Journal of the Geological, Mining, etc., Society of India ", 1932.

[3] B. Sahni, *The Himalayan Uplift since the Advent of Man*, " Current Science ", Vol. V, 1936.

floods that frequently devastate the plains of Central China.[1] If the excoriated moraine rocks recently discovered by the Chinese professor J. S. Lee as " islands of rocks " in the alluvial plain beside the lower Yangtse, are really glacial formations from an earlier Ice Age, which now seems almost certain, this view has received additional confirmation.

More and more discoveries are being made which bear witness to a hitherto unsuspected mobility in what we have been wont to speak of as the " fixed crust of the earth ". Teilhard de Chardin[2] showed the geologists assembled in Congress at Washington in the year 1933 photos taken by him as a member of the Citroën Expedition through Central Asia from Tienshan. They exhibited rocks with an inclination of 60°, composed, not of gneiss, but of up-ended quaternary detritus cones.

In Kashmir, de Terra and Sahni have found sedimentary deposits of an ancient sea-bottom which in places has been elevated to an altitude of 5000 feet and up-ended to an angle of as much as 40°. These deposits contain paleolithic fossils and other organismal fragments belonging to the Quaternary period. Who, in face of such facts, can venture to repudiate the bold hypothesis that since the appearance of man on earth the passes leading into Tibet have become more difficult owing to a rise of 3000 feet or more in the height of the mountains — however fantastic changes so extensive may seem to a modern geologist ? Prior to the discovery of the before-mentioned facts, it was known from zoological and botanical data that not so very long ago Tibet was a comparatively fertile land which only later was cut off from India by the elevation of the Himalayas. In this connection I may remind the reader of the hypothesis advanced in Peking by Professor Grabau,[3] to the effect that Tibet was the cradle of mankind. There, he suggests, our ancestors of the Pliocene or Late Tertiary period, when the climate grew worse and it was impossible to return to Hindustan, were compelled to cultivate their intelligence and have recourse to the use of fire and clothing. May we not attribute the abandonment of the cave-city discovered by Gansser, and that of Takla Makan, the dead city of the desert visited by Sven Hedin and Aurel Stein, to the increasing desiccation of the respective regions, and to the same cause ascribe the

[1] Heim, *Minya Gongkar, Forschungsreise ins Hochgebirge von Chinesisch-Tibet*, Berne 1893, p. 219.
[2] P. Teilhard de Chardin, *The Significance of Piedmont Gravels in Continental Geology*, " Proceedings of the Sixteenth International Geological Congress ", Washington, 1933 (published July 1935).
[3] A. W. Grabau, *Tibet and the Origin of Man*, in the *Sven-Hedin-Festschrift*, 1935, p. 317.

218

decline of the huge Mongolian Empire which flourished in Central Asia during the Middle Ages — all this being dependent on the increasing height of the Himalayas ? [1] Very remarkable indeed is the way in which observations made from various view-points in widely separated parts of Asia all lead to the same result.

But whereas, with the rise of the Himalayas, the rainfall and snowfall of the hinterland were reduced, in the actual mountain region they increased. Associated therewith was a steady lowering of temperature, so that glaciers were formed. There, as elsewhere on the surface of the globe, in the Quaternary Ice Age, they reached down to lower levels than to-day, though not so low as those they would have reached had the mountains then been as high as they are to-day. Even apart from these tectonic considerations, the question how far down the glaciers may at one time have extended is of primary interest and importance. Our studies in two of the main valleys of the Himalayas have provided some valuable data. In the Kali Valley, on the Nepalese frontier, we found the outermost moraine at an altitude of 7050 feet, and in the Alaknanda Valley, in Garhwal, at an altitude of 6550 feet. In both these places, therefore, during the days of the last Ice Age (the Würm Ice Age), the tongue of the glacier did not stretch beyond the gorge into the foothills, as happened to the north of the Alps. Nevertheless there was an extensive difference between the ancient and the latter-day levels, for the glaciers in those two main valleys have practically disappeared, while the lateral glaciers have receded to somewhere about 13,000 feet.

When we consider these contemporary glaciers, we are struck by their sluggishness in comparison with the power of erosion by water. We rarely find evidence of glacial excoriation on the walls of the valleys. Often, indeed, between the sub-recent marginal moraines and the rocky walls of the gorges there exist little valleys with a gravelly floor or partially filled by a small lake, this showing that the glaciers even in their more vigorous days had no power of lateral expansion. The glaciers in the larger valleys, such as the Satopanth, the Bhagat-Kharak, and the Milam, are not only covered with detritus for several miles (3 to 10), but float, so to speak, on their moraines, which they are no longer capable of sweeping away. Thus not merely do glaciers fail to excavate valleys (as geographers believed so late as the beginning of the present century) but they actually preserve the earlier forms of erosion and fill the floors of the valleys with moraine detritus.

[1] Cf. H. de Terra, *Zum Problem der Austrocknung des westlichen Innerasien*, " Zeitschrift der Gesellschaft für Erdkunde ", Berlin, 1930.

Stupendous though the scenery of the Himalayas is, it is possible during springtime in the Alps to gain a good idea of the sublimity of the Himalayan peaks. In April, recently, when travelling by train from Lausanne to Geneva, I enjoyed a view of Mont Blanc which aroused in me vivid memories of a Himalayan peak. In the Himalayas, of course, the rocky walls are steeper as well as higher than those of the Alps, and no Alpine gorge can seriously compare with the majestic, almost incredible, transverse gorges of the Himalayas.

But one magnificent Alpine phenomenon is lacking in the Himalayas, namely the big marginal lakes. The Himalayas are still rising, whereas the Alpine masses have been sinking since their lateral protrusion, so that the marginal valleys have been depressed to form fiord-like lakes. In the Himalayas, too, glacial action is less marked, so that only here and there do we come across small moraine lakes. On the other hand, as was to be expected, recent landslips are numerous. But if a landslip dams up a valley, the lake thus formed is of brief duration, for it soon fills up, and then the silt is washed away again.

We see, then, that, both from within and from without, the Himalayas are in a condition of extremely active change.

No geologist will be surprised to learn that the highest mountains in the world are also the youngest. Only recent elevations, whether of volcanoes, plateaus, or mountain chains, can maintain themselves at a great height through lengthy geological periods. But the Himalayas do more than maintain their altitude, for these mountains are still rising more rapidly than they are being lowered by erosion — just as man, in spite of depressing influences, can rise to increasing spiritual heights.

If we contemplate the Himalayas as a whole, we come to regard them as representing a mighty upward flow of the earth's crust, resulting from a struggle between the two ancient continents of Angara and Gondwana as pictured by Argand and R. Staub, these two continents clashing together, and thus pushing up into mountains the less rigid oceanic zone by which they were originally severed. Angara, occupying a higher position, got the better of the thrust, so that the mobile mountain masses flowed over the sinking lowlands of Gondwana. Thus to the eyes of the geologist, who is used to thinking in great periods of time, the Himalayas seem a mobile organ of our planet—a planet which is not merely rolling on its course through the universe, but within its own framework is continually undergoing the throes of an active life.

PALEONTOLOGICAL RESULTS

Although the labours of our friend Professor Jeannet are not yet finished (and, when finished, will be published in a technical treatise) we may epitomise a few of his provisional results.

From the Ordovician in the Shiala Pass we secured several new kinds of brachyopods, which have been sketched under the lens.

Two magnificently preserved ammonites, found by A. Gansser in the black schistous clay on the top of Lebong Pass (17,400 feet), proved to be rare specimens of the genus *Cyclolobus* (new and exceptional species) from the Permian.

From the Lower Trias came various ammonites found at Kuti (*Ophiceras*).

Remarkably well preserved were the numerous ammonites found at 17,000 feet, in Tinkar Lipu, Nepal. The lower stratum, a silicious-calcareous bed, contained a rich fauna belonging to the Noric Trias.

The fine ammonites shown in Plates 67 and 68 from the black calcareous schist, containing a number of new species, belong to a Noric bed in the Upper Trias, hitherto not known to be fossiliferous in the Himalayas.

Useful as giving a clue to the age of the strata were some ammonites found in a thin bed of iron-oolith in the Kiogar region, which can be ascribed to the Callovian (Upper Dogger).

Previously recognised and described, on the other hand, are most of the numerous fossils we found in the black Spiti shale, a transitional bed between Jurassic and Cretaceous.

BOTANICAL RESULTS

(By Dr. E. Schmid)

The botanical collection made by the Swiss Himalayan Expedition, and presented to the Botanical Museum of the University of Zurich, comprises 272 specimens consisting of about 187 species of flowering plants. Most of them came from the high-mountain regions of the Central Himalayas and the Transhimalaya, at levels of more than 13,000 feet. In conjunction with the verbal reports and photographs of Messrs. Heim and Gansser, they give a very vivid picture of the flora in those alpine belts which hitherto were least known.

The vegetational zones along the line of route, as characterised by the predominance of different kinds of tree, displayed the following characteristics. The damp marginal zone among the lower levels of the foothills was occupied by tropical monsoon-forests though this cannot be described as a true " rain-forest ". As we pass inwards up the mountains, there begins at about 3250 feet a belt of such leafy trees as evergreen oaks and rhododendrons; the northern slopes being characterised by the predominance of various species of *Acer, Aesculus, Juglans, Ulmus, Carpinus*, with species of yew, ilex, and bamboo. This belt extends up to 10,000 feet, being there replaced by a belt rich in conifers, such as *Picea morinda, Abies*, and *Cupressus*. The birch-belt forms the uppermost zone of forest trees. Above this we find a scrub and shrub belt; and higher still the alpine steppe.

The Birch-forest Belt

There still remains an abundance of virgin forest in the more rarely visited valleys of the Central Himalayas. As everywhere in the northern hemisphere in regions where there is a heavy rainfall, one of the birches (*Betula utilis*) is the tree which grows at the highest altitudes. In these regions there is a well-marked rainy season. During the exceptionally wet summer of 1936 there were monsoon rains almost every day. Immature, fine-grained soils of a clayey schist are common. Limestone subsoils are rare; but there are extensive layers of red humus, the product of the dampness of the climate, lying in many of the slopes directly upon the rocks and the detritus.

The horizontal line of the forest belt is only broken by steep precipices, avalanche channels, and movable lines of detritus, not being interrupted, as in the Alps, by pastures reaching far down where the soil is good. Especially on the northern faces of the valleys, the forests are still untouched. On the southern exposures, which are dryer, forest fires, often caused by man, have made extensive clearances. Such fires are common, spreading far more rapidly upon the southern slopes. As we approach the Tibetan frontier, local climatic influences play their part, thinning out and interrupting the forest on these southern exposures. There has not been much purposive deforestation. The inhabitants use very little wood as fuel, not being dairy-farmers, such domestic animals as they have being kept for wool and as beasts of burden.

In the western parts of Heim and Gansser's route, the end of the forest belt was comparatively low — on the Kurai Pass, for instance it was about 12,000 feet. *Abies webbiana* extends there up to 11,650 feet, *Pinus excelsa*, here and there, near Kalapani in the Kali Valley, ranges as high as 12,450 feet; in the more easterly regions, on the Nepalese frontier, the forest ranges up to 13,000 feet.

The undergrowth of the birch belt consists mainly of rhododendron bushes, such as *Rhododendron lepidotum, Rhododendron campanulatum,* etc. Besides this, we find here, as undergrowth, such plants as love a rich humus, and especially woody growths. Tall bushes are rarer than in the homologous forest belts of the Caucasus or the Alps.

The Alpine Scrub and Shrub Belt

Above the topmost forest belt we come to small shrubs, which include various species of rhododendron (*Rhododendron anthopogon, hypenanthum, lepidotum*) and various Ericaceae, such as *Cassiope fastidiata,* and *Gaultheria* — an alpine tundra covered with a mossy, acid humus. This belt extends through a range of altitudes amounting to about 1200 feet, rising in the eastern regions that were visited as high as 13,750 feet; while isolated rhododendron bushes may be found even at 15,400 feet (*Rhododendron anthopogon,* beside the Satopanth Glacier). Like the birch belt, the shrub and scrub belt is interrupted only by avalanche channels, mobile detritus, and steep precipices. Here, likewise, the naked rock is thinly colonised by *Delphinium brunonianum,* and species of *Aconitum* and *Caltha* or other shrubs. Pastures between the patches of heathland are rare.

On the declivities facing south, small heaths growing in humus are no longer found. The only vegetation consists here and there of *Juniperus wallichiana* and *Juniperus macropoda,* interspersed with grassy patches of one sort and another.

On the moraines, *Rheum webbiamum* is found in thick patches, its growth resembling that of a tall shrub. In the depressions where the snow lies long there are to be found plant communities in which the species of primula play the same part as do the soldanellas in the snow-valleys of the Alps (for instance, on the northern slopes of the Ralam Pass, the primulas were in full flower on July 22nd at 14,750 feet). *Soldanella* is an unrepresented genus in the Himalayas, being indigenous to the Alps alone. In boggy depressions are to be seen the white heads of cotton-grass (*Eriophorum*). Pastures for bovines are found almost exclusively in the neighbourhood of the caravan routes. Sheep-pastures are commoner. Wild quadrupeds are too scarce to affect the vegetation by the production of pastures. At the greatest altitudes to which vegetation extends among the rocks various species of juniper flourish, this forming the only fuel available in most of the lofty valleys, though beyond the Tibetan frontier various species of willow are obtainable for the same purpose (the Mangshang).

The Alpine Steppe

The high rainfall in the Himalaya valleys is shown by the comparative lowness of the snow-line. It varies from 16,000 feet to 16,500 feet; in the innermost valleys being about 17,000 feet, lower than in the neighbouring Tibet, which is drier. Plants that like to grow on the snow-line, solitary dicotyledons, will occur in spots as high as 18,000 feet. Vegetation in the form of adventurous grass-patches ranges up to 16,000 feet; on Tinkar Lipu up to 16,400 feet, and on the Chaga Pass up to 15,800 feet. The continuous grass-belt above the alpine scrub and shrub zone ranges through an altitude of about 1600 feet, topping the scrub zone by as much as 700 feet. It is much interrupted by erosion furrows, rocks, and detritus. Owing to the steepness of the declivities, collections of humus can be formed only in the necks, and in the depressions formed by moraines. There are a great many different species in these alpine meadows. Such vigorous plants as *Pedicularis*, and species of *Primula* and *Rheum*, are found making their way here and there even above the snow-line. The rock-flora is very extensive. On the accumulations of humus in the damp depressions of Tinkar Lipu, at 16,750 feet, there were picked at the end of May: *Ranunculus pygmaeus* (not previously found in the Himalayas), *Oxygraphis glacialis, Braya rosea, Draba alpina, Ermania himalayensis, Lagotis.*

Tibet

To the traveller who approaches Tibet, not by way of the longitudinal valleys of the Indus, the Brahmaputra, or the Yangtse, but going straight across the Himalayan chains from the south, the change in vegetation is extraordinarily rapid. A few days before, he was struggling with a luxuriant tropical jungle, and now he finds himself in search of scanty steppes and matted oases amid the snowy or stony deserts. This phenomenon is dependent, not only on the increase in altitude, but also upon the change of climate. Having crossed the mountain chains to reach the plateau, the monsoon deposits there less moisture. At these high altitudes, evaporation is extraordinarily rapid, so that the ground dries very speedily after rain. There will be a thunderstorm in the night, producing a freshet in the neighbouring brook, but by noon the water will have ceased to flow. When the snow-line is at 20,000 feet, the nival moisture-preserving belt which ranges through an altitude of about 1500 feet is so high as to be practically above the vegetation belts. In the drier regions of western Tibet we no longer find any nival flora, this being a great contrast with the Central Himalayan valleys, where dicotyledonous plants can flourish up to and beyond the snow-line, and where the uppermost forest zone lies about 5000 feet lower down. In the Alps, the limit of altitude between the tree belt and the snow-line is, according to Imhof, about 3000 feet; but in Patagonia, which is both damp and cool, the lower line of the " eternal " snows comes right down to the edge of the forest belt. A coherent coat of vegetation is limited to the alluvial tracts of sand and gravel where their roots can get down to the subsoil water. These are the only spots where humus colours the soil dark. The temperatures, too, are extremely unfavourable. In the narrow Himalayan valleys, with their precipitous slopes, the radiation at night is much less extreme than in the level plateaus of the lofty upland. As you approach the Tibetan plateau, the differences between the night and day temperatures of the Himalaya vary more. If upon a northern exposure you still find a small-shrub tundra and birch-forest, you will be apt to discover upon the opposite side of the valley, facing south, but no more than two miles away as the crow flies, that there is nothing better than a dry alpine steppe. This is what we see, for instance, in the Kuti Valley. The transition from forest area to steppe is so sudden that we make it in passing over one mountain chain.

In the Central Himalayas, man has an influence on vegetation only along the pilgrim roads, and through forest fires and the formation of pasturage. It is much the same in Tibet, where the density of population is even less, but where great flocks of sheep traverse the wide valleys and forgather upon the grassy islands in the steppes.

At the uppermost levels of the travelled areas, most of the vegetation is of the alpine-meadow type, whereas in the floors of the deeper valleys it is of a Central Asiatic half-desert and steppe character.

The flora of the alpine meadows of the Tibetan uplands contains very few species, consisting mainly of the oreophytes of the Central Asiatic mountains; cruciferae belonging to the genera *Draba*, *Parrya*, and *Braya*; leguminosae of such genera as *Astragalus*, and *Oxytropis*; such composites as *Saussurea*, *Leontopodium*, and *Senecio*; varieties of aster; and xeromorphous species of genera that abound in the Himalayas. Local varieties are by no means rare. Thus we find societies in which *Carex melanantha*, var. *Moorcrofti*, or *Cobresia*, var. *Elyna myosuroides*,

225

dominate, comparable with the *Elynetum* of the Alps, which is also prone to exhibit local variations.

On the lower-lying levels of the uplands, the semi-desert and steppe vegetation comes into direct contact with the alpine. All the types of vegetation which, in other regions, are usually found between these two — such as deciduous forest trees, pine-trees, tundra, etc. — are completely absent in Western Central Tibet; this being a phenomenon which, as far as the rest of the world is concerned, can be found only in the South American Andes. The *Artemisia* semi-desert and the *Stipa* steppe are not very well developed floristically, but they contain the characteristic representatives of the Central Asiatic area: species belonging to such genera of the chenopodiaceae as *Eurotia, Halogeton, Haloxylon, Halocharis,* and *Chenolea*; the zydophyllaceae, *Nitraria* and *Zygophyllum*; the cruciferae, *Christolea, Desideria,* and *Chorispora*; the leguminosae, *Caragana, Astragalus, Alhagi*; the graminaceae, *Bromus, Brachypodium, Stipa, Elymus*; also *Ephedra, Myricaria, Peganum,* etc. Very frequent are the low shrubs of *Caragana pygmaea,* which grows in masses extending to several square yards; and the hard cushions of *Thylacospermum rupifragum.* The number of endemic species is smaller than in the case of the alpine flora. The Tibetan flora which is so poor in species is largely dependent upon those of the neighbouring regions, these invading plants producing local varieties, as we see especially in Southern Mongolia and in the Western Chinese and Eastern Himalayan mountains.

The vegetation of the sub-alpine and alpine belts of the inner valleys of the Central Himalayas can certainly be compared with those of our inner Alpine valleys; but in the Himalayas the belts stand at an altitude from 5000 to 6500 feet higher than in the Alps; while in the sub-alpine forest, the birch prevails instead of the larch and the cembra pine. Many plants with which we in the Alps are familiar are not found in the Himalayas; such as the tall gentians known as *Coelanthe*; some of the primulas (*Auricula*) which adorn our rocky mountains; or, among the wealth of flowers that variegate our Alpine meadows, *Euphrasia, Alchemilla, Hieracium, Achillea,* and *Soldanella.* But their absence is compensated by many other beautiful flowers met with in the Himalayas, such as *Pedicularis,* species of gentian, primula, saussurea, and *Leontopodium* (edelweiss), *Astragalus,* and numerous others, which make the Himalayan mountain flora even more beautiful than our own Alpine flora.

APPENDIX

EQUIPMENT

Much has already been written by other mountaineers concerning the equipment of Himalaya expeditions. If, nevertheless, we think it expedient to mention our own experience, we have two good reasons for this. Almost every year new and useful accessories become obtainable. Every new expedition is thankful for the hints given by predecessors. Also our own little expedition was conspicuously different from most earlier ones in respect of our food supply, for most of the previous Himalayan mountaineers took all sorts of tinned food along, and even supplies of bottled beer. Our own experience coincides with that of Shipton and Tilman, who proved how economically one can live in the Himalayas. A small group of weather-proof and easily contented men who are willing to live on cheap native produce will be much more efficient and mobile than a huge expedition which needs hundreds of porters (so that the energies of the leaders must be largely concerned with the organisation of the coolies). Had it not been that our good friends had supplied us so liberally with excellent provisions, we should from the start have lived precisely as we did during the last two months in the mountains, when we had eaten our original supplies. After inaugurating this reduction in our diet, we needed only eight porters instead of thirty. Our diet, consisting mainly of rice, barley, wheat, and millet, cost us during these last two months about 12 annas per day for the two of us, this being, at the then rate of exchange, less than a Swiss franc.

We found, like E. Shipton, that delicacies of one sort and another to stimulate the appetite are superfluous. On the contrary, the simpler and more primitive the nutriment, the healthier the mountaineer Apart from the disaster which deprived us of our most skilled mountaineer in the early days, and from two brief minor ailments mentioned in the text, we enjoyed the most excellent health throughout, on an almost strictly vegetarian diet with no alcohol and no tobacco.

Stores of Food from Switzerland

I mention the chief of these, which may be of interest to the organisers of future expeditions.

Vierkorn (Four Corn) Biscuits by Nobs & Co. This seems to be one of those rare biscuits of which one cannot get tired. It is a complete diet in itself,

227

consisting of wheat, barley, rye, and oats, very slightly sweetened with un-refined sugar. One packet, with a handful of hazel-nuts, forms an admirable emergency ration for use at great heights when weight is of the utmost importance.

Pomol, prepared by Tobler of Bischofszell, is a pure concentrated apple-juice. Diluted with seven parts of water it makes an agreeable beverage, and compensates for the lack of fresh fruit. It can also be usefully drunk with hot water instead of tea. Since malic acid attacks aluminium, we had special pocket-flasks made which were resistant. Each of us carried a flask charged with a few teaspoonfuls of Pomol, and filled up with water on the way.

Sport-Ovomaltine (also called " Ovo-Sport ") prepared by Dr. A. Wander of Berne, in accordance with a recipe by Heim, is a readily soluble mixture of Ovomaltine with milk-powder and sugar. The addition of hot or even of cold water converts into a ready-for-drinking valuable beverage. As long as our stores lasted, we had a cup of this daily for breakfast.

Nestlé-Pulvermilch (" Nestogen "), a malted, powdered milk, when dis-solved in water produces a beverage which the palate cannot distinguish from fresh milk. Not only because it is so much lighter, but also in the matter of flavour, this milk-powder is superior to unsweetened condensed milk.

Dried fruits, above all sliced apples, are a valuable portable food for use when actually on the march. They are also excellent as a sweet when lightly boiled, and better still when boiled after having been swelled by overnight soaking.

As regards *Meat*, we took only a couple of pieces of Bündnerfleisch, an extremely concentrated food, which was excellent as long as it lasted.

Packet Soups. These were by the firm of Maggi. We took by preference slabs of barley or oats soups, both of which are extremely digestible by persons suffering from gastric disturbance. But though they were very useful to travellers in the lowlands, they are inconvenient at great heights, for there they need such extremely long boiling. Not merely is the boiling point lowered by the ascent, but fuel is extremely scarce. Perhaps the firm of Maggi (Kemptthal), in accordance with our advice, will make packet soups of tsamba, the roasted barley meal which is the staple article of diet in many of the regions we visited. These will not need prolonged boiling, being already cooked, so that the mere addition of hot water will suffice.

Issro-Haferflocken, when boiled for a very short time, make a delectable oatmeal porridge.

Our chief nutriment, as already said, was rice and other cereals, such as barley, wheat, and millet, which can usually be bought at a very low price in the Himalayan villages. Also dark-brown raw sugar, in the form of slabs rolled in leaves, is usually obtainable. It tastes like honey, and is much cheaper and more wholesome than white sugar, a product of " civilisation " and refinement, and apt to be very dirty in out-of-the-way places. Dirtier still are frying oil and butter, which are also dear and not universally obtainable. To dirt the traveller in remote parts must learn to shut his eyes indulgently.

DRUGS

I do not propose to speak here of first-aid cases with bandages, Z.O. plaster, etc., but only of a few novelties. Since we ourselves and our porters were lucky enough to get off without any serious accidents, we had not much experience in this field.

For the treatment of wounds and scratches, instead of the customary but exceedingly painful tincture of iodine, we have long been accustomed to use *Mercuro-Chrom*, as universally employed in America. It is a reddish powder, easily soluble in water. When the feet are chafed, as by the wearing of boots which have not been properly broken-in, Mercuro-Chrom relieves the smart.

Quite new is the treatment of wounds with *Uuguentolan-Salbe* (the German trade-name is a pleonasm, for Salbe=unguentum=ointment). This preparation, made from cod-liver oil, disinfects the wound and hastens the regeneration of the tissues. A deep incised wound in the foot of one of the porters healed with marvellous quickness under this ointment and an ordinary bandage.

Against dysentery, instead of using Iatren, which is a laxative, we recommend *Spirocid* ; while instead of quinine, we used *Chinoplasmin* as a prophylactic against malaria whenever we were in the mosquito-infected regions. Certainly we escaped without a trace of malarial fever. This prophylactic, in conjunction with the use of fly-tox or some similar spray, unquestionably reduces the danger of being attacked by malaria to a minimum. To the coolies we gave quinine sulphate, which is cheaper ; and we also had with us a sufficiency of acetyl-salicylic acid (which is cheaper than the proprietary aspirins) to relieve the headaches of which our men often complained at high altitudes.

We forgot one extremely important requirement which, unfortunately, was not obtainable in the Himalayas — though much needed there — a trustworthy brand of insect-powder to ward off the attacks of fleas, bed-bugs, and lice.

SPORTING REQUISITES

We were well, though not luxuriously, equipped for our modest wants. To travel as light as possible, we renounced the idea of camp-beds, and for six months lay on the ground in our sleeping-sacks. Nor did we bother about camp-stools or camp-tables, getting on as best we could with our wooden cases. Before starting, we had 26 of them made — 12 × 15 × 22 inches, each with a hinged top and a lock, and marked S.H.E. with a number. The equipment was got together in the sports department of Jelmoli's by W. Weckert, who is an expert in these matters. Besides the personal equipment which each of the three participators in the expedition provided at his own cost, we needed for ourselves and the porters :

Mountain Boots (Bally), in addition to those we already had, a pair each of
    ordinary mountain boots and a pair of extra-stout ones for the high
    mountains ; also three pairs of porters' mountain boots No. 42.

Mountain Tweeds, a new suit for each of us made of " Everest " woollen cloth, very tough and not heavy. Also four old suits for the porters.

Raincoats, " Protector ", 6.

Underclothing, flannel, with woollen socks and flannel shirts.

Pullovers, 3 + 3.

Air-Pilots' Hoods, lined with sheepskin.

Leather Gloves, 6 pairs.

Woollen Mittens, 6 pairs.

Tinted Spectacles, also for the porters, 3 dozen.

Skin Rugs, 3, for use in tent and under sleeping-sacks.

Gaiters, 3 pairs.

Ice-Axes, light, 7.

Crampons, 3 pairs.

Ski, 3 pairs, hinged, with ski-ing sticks — made by Attenhofer.

Tents, 7 in all, of which 5 were used.

Eiderdown Sleeping-sacks, 3 new ones, and 3 old ones for use by the porters.

Rubber Sheets, 5, for use under the sleeping-sacks.

Portable Flasks, of metal resistant to fruit-juices, 6.

Primus Stoves, for petrol, 3.

Meta Stoves, 2, with 4 packets of Meta fuel.

Rucksacks, 3 new ones with a metal framework to avoid pressure on the back ; and 5 ordinary sacks for the porters, 3 old ones and 2 large new ones.

Ropes, for Mountaineering, 6 ($\frac{1}{3}''$ and $\frac{1}{2}''$).

A few *Avalanche Cords*.

Snow Shovels of duraluminium, 3.

Saucepans, 2, also some aluminium plates and cups.

Storm Lanterns, 6, with candles, and electric pocket torches with reserve batteries.

Sailcloth Buckets, 4.

Grapples, for use in ice-work.

Large water-proof *Gunny-sacks* of sailcloth, with locks, 8.

As part of our geological equipment I need hardly say we needed hammers, chisels, compasses, bottles of hydrochloric acid in vulcanite cases, aneroids with a scale ranging up to 26,000 feet, and Zeiss prismatic binoculars magnifying 8 diameters, made by Kern & Co. of Aarau with light aluminium framework.

At the lower levels, our eiderdown sacks were too warm, and if we lay on the top we began to freeze towards morning. Two lighter sacks which, if necessary, could have been inserted one within the other would have been more practical. Most useful were the light rubber sheets to place beneath the sleeping-sacks.

In many books we are told that a solah topee should be worn by Europeans, even in the high mountains, to escape the risk of sun-stroke. This seems to me an exaggerated precaution. One of us wore a light white drill cap, like

that used by the natives, and the other an ordinary ski-ing cap. Neither of us had any trouble from the sun.

Instead of using thick and heavy outer garments, it is preferable to use a strong but light woollen stuff for this purpose, and when necessary to wear more underclothing and overcoats.

PHOTOGRAPHY

People are constantly asking what my equipment could have been to produce such admirable pictures. First let me confide the fact that all the duds have been kept for my private collection. Many were the failures, due in large part to inadequacy in the quality of our apparatus, which we had imagined to be the best obtainable. Here the manufacturers must bear the brunt of the blame ; for, though they have devoted themselves to the production of lenses such as were beyond the realm of fancy some thirty years ago, they have remained somewhat indifferent to the quality of the film. To them, too, it seems a matter of small concern whether the focussing is perfect. Since it is impossible for the traveller in high mountain ranges to do any developing as he goes along, and since in varying climatic conditions the emulsion tends to stretch or to contract as the case may be, the photographer has to be prepared for surprises. The plain fact is that some hundreds of pictures, though exposed under the most favourable conditions, were failures. It remains a puzzle why manufacturers have not yet introduced and placed upon the market automatic film-tensers. A. Oschwald, the photographic mechanic in Zurich, placed such a device in my old Icarette and Cocarette apparatus, with highly satisfactory results. In more modern cameras there is no chamber for such a gadget. We had four cameras in use on the present expedition, namely :

Rolleiflex 6 × 6 cm.
Superikonta 4·5 × 6 cm.
Plaubel-Makina 6 × 9 cm. fitted with a Tele-Makinar lens f = 21 cm.
    (all three of these loading a 6 × 9 cm. reel).
Finally, August Gansser used a Leica camera.

As is well known among photography-fans there exist two outlooks regarding the best size of film to use. One group maintains that the finest results can be obtained with a small cine-camera containing the usual movie safety film (perforated) ; the second group refuses to work with any size smaller than a 6 × 9 film.

I myself formerly preferred the larger-sized film and even during my wanderings in eastern Hindustan and in North America I toiled about with an 18 × 24 camera, fitted with double chambers and heavy plates. This camera, with its duplex protar and its wide-aperture lens, procured pictures of mountainscapes such as no camera fitted with an ordinary film-roll could ever achieve. But its weight, and the fact that plates are breakable, make its use unpractical.

Improvements in the manufacture of the roll-film have led me to reduce the size to a 6 × 9 and even to a 4½ × 6 model. But this is the smallest I have worked with so far. If these small pictures are taken on an exceptionally fine-grain emulsion and treated carefully in a soft fine-grain developer (hardly possible to do while travelling), they may successfully be enlarged to the size of the larger plates and secure almost equally good results. But no detail can be selected for further enlargement. A small-sized film of 24 × 36 mm. does not procure as sharp a picture as that obtained by an exposure on a larger size, for distant contours cannot be brought sufficiently into relief against their backgrounds. Of course this does not apply to close-ups (portraits, etc.), since sharp outline is not necessary when the negative is enlarged to 13 × 18 or 18 × 24 cm. The Leica camera proved its worth during A. Gansser's excursion into Tibet when facility for inconspicuous use was the main requirement. In the circumstances a Rolleiflex would have been useless. But so far as I am concerned such cameras as the Leica, Kontax, and others, are, in spite of un-questionable advantages, not so good for geological expeditions.

Of all the cameras we took with us on this trip, our Rolleiflex 6 × 6 proved the most trustworthy. It has no bellows, the framework being solid, not collapsible. Often it has happened during other journeys through deserts (Sahara, western Arabia) or among the wintry Tibetan highlands, in places where an especially dry atmosphere is the rule, that I have noticed all too late the presence of tiny holes in the folds of the bellows. Possibilities of the sort lurked in both the Superikonta and the Plaubel-Makina. In the former, the film was not in perfect focus (though in previous use this flaw did not occur); while with the latter we could not profit by the superb illuminating speed of the lens because the film-roll in its special container did not lie flat. This model was, therefore, reserved for time-exposures with a minimum of glare. There are other faults in the Makina, but this is not the place to discuss them. The pictures we took with it are of dubious value.

In addition to vast improvements in present-day lenses, immense strides have been made in the preparation of films. These are not only more sensitive and finer grained, but the emulsion is now *panchromatic*. We used panatomic and perpantic films on this expedition. Another time we shall give the pre-ference to yet finer-grained films on account of their higher sensitiveness. With a panchromatic film, a red filter, and an exposure of from five to eight times longer, all the distant details are recorded in so far as the fine grain of the film allows. In such conditions the sky comes out a fine dark hue. At times the red filter proved too strong, so that in photographing snow-mountains we made sole use of the ultra-violet filter. We took no films peculiarly sensitive to infra-red rays, not only on account of their more perishable nature, but be-cause they produce undesirable exaggerations and differ entirely from the usual emulsions, so that blue is reproduced as black, and green as white. Similarly, on this expedition, we abandoned the idea of using autochromatic preparations, though I had got excellent results as early as 1909 in Greenland with Lumière autochromatic photographs. My experience during a ten months' journey through China and Chinese Tibetan territory in the years 1930 and 1931 had been to find that autochromatic plates suffered from changes in climate and
232

from being kept too long. For this reason my pictures were failures. On the other hand if any further expedition be organised, the question of taking colour films as part of the equipment must be seriously considered. The slides I use in the course of lecturing have been painted by myself.

Of supreme importance is the developing. A soft fine-grain developer should be used. To our horror on our return we found that some of the films had been far too strongly developed, so that in the background grain could be detected which created a bad effect in an enlargement by three or four diameters. Many of the plates here reproduced are defective for this reason, although the pictures were photographed on irreproachable fine-grain emulsions.

For movie making we had two Siemens cameras with small-sized films, one of them possessing three alternative lenses. In spite of the troublesome method of loading, which sometimes held up the shooting, we found these cameras could be relied upon. Another time we should prefer to use a negative film rather than the Kodak reversible, since, in the case of the reversible, over-exposure cannot be remedied.

What we geologists and geographers lack is a light-weight handy camera, non-collapsible, but with the following specifications : size 6×9 cm. (not 6×6 cm.) ; a film-roll with automatic film-tenser, which will guarantee perfectly flat focussing ; supplementary lenses for distant views. That is to say a larger and yet not too heavy Leica, or a light-weight Reflex-Korelle, or an Exakta 6×9 cm.

GLOSSARY

(A dot beneath a vowel means that the syllable is stressed)

ạta, wheaten flour

Bara Sahib, " big sahib " (Heim)

Bhotias, a Mongoloid tribe of Nepalese mountaineers

chaloo ! gee-up ! get on !

chit (from Hindi chitthi), word universally applied in India and the Far East to any short written document—a note, a certificate, an I.O.U., etc.

chokidar or chokedar, a watchman or caretaker

chort, Buddhist religious monument

Chota Sahib, " little sahib " (Gansser)

chua, a motley wheat-like plant cultivated in the Garhwal Hills (Aramantus frumentaceus)

chupatty, flat cake of unleavened bread

cummerbund, sash worn inside for warmth, or outside for ornament (Persian for " loin-band ")

dak-bungalow, a rest-house for the accommodation of white travellers in out-of-the-way parts

Dhotials, men of a Nepalese tribe, employed as porters

dzo, hybrid offspring of yak and ordinary cattle

ganga, river

gọmpa, same as lamasery

kiang, wild ass

la, pass

lal, paprika

lạma, Tibetan Buddhist monk : " red lama "—the red refers to the colour of the monk's gown or caftan

lạmasery, Buddhist monastery

lek, pass

pạtwari, head policeman of a district

sadhu, a Hindu ascetic or holy man

Sherpa, a people of the high southern slopes of the Himalayas, in south-eastern Nepal. Half-Mongolian by race. Sherpas, nicknamed "tigers", accompanied the expedition as porters

sirdạr, overseer, commander, boss

sụdji, semolina

tạhsildar, commissioner's native subordinate (originally a native tax-gatherer)

" tiger ", used as nickname for a Sherpa porter

tọnga, a two-wheeled cart

tọpi, a pith-hat or helmet

tsạmba, roasted barley meal

THE END

Printed in Great Britain by R. & R. CLARK, LIMITED, *Edinburgh.*